The CARIBBEAN and its environs

0	100	200	300	400

Statute Miles

0	200	400	600

Kilometers

ATLANTIC OCEAN

LANDS

INAGUA

DOMINICAN REPUBLIC

Ciudad Trujillo

Port-au-Prince

HAITI

Mona Passage

San Juan

Ponce

PUERTO RICO

ST. CROIX

VIRGIN IS.

ANEGADA

ANGUILLA

BARBUDA

ST. KITTS

ANTIGUA

MONTSERRAT

GUADELOUPE

AVES

DOMINICA

MARTINIQUE

ST. LUCIA

ST. VINCENT

BARBADOS

SEA

ARUBA

CURAÇAO

BONAIRE

LOS ROQUES

BLANQUILLA

GRENADA

UAJIRA

ORCHILA

MARGARITA

TOBAGO

Port of Spain

TRINIDAD

LENA

FALCON

La Guaira

Guanta

acaibo

Puerto Cabello

Caracas

Caripe

L. Valencia

Barcelona

VENEZUELA

R. Apure

Río

Orinoco

Georgetown

Paramaribo

BRITISH GUIANA

SURINAM

FRENCH GUIANA

LA GRAN SABANA

R. Orinoco

MBIA

AMAZONAS

BRAZIL

BIRDS
OF THE CARIBBEAN

Robert Porter Allen

BIRDS
OF THE CARIBBEAN

A Studio Book • *The Viking Press* • *New York*

FIRST PUBLISHED IN 1961 BY THE VIKING PRESS, INC.

625 MADISON AVENUE, NEW YORK 22, N.Y.

PUBLISHED SIMULTANEOUSLY IN CANADA BY

THE MACMILLAN COMPANY OF CANADA LIMITED

DESIGNED BY MYRON S. HALL III

LIBRARY OF CONGRESS CATALOG CARD NUMBER: 61–13732

TEXT PRINTED IN THE U.S.A. BY ARDLEE SERVICE, INC.

ILLUSTRATIONS PRINTED IN HOLLAND BY JOH. ENSCHEDÉ EN ZONEN

Contents

Foreword

In 1951 a book was published called *Flowering Trees of the Caribbean*. With its beautiful pictures in color, it met with such a wide and enthusiastic reception that the sponsors, the Alcoa Steamship Company, a subsidiary of the Aluminum Company of America, decided to undertake research for a second book, devoted to the birds of the region. The result of this project is to be seen on these pages.

Many who are interested in birds are unable to visit them in their native habitat, and even if they could, to find them all would no doubt take a lifetime of study and travel. This book, about an ornithological paradise, brings some of the charm of tropical birds to you, and we hope it will prove of special value for future travelers to the Caribbean. The pleasure of seeing and hearing these tropical birds is greatly enhanced by a knowledge of their habits as described in such an interesting way by Mr. Robert P. Allen. Without this information a visitor would not be able fully to enjoy one of the greatest attractions of this area.

When I was asked to write the introduction to a book on tropical birds, the only qualifications I could muster for such an assignment were a lifelong interest in almost everything having to do with natural history, particularly with its manifestations in that rather vague area popularly referred to as "the outdoors," and, more specifically, an intimate association with the habitat of many of these birds during my early years as a geologist. In that period I spent many months in the tropical jungles, and while my first attention and efforts on those expeditions were focused on the ores of aluminum for which I was searching, I was at the same time keenly and pleasurably aware of the animal and bird life around me. In these pages I have recognized some old friends of those days.

Now, taking a few liberties with the power of imagination to correlate the apparently unrelated, I can see that if there is any analogy at all between birds and the world of metals, if there is any metal that can be said to fly, it is certainly aluminum, for what other metal has in equal degree enabled man to rival the birds in airborne flight?

The ore from which aluminum is made is called bauxite, and this comes in generous supplies for the aluminum industry from the area in which these birds are found. So, both by reason of the analogy mentioned above and of our identification with the area, we feel doubly justified in making this contribution to the general literature on the Caribbean, and, more specifically, to add a much needed reference and picture book on the beautiful birds that live there. In so doing, special tribute should be paid to Mr. William C. White, President of the Alcoa Steamship Company until 1959, whose idea it was to inaugurate the program for this book as well as the first one.

LAWRENCE LITCHFIELD, JR.
President, Aluminum Company of America

August 1961

Introduction

The Caribbean: a Sea, a Region, and a State of Mind

Caribbean is a magic word with a multitude of meanings. It is the name of a sea that is more than 1500 miles in width from east to west, and some 400 to 700 miles across from north to south, a sea that contains isolated shoals and reefs that lie exposed at low tide, but has depths that exceed 16,000 feet. The Caribbean is a geographical entity in itself, but it encompasses a variety of widely divergent geographical units and sends its surging tides against such vastly different shores as those of Central America, the Antilles, and South America. It is a medium of transport and trade, a way of life, and, under certain conditions, a state of mind. It is attractively haunted with history, and from shore to shore and island to island it is a place of dreams and music and beauty. Yet, with all its soft tones and romantic rhythms, it is energetic, bustling, and bursting at the seams with aspiration and promise. Its future is boundless.

For the purposes of this book it will be well to establish our understanding of the broad limits of the Caribbean in a geographic sense, as well as in other respects. When we speak of "the Caribbean" what area does this term convey? Some will think at once of the Lesser Antilles—St. Kitts, Guadeloupe, Martinique, St. Lucia—or of Jamaica or Trinidad. But the Caribbean is larger than the usual itinerary of a cruise ship, and extensive coastlines that are undoubtedly Caribbean are not served by the regularly scheduled airlines. Actually, the Caribbean Sea is one thing, and "the Caribbean," as a region, is another. The sea extends from the Yucatán Channel on the northwest, eastward along the south coasts of Cuba, Hispaniola, and Puerto Rico to St. Croix in the Virgin Islands and the Dutch islands of St. Martin, Saba, and St. Eustatius. On the west it reaches from the

Yucatán Peninsula southward, along the deeply indented coast of Central America to the Gulf of Darien, where Panama and Colombia meet, and east along the northern coast of South America to Trinidad and Tobago. Along the eastern rim lie the Lesser Antilles, from the Anegada Passage south to and including Grenada.

The Caribbean as a region is not so easily described. At least, not in specific terms. To do so we would have to draw an arbitrary line at a debatable distance inland from the coast, at a place where, from this viewpoint or that, we feel that the Caribbean influence no longer holds. Regardless of your personal interest—political, historical, geological, or whatever—you might as well say that when you go inland so far that the natives have never heard of the merengue or of a steel band, then you are beyond the Caribbean influence. But this won't work, because in this day of jet travel, easy-payment travel plans, and a hi-fi in every living room, the Caribbean, its people and its cultures, now extends far beyond its normal range of only a few years ago. Vacationing schoolteachers from Brooklyn and retired couples from Keokuk know all about steel drums, and if they don't do the merengue with the aplomb of a born native, you can't say they haven't tried.

We are not much better off when it comes to describing the limits of the Caribbean with relation to the birds of this region. Sprawling across a large part of the Caribbean lie the West Indies, but their boundaries are reasonably exact and we know how many species of birds have occurred within these boundaries. To understand the distribution of the birds of the Caribbean as a whole, we must examine the subject in more detail.

The Origin and Distribution of Caribbean Birds

When Sir Henry Morgan was Lieutenant-Governor of Jamaica and, indeed, long before that, solitaires were singing their sweet sad songs in the cool ravines of the Blue Mountains, high above sweltering Kingston and Port Royal. And they are still there, singing the same songs today.

Morgan probably never heard the song of the solitaire, for it is unlikely that he, or many other Europeans of that day, had reason to climb the steep, heavily wooded slopes that rise abruptly beyond the outskirts of the city and veil their serene heads in the clouds. Sir Henry was a man of many interests, but it seems doubtful if bird-watching was one of them. Nevertheless, he must have seen and admired the long-tailed "doctor bird," which only a blind man could avoid, and no doubt he smiled with amused tolerance, befitting a gentleman of his station, when the little "beany bird" dipped its bill into the sugar that remained at the bottom of his empty rum glass.

We could carry these conjectures much farther into the past than this, of course, but the only point to be made here is that birds have been around for quite a long time and, with certain exceptions, haven't changed their appearance or their habits or their songs very much since the Pleistocene, or even longer than that.

Where did these birds come from and how did they get there? For many years, zoologists theorized that birds originated in the great land masses of the major continents and reached isolated offshoots, such as the Antilles, by way of "land bridges." The land-bridge theory might account for the presence, especially in ages past, of certain large animals in regions where they have since disappeared, following a settling and subsidence that left the coast lines and land areas much as they are today, but with regard to vertebrates in general, and even more emphatically in the case of birds, the land-bridge theory has been largely discarded by modern zoologists. In a highly enlightening discussion, "Origin of the Bird Fauna of the West Indies," James Bond in 1948* reviewed recent thinking on this subject. He pointed out that most zoologists now consider these islands "oceanic" at least in the sense that "their vertebrate fauna was received across the sea." Geologists believe that no land bridge may have connected any of these islands since Oligocene time, during which the Antilles were almost completely submerged. Mammals such as ungulates and carnivores, which are abundant on the adjacent continents, are entirely lacking in the West Indies, and yet could easily have arrived there by way of a land bridge. The evidence of mollusks suggests that there has been no direct connection between Central America or Yucatán and Jamaica or Cuba later than the Eocene.

Finally, noting the complete absence in the West Indies of members of the primary division of fresh-water fishes, which swarm in all waters of the mainland continents, Bond quotes Ernst Mayr as stating that if we are to suppose that these aggressive fishes originally made their way southward through Central America and thence into South America, what we know of geological conditions forces us to "push any such continental bridge back into the Mesozoic, if indeed it ever existed at all."

It is Bond's belief that birds probably reached the West Indies over water, "for the most part at times when the water gaps were smaller, as during the glacial periods of the Pleistocene." Numerous species of birds migrate considerable distances, and open water is evidently no great barrier, but, on the other hand, as Bond indicates, "numerous families of birds are remarkably sedentary."

During most of the Tertiary, North and South America were separated, to be united in the Pliocene when the Isthmus of Tehuantepec emerged. At one point in this everlastingly long period, the Miocene, there must have existed a "Caribbean Archipelago," as Bond terms it. The climate of much of North America was tropical at this time, and over the southern half of the continent there probably

* Source references, indicated in the text by author's name and (where necessary) date of publication, will be found in the Bibliography beginning on page 249.

existed a fauna that was quite distinct from that of South America. The West Indian avifauna, in large part, may have derived from these tropical North American forms, which had to move south as the climatic conditions became unfavorable for them.

Bond is of the belief that while the birds of the West Indies are "fundamentally and predominantly tropical North American," there is also a South American element, of comparatively recent arrival and comprising only members of aggressive families, that entered through Jamaica on the one hand and the Lesser Antilles on the other. The Central American avifauna may once have included similar forms from tropical North America, but since the continents were joined together this last time, these have been largely pushed out and replaced by South American forms. The birds of the Bahama Islands were evidently derived first from Cuba and later from Florida. The presence of some species on oceanic islands can be explained only as a result of natural causes, often fortuitous. "There can be no doubt," Bond concludes, "that dispersal of birds in the West Indies has been largely brought about by hurricanes, but the prevailing easterly trade winds have had little effect on bird distribution."

Ludlow Griscom pointed out in 1932 that Guatemala, with its strategic location, highly complex topography, and five distinct climates, has an unusually rich avifauna. Also, it has been a "buffer state" between two growing continents since Palaeozoic time. "It has been separated and united with one or the other or both on several occasions. Many times has the tide of life flowed through it both north and south, and at the same time it has managed to create endemic forms of its own and safely preserve them against a horde of later immigrants. It is no exaggeration to say that Guatemala is the [ornithological] key to Central America." Although Guatemala is the largest of the Central American countries, it has an area of only 48,250 square miles. Griscom recorded 736 species here, a remarkable total. The entire West Indies list is 463.

Of the avifauna of Central America as a whole, Alexander Skutch (1954) says: "Lying between two great continents each with its peculiar avifauna, the thousand-mile-long isthmus known as Central America has a wonderfully rich bird life. The greater part of the region is comprised in the Caribbean lowlands, where the rainfall is high and rather uniformly distributed through the year and the forests tall and heavy. The colorful bird life of these warm and humid lowlands is closely related to that of northern and eastern South America. Nearly all the genera, and the majority even of the species of these Caribbean birds, are found also in the southern continent; many of the species extend across the tropics to Paraguay and northern Argentina."

Wagenaar Hummelinck (1957) notes that "the Caribbean element in the islands of Aruba, Curaçao, and Bonaire is stronger than would have been expected from the short stretch of sea separating the islands from the continent. Indeed, the South American element is dominant, but such North American and

Caribbean species as *Ardea herodias* (against *A. cocoi* from South America), *Butorides virescens* (against *B. striatus*), *Elaenia martinica* (against *E. flavogaster*), and *Vireo altiloquus* (against *V. chivi*) have their southern distributional limits south of Aruba, Curaçao, and Bonaire, instead of north of these islands. The absence of many typically South American families of pro-passerine and passerine birds, which on the South American mainland occur in a great variety of species, is also indicative of the fact that the avifauna of the islands is not purely South American."

Hummelinck finds that of the 137 species recorded from these islands, 88 per cent also occur in continental Venezuela, and 82 per cent in Colombia. He adds that of 48 species breeding in Aruba, Curaçao, and Bonaire, 29 (59 per cent) probably are of a South American origin, 13 (27 per cent) are of a Caribbean or at all events northern origin, and 6 are of unknown or indefinite origin.

A similar comparison has been made by G. C. A. Junge and G. F. Mees with regard to the birds found on Trinidad and Tobago, as they relate to those of Venezuela and the Guianas. They conclude that "...the main part of the avifauna of both islands consists indeed of purely South American forms. This, however, appears much more in Trinidad than in Tobago. Many South American species did not reach Tobago, which has been colonized by more widespread forms and some Antillean elements (*Buteo platypterus*, *Progne subis*, *Tiaris bicolor*). The more isolated position of Tobago is also expressed in a relatively much larger percentage of endemic races. Trinidad and Tobago have 6 endemic races in common. Besides Trinidad has 18 endemic races among 284 forms (6 per cent) and Tobago 22 among 106 forms (20 per cent).

"Chapman as well as Hellmayr suggested that the avifauna of Trinidad and Tobago, though mainly showing Venezuelan affinities, also possesses some Guianan elements. Our increased knowledge of the distribution of many species in northern South America now shows that these Guianan elements can be neglected. Of the purely South American forms on Trinidad there are 28 occurring in Venezuela that are not known from the Guianas. On the other hand there are only 2 species occurring in Trinidad and the Guianas that are not (yet?) found in Venezuela...Tobago does not show any Guianan affinities. Of the 13 resident species in Tobago, not known from Trinidad, 5 occur in Venezuela, but not in the Guianas; the reverse is not found. The main part of the South American forms of course occur in Venezuela as well as in the Guianas. The species occurring in Tobago that are not found in Trinidad, most probably reached Tobago from the South American mainland by chance."

It is now generally accepted that there are some 8,600 species of birds in the world, and these are divided into 170 families which may include from one to more than 300 species each. The total number of bird species occurring within what we choose to call the Caribbean region is around 1000, although, because the limits of this "region" are indefinite, we cannot arrive at an exact figure.

This impressive array of Caribbean birds is represented in this book by 98 species, comprising in all a total of 50 avian families. As you would expect for a region that is mainly tropical, most of these species—about 71 percent of the list—are resident within the Caribbean area, but this statement must be qualified by pointing out that many of these species are of wide distribution and so can be said to be resident over considerable areas (the whole continent of South America, for example). A few of the resident species are very local in their distribution—for instance, the tufted coquette, a tiny and lovely hummingbird that occurs only in northeast Venezuela, the Guianas, and Trinidad. Others are endemic species, restricted to a single island, perhaps, and found nowhere else in the world. Examples of this are the streamer-tail hummingbird of Jamaica, the blue-headed quail-dove of Cuba, and the St. Vincent parrot, which is found only on the island of that name.

Some of the seabirds, like the tropicbird, the frigatebird, and the sooty tern, are pan-tropic, occurrring in all tropical seas around the world. Other species are of universal distribution in a global sense—such birds as the osprey and the black-crowned night-heron, for example—but occur in the Caribbean chiefly as migrants from North America. In addition, a number of Caribbean birds are both migratory and resident—black phoebe, house-wren, rough-winged swallow—migrants from North America meeting and mingling with resident races of their own species that live in the tropics.

Migration is a way of escaping from unfavorable changes in the environment, such as low temperatures and lack of food, and the Caribbean is the winter home of a great many North American birds, which are only known there as winter visitors. Not many of these have been included in this book because they are more typical of the United States than of the Caribbean. In a strict sense, even so-called "resident" birds may make local migrations, moving to lower altitudes in winter, for instance, or flying short distances at the end of the breeding season to new feeding grounds, as does the flamingo. The swallow-tanager is an excellent example of such a semi-migratory species.

Bird-Watching in the Caribbean: 1492 to the Present

Isabella, Queen of Castile, was evidently one of those remarkable individuals who are years ahead of their time. In addition to the important role she played in sending Columbus on his way, it was she who first raised a voice against slavery in the New World and who first sponsored an interest in the natural history of the new lands beyond the sea. Isabella, it is recorded, charged Columbus with the extracurricular task of collecting such unusual and exotic birds as he might come across in his travels. *El Almirante*, we can surmise, had no personal interest in such a project, but who could deny Isabella? Undoubtedly he gave no more thought to the matter until it was almost time to return to Spain. Then, at the last minute, we can imagine him gathering as many brightly colored birds as he could find to bring back to the Queen.

On his first voyage, Columbus wrote of Hispaniola: "Its lands are high, and there are in it very many sierras and very lofty mountains. . . . All are most beautiful, of a thousand shapes, and all are accessible, and filled with trees of a thousand kinds and tall, and they seem to touch the sky. And I am told that they never lose their foliage, as I can understand, for I saw them as green and as lovely as they are in Spain in May, and some of them were flowering, some bearing fruit, and some in another stage, according to their nature. And the nightingale was singing, and other birds of a thousand kinds, in the month of November there where I went." Alexander Wetmore (1931) notes that this was at Baie des Moustiques, Haiti, and he identifies the "nightingale" as a mockingbird. Columbus heard it again at Gros Morne, singing both day and night, even in December. He was obviously entranced.

These are the first ornithological notes from the New World, and it is not surprising that the first bird to be recorded was misidentified. Incidentally, mockingbirds are still called nightingales in the West Indies and on the Spanish-speaking islands they are "ruiseñor," which means the same thing.

Of course, ornithological knowledge scarcely existed at this time, and although there was an increasing interest on the part of many of the early travelers and explorers in the natural history of the New World, it was not until the early nineteenth century that the first ornithologists did any serious work in the Caribbean area. By the end of that century a solid groundwork had been laid and over the last forty years great strides in our knowledge have been made. Until very recently, most of these labors in the ornithological vineyard have been the co-operative efforts of the collector of bird skins in the field and the taxonomist or classifier in the museum. There are still many problems in this basic field that can be solved only by more collecting and further study, but we are now on the threshold of detailed life-history and ecological studies that will necessarily result from the careful observations of living birds. In the Caribbean region some of these studies have already been made, such as Ernst Schaefer's work on the swallow-tanager and Skutch's numerous contributions from Central America. Undoubtedly these are only a beginning, and considering the rich and colorful avifauna of this region, we can look forward to an as yet unborn ornithological literature that will be equally rich and filled with unusual color and interest.

Finally, another comparatively recent arrival on the Caribbean scene is the amateur bird-watcher. It is probably significant of this increasing curiosity about the birds of this area that so many of the reference works in our Bibliography have been published during the last decade, including all of the important guide books except two old standbys—Bond and Sturgis—which have been available for some years. There are now specially conducted bird tours to Caribbean countries, and these will doubtless become increasingly popular.

Not only is all this a happy development for those who take a personal interest in such matters, but a wider knowledge of Carribbean birds on the part of a large number of visitors is bound to result in a more widespread concern for birds such as the flamingo, certain of the parrots, and a number of additional species that will require special conservation measures in their behalf if they are to survive. The relationship that has long existed in many countries between amateur bird-watchers and conservation practices is well-known and may be classed as a sort of natural phenomenon. As bird-watching tourists burgeon in the Caribbean, you can expect to find in their wake a new set of values with regard to the local birdlife, and a new understanding of the meaning of conservation.

It would have pleased me very much (and no doubt the reader as well) if a great many more species of the birds of this region could have been included in this volume. Unfortunately, this could not be done, mainly because the book was built around color photographs, and really good color photographs of Caribbean birds are still something of a rarity. As a result, our selection was limited by the number of such pictures that was available. This is an explanation rather than an apology, for these pictures can stand on their own and require no special pleading.

It should be apparent that this is neither an out-size field guide nor a complete reference work, although we have mentioned the several excellent handbooks that are now available, and the Bibliography is in itself a pretty fair reference guide. It should also be apparent that this book is chiefly for the layman rather than the post-graduate bird-watcher, although we hope that many of the latter group will enjoy it, too. But our interest is primarily in the average tourist and jet-age *voyageur* who travels to the Caribbean and has a healthy interest in all aspects of the Caribbean scene. Since birds are an inescapable part of this scene, perhaps this collection of pictures will serve as your introduction to some of the Caribbean forms, and create for you new interests and thus enrich your present and future, both in the Caribbean and wherever you may go. If it accomplishes any one of these things it will have achieved its main purpose.

The following presentation of the birds in text and pictures conforms with the usual ornithological order except in a few instances where the arrangement has been slightly changed for artistic reasons.

The Birds

No other large white seabird observed over the open waters of the Caribbean, or near rocky and precipitous headlands, is as quick and graceful or trails behind it such delicate, elongated white tailfeathers as the tropicbird. There are two species in the area, but the white-tailed (also called yellow-billed) is the more widely distributed. On the surface of the sea it floats and swims with grace and buoyancy, its elegant tail held daintily aloft; but on dry land it is one of the most awkward of birds, its feet placed so far aft that it cannot stand erect and must shove itself along on its breast.

I have seen these birds come ashore at their breeding places on Great Inagua in the Bahamas. As I clung precariously to the steep sides of the cliff, far above the surging waters that beat against the jagged rocks below, they dashed in by twos and threes, landing with inherent skill on a narrow ledge of jutting rock, then pushing themselves with jerky, labored movements beneath an overhanging shelf or into a tiny slit or crevice in the heavily eroded coral limestone. Inside these crevices we found the lone pinkish, brown- and purple-splotched egg, or the single fluffy chick, quite at home on the hard, bare floor. The adults are fearless and can readily be handled at such times, if you don't mind their sharp bites.

Tropicbirds feed by diving into the sea, often from a considerable height. Flying fish are a staple food, as are squid. A common call note can be described as a sharp *kik*, but in flight they have a harsh, even sharper note, *kik-et-kik-et*, repeated in series.

The red-billed tropicbird (*Phaethon aethereus*) has narrow black bars across its back and a small area of black on the scapular region of the wings. The bill color

Plate 1
White-tailed
tropicbird

17

is a deeper red than in the white-tailed form. It is most often seen in the Virgin Islands area or around certain of the Lesser Antilles (St. Vincent, Grenada, Bequia, Carriacou), but rarely in the vicinity of the Greater Antilles. Although it breeds on islands off Venezuela (Los Hermanos, Los Roques), it also occurs off the Pacific coast of Mexico, off Panama (Almirante Bay), and among the Galápagos Islands.

Plate 2
Brown
pelican

The brown pelican is a colorful and characteristic bird of many southern shorelines and a great favorite of tourists from Florida to the most distant corners of the Caribbean. In many places, where they gather to feed on scraps from the fishing boats, these birds have become quite tame and can readily be fed by hand. At a dock on Key Largo a young pelican known locally as Bill became so accustomed to the inexplicable behavior of its human friends that it did not protest when picked up by its bill and landed bodily on the dock, where it simply continued its entreaties for more fish. In repose the brown pelican is rather absurd in appearance, but its solemn expression is belied by the twinkle in its small white eyes. It is a bird that seems to have a sense of humor, and if you get to know it on the right terms, it is appealing and admirable in every way.

Recently, when a severe hurricane was approaching the Florida Keys, residents were urged to move to the safety of more protected communities on the mainland. One couple started to leave, but remembered their tame, free-flying brown pelican. They went back, picked up the bird, and drove on, with their avian friend in the back seat of the car, to Miami. There the hotel management objected to giving the pelican a room, so it rode out the storm inside the car in a parking lot. Next day the couple returned home by air taxi, pelican and all, and everyone—especially the pelican—was very happy about the entire experience.

In spite of their bulk, pelicans are extremely graceful in flight and adept at skimming within inches of the surface of the water or diving from a height of thirty feet or more in a headlong plunge that is truly spectacular. This dive is made to catch fish, which are their only food. For many years commercial fishermen looked on the pelican as an arch-enemy and exterminated thousands of them, chiefly by visiting their nesting colonies and destroying the young and eggs. In the United States the federal government and the National Audubon Society waged a number of campaigns to save the pelican, conducting surveys that revealed the true nature of its diet—predominantly species of fish not used by man for food—and gradually educating the public to an understanding and appreciation of these amusing and harmless birds. Today the brown pelican is an abundant and highly regarded resident throughout most of its range as well as a conspicuous, beloved inhabitant of countless tourist resorts.

Brown pelicans usually build their rather flimsy nests in mangrove trees, close to water and five to ten feet high. In Florida they may nest in every month of the year. Infrequently, owing to local conditions, they nest on the ground or on rocky ledges. The plain white eggs number from one to three to a clutch. The nestlings can produce various sounds, from low groans and grunts to shrill, high-pitched begging notes. Adult pelicans are voiceless, although they can make a low clucking sound, seldom heard except by other pelicans.

The pelican has often been misunderstood and its behavior misinterpreted. Alfred Newton wrote: "It may be necessary to state that there is no foundation for the venerable legend of the Pelican feeding her young with blood from her own breast, which has given her an important place in ecclesiastical heraldry." But a place in modern heraldry still exists, and in addition to its presence on the Great Seal of the state of Louisiana, the brown pelican has been adopted as the crest of the University College of the West Indies.

It is easy to overlook the cormorant as a common, uninspired, and uninspiring species that does not seem to have any special charms. Of course, this attitude is a mistake, for cormorants often reveal hidden qualities that are quite surprising. My home is in a seacoast community where fishing is the chief local interest and pursuit, and cormorants are a dime a dozen. They even nest nearby on several mangrove-fringed islands in Florida Bay; but with so many other birds in the vicinity—more exciting birds such as roseate spoonbills, reddish egrets, and great white herons—we never gave the lowly cormorant much attention. Then one day my daughter and I went across the harbor to fish for mangrove snappers. It was late afternoon and several fishing boats had come in with their day's catch, so that a whole bevy of pelicans and gulls and cormorants hovered around the fish house. We caught a few snappers, and as I started cleaning them several birds left the fish dock and settled on the water close to our boat. The boldest and most eager among them were five or six gimlet-eyed cormorants.

This description stems only from a certain characteristic alertness of bearing and manner. Actually, their eyes, seen at close range, are a beautiful sea green or turquoise. They are bright, intelligent eyes, but at the same time cold and calculating and quick, so that one gets the feeling that these birds will miss nothing that comes their way. We enjoyed throwing fish and bait scraps to them until there were none left, and in the end they were nearly taking it right out of our hands. All this time the pelicans and gulls, the usual charity cases, were hovering dismally in the background, thoroughly beaten at their own game. From that day on the cormorant has been a special friend of mine.

Cormorants are highly successful birds, numbering some thirty species throughout the world, six of which occur in North America. In certain remote parts of the globe they gather in huge nesting colonies of a million or more individuals, and the accumulated guano is of considerable value as commercial fertilizer. It is also believed that the high percentage of nitrates and phosphates deposited in the waters surrounding a cormorant rookery stimulates the growth of marine plants, resulting in a local abundance of marine animals, especially fish. Thus the lowly

Plate 3
Double-crested
cormorant

cormorant is an essential link in an ecological pattern so perfectly arranged and so complicated that we have only recently begun to understand it. In addition, cormorants as a rule eat only scrap fish of little or no economic value.

Cormorants of whatever species are much alike in habits. They nest in trees, on rocks, or on the ground, in the vicinity of salt or fresh water. They lay from two to four eggs, bluish-green in basic color and covered with a chalky white deposit. Their voice is seldom heard away from a colony or roost. It is harsh, and on occasion may sound like the grunting of a herd of hogs. But the cormorant does have beautiful eyes.

Plate 4
Anhinga

This strange, reptile-like bird was first described by the seventeenth-century naturalist Marcgrave, who wrote that "anhinga" was the name by which it was known to the Indians of its native Brazilian haunts. I have always liked "snake-bird," which seems to suit its peculiarly reptilian appearance, but "water-turkey" is the appellation commonly given it in the southern United States.

Once, in Florida, I was patroling by airboat with one of the rangers of Everglades National Park. We skimmed out of the sawgrass and into the clear, dark headwaters of the Shark River. Coming around a bend in the narrow stream at top speed, we swerved to avoid an overhanging branch and, in the split second it took to pass it, saw that it supported a snakebird nest. In it were three well-grown young. Almost before we realized what had happened, all three youngsters had dropped like stones into the water. There was absolutely no hesitation; they simply went over the side and *plop* into the water! Naturally, we slowed down and worked our way back to the nest, but it was some time before we found even one of them. The bird was lying in the water, close against the bank, completely submerged except for its bill and part of its head. When we tried to catch it, in order to return it to its nest, the youngster, which had certainly never been in the water before, swam swiftly out of sight.

The adult birds will plummet from a perch in the same manner when disturbed, and even when merely going into the water to fish. They knife beneath the surface with scarcely a splash, and swim underwater with great skill and dexterity. Their food consists of such fish as bream, sunfish, and mullet, as well as occasional insects and insect larvae.

The neck vertebrae and related muscles are curiously constructed to enable these birds to twist and turn when in pursuit of a rapidly moving fish.

Most people seem to consider the anhinga an enigma, with even a shade of the occult about it, doubtless because it is virtually voiceless, has a somewhat aboriginal appearance, and dwells in dark, silent, water retreats. Gilbert Pearson wrote of them: "Their whole life seems to be pervaded with a haunting mystery. It is undoubtedly the bird to which the rural preacher referred when he said, 'Where the Wangdoodle mourneth for its first-born.'" But in the spring, when the male rises several hundred feet above the treetops, spreads his gaudy tail, and soars splendidly in wide, effortless circles, there is no mystery about it. He is showing off for the benefit of a glittering-eyed, long-necked, buff-breasted female snakebird watching below.

Once you have seen a frigatebird soaring effortlessly on trim, graceful wings, outlined in black against the warm blue of a tropical sky, you will no longer wonder why this bird has been given such an extravagant name. For it is indeed magnificent. The ease with which it "hangs" in the sky is not without explanation, however. In addition to a highly specialized skeletel structure, with unusual rigidity, the great wing expanse must support only about three and a half pounds of body weight. Even the bones themselves, being hollow, are extremely light.

*Plate 5
Magnificent
frigatebird*

No doubt the commonly used English names (such as man-o'-war bird and man-o'-war hawk) were first given these birds by sailors familiar with their habits. They are daring robbers, snatching fish from other birds, and so swift on the wing that few birds can escape them in outright pursuit. Heavy, slow-flying boobies are favorite victims, and once a frigatebird gets on a booby's tail it is almost certain to cough up the fishy morsel that is the usual prize. Other victims include gulls, terns, cormorants, and pelicans. In the Florida Keys they seem to pick most often on the royal tern, which is quite nicely streamlined and no mean flier itself. But it hasn't much of a chance against this dark, relentless pirate. With shrill cries of fear and frustration the tern streaks across the sky under a full head of steam, the grim-visaged man-o'-war close on its tail. They weave this way and that, up, down, off in wide circles and long swooping descents. In the end the tern is forced to drop its mouthful of fish, and with easy grace the frigatebird pulls out, spirals downward, and catches the morsel before it hits the water below.

In the Dry Tortugas off the Florida coast these birds occasionally prey on the young of the noddy and sooty terns that nest on Bird Key, scooping them up and swallowing them whole while still on the wing. Such depredations, however, are possible for a limited period only, when the chicks are old enough to move about but still too young and helpless to seek the protection of surrounding vegetation. At sea frigatebirds feed on many varieties of surface fish, and flying fish are high on the list.

These birds breed in colonies that may number a few pairs or as many as two or three thousand. Their frail, rather small nests are built at various elevations in mangroves, or sometimes directly on the ground or on rocks. In Yucatán, Raymond Paynter found them nesting on clumps of sea lavender (*Limonium sp.*). The bird usually lays a single plain white egg.

*Plate 6
Great
blue heron*

When I was a small boy, I had the unforgettable experience of visiting a nesting colony of great blue herons. It was hidden away in the dense riverbottom growth of an island in the West Branch of the Susquehanna River in northern Pennsylvania, and to my young eyes the willows, sycamores, and heavy stands of Joe Pyeweed were as authentic a jungle as any tropical forest I had ever read about. The big nest platforms were high up in the towering sycamores, and the steady, monotonous *yek-yek-yek-yek* cries of the young added to the sense of mystery and the thrill of exploration and discovery. I have seen many heronries, large and small, since that memorable day—in the Big Cypress and Everglades regions of Florida, on remote islands off the Texas coast, along uninhabited stretches of Yucatán lagoons, and in mangrove swamps in the Caribbean—and I still measure their appeal by the yardstick of that experience long ago.

Great blue herons are one of those highly adaptable species that can fit its way of life to all sorts of habitats and conditions. They seem equally content in either salt or fresh water, in the far North or the deep South. In Canada you will see a great blue stalking its prey in the reedy shallows of quiet backwater, and on the shores of a West Indian island the same species is perfectly at ease feeding in the surge of the tumbling ocean surf.

They build their big nests in the tops of cypresses or pines nearly one hundred feet high, in tule rushes just above the water, in mangroves and cabbage palms, prickly-pear cactus, fir or maple. It makes no difference to *Ardea herodias*. The eggs number from three to six and are blue or greenish-blue in color.

In the Florida Keys and many places in the West Indies, Yucatán, and the Caribbean, herons of the same size and general outlines of the great blue occur in all-white plumage. For some years ornithologists have disagreed whether this is a separate species (the great white heron) or merely a color phase of the great blue. There is interesting evidence on both sides of this discussion, and as our knowledge increases, especially in the fields of genetics and comparative animal behavior, new light will be shed on this and many related problems.

Plate 7
Green heron

One of the by-products of the digging of the Panama Canal was Gatun Lake, the natural result of the building of Gatun Dam, which raised the water depth in the Chagres Valley more than eighty feet and flooded 165 square miles of surrounding country. In one of the many by-waters of this man-made lake are the Grassy Islands, formed by a gradual succession of floating debris and plant growth that got its start around half-submerged tree trunks and broken limbs. As Frank Chapman noted, these islands have no shores and offer no foothold for shorebirds or for most of the herons. But the wonderfully adaptable green heron soon found a place there, and "made do" with its usual energy and persistence.

This species may be the smallest heron of our acquaintance, but it has twice the vim of many of its larger relatives. Its darting, competent flight and confident if raucous voice are in singular contrast to the poised, leisurely behavior of a great blue or a common egret.

No wonder the green heron is so widely distributed and so successful, even under conditions that may actually appear to be adverse. Andrew Meyerriecks made his valuable studies of the breeding behavior of the green heron on an island in Jamaica Bay, near the teeming New York metropolitan area. The nesting territories of the herons, also teeming, were located in marsh on either side of Cross Bay Boulevard. Apparently the heavy traffic in no way discommoded the herons, who went about the ordered ritual of their courtships and family duties without fear or frustration.

The green heron is extremely tame, but it must not be considered stupid. When a bird meets a human at close range, it requires considerable "savvy" on the part of a bird to estimate correctly the tolerance threshold, and the green heron seems to have this ability. Often, when fishing along a mangrove shore in Florida, I have seen one of these little birds land on an arching aerial root a few feet away and proceed with its own fishing as if there were no one else around. It was quite evident, however, that the heron was acutely aware of my presence and had gauged the situation perfectly.

The green heron makes its home in both fresh- and salt-water environments. Less gregarious than other herons, it gathers in small breeding groups rather than in large colonies. The nest is a frail structure of small sticks, often including green twigs, cleverly woven so that it can hold together in a high wind. The bird lays three to five pale bluish-green eggs.

Young green herons are as remarkable as their parents, using their wings and bills to clamber agilely about the nest tree. Even more amazing, their toes are partially webbed, and, should one fall into the water, it will swim like a fish. In a word, the green heron can look after itself—from the state of Washington all the way to the islands off Venezuela.

Most herons are wanderers, but the trait is more marked in the little blue heron than in any other. The so-called survival value of such a habit was well illustrated in the past, when drainage of the vast Florida Everglades resulted, during drought periods, in prolonged and devastating fires. During the 1930s in particular, great numbers of little blue herons and other wading birds appeared along stream banks and in any available water habitats throughout many Northern states. The first reaction of observers in those areas was to congratulate the Audubon Society on the magnificent conservation work it had done in the South, but in recent years it has become apparent that, while the value of this work cannot be denied, these many thousands of wading birds were fleeing from nesting and feeding sites that had been destroyed by the lethal combination of drainage, drought, and fire. Probably those species with the strongest ability to disperse survived these evil times in the best condition.

The little blue heron is at home in fresh-water sites inland, but it does very well, especially during its winter migrations, in brackish and salt-water environments. Consequently, its food must be quite varied, although basically it is the usual heron menu of small fish, crayfish, fiddler crabs and other crustaceans, frogs, and

Plate 8
Little
blue
heron

many kinds of insects. Grasshoppers may be a favorite item, if available, and at Orange Lake, Florida, Oscar Baynard found that fifty meals of young little blues included 1900 of these creatures.

Little blue herons nest in congregations of their own kind, often quite a number together, and sometimes in company with Louisiana herons. Julian Huxley, who studied these two birds in a Louisiana heronry some years ago, thought that their breeding behavior was essentially similar.

*Plate 9
Cattle
egret*
How did the cattle egret, a native of southern Europe, Africa, and Asia, reach the New World? Since the astonishing transoceanic colonization of these birds first came to the notice of ornithologists some years ago, and especially since 1952 when they made a sudden, almost whirlwind invasion of the United States, there has been much speculation. The theories are numerous. Some claim that they were brought to British Guiana as household pets by transplanted East Indians or arrived as stowaways on a cattle boat; others say that a few escaped from the zoo in Georgetown or that someone introduced them deliberately, without publicizing the fact. But as time went on, and the really tremendous number of these birds was noted, the more certain it has seemed that they must have come across voluntarily from the bulge of Africa and, borne by favorable easterly winds, landed in South America under their own power. Their adventurous journeys have also taken them to Australia, for the cattle egret now occupies all continents except Antarctica.

They are so firmly entrenched in the United States that in many respects they seem more at home than some of the native herons. Bird citizens of the world at large, they have an advanced, cosmopolite attitude toward all fellow creatures, and would as soon pick a tick from the ear of a hippo in Kenya as from the shoulders of a red bull on the Kissimmee Prairie of Florida. Toward man they exhibit a fearlessness, or degree of sociability, that is hard to believe. During their regular movements or migrations into Florida, scores of cattle egrets can be seen searching for insects in fields, pastures, and lawns. A man can walk up, slowly, within four or five feet of them before they decide to move unhurriedly away.

Although they nest on islands and along streams or swamps, cattle egrets do not spend much time in watery environments, but feed in fields, pasture lands, or dry open country, preferably where cattle are present. Evidently it is their habit to pick up the insects that are disturbed by the animals' movements. Insects are not their only food, however, and the fact that they have been observed taking frogs and small birds suggests that these capable newcomers will get along on whatever is most available.

As further proof of the sociability of the cattle egret, they are now nesting in several colonies in the United States together with native herons, egrets, and ibises. It seems certain that they are in the United States to stay, although the limits of their distribution and the peak of their abundance have not yet been established.

What caused their sudden burgeoning in the first place is anyone's guess. Whatever the answer, the cattle egret is unquestionably the number-one tourist of the avian world.

Plate 10
Snowy
egret

In less enlightened days, the snowy egret was slaughtered by the tens of thousands to provide plumes or aigrettes for the millinery trade. In 1910 the "plume trade" in the United States received its death blow when the sale of wild birds' feathers was outlawed. This action was followed both by additional legislation and the protection of the remaining nesting colonies, chiefly by Audubon wardens. Public opinion gradually changed. Women who had worn egret plumes on their bonnets heard these fragile and expensive ornaments referred to as "the badge of cruelty." The horrors of the plume trade were widely publicized. One eye-witness account, circulated by the Audubon Society, told of a visit to an egret colony after the plume hunters had left: "There, strewn on the floating water weed, and also on adjacent logs, were at least 50 carcasses of large white and smaller plumed egrets—nearly one-third of the rookery, perhaps more—the birds having been shot off their nests containing young. What a holocaust! Plundered for their plumes. What a monument of human callousness! There were 50 birds ruthlessly destroyed, besides their young (about 200) left to die of starvation!...Picture the cost of a plume!"

It is a wonder the egrets lasted as long as they did. The destruction had been in progress, at an increasing pace, for several decades, reaching its height during the Gay Nineties. The British stopped the slaughter of their birds by an act of Parliament in 1869, but it continued elsewhere. By 1902 the snowy egret was at low ebb in Florida, where, in that year, Arthur Cleveland Bent saw only a few of these birds and found none of them nesting. The monetary value of the plumes became so great that they were actually worth twice their weight in gold! Agents of the "trade" hunted down every last colony and finally moved on to Venezuela and Colombia.

Early in this century two Audubon wardens were killed by plume hunters and the protection movement nearly ran out of steam. But with the outlawing of the feather market the battle was won, and the job of searching out and finding the remaining birds began. Today the snowy egret is safe, but it is doubtful if it will ever again regain its original numbers. Only four large breeding rookeries exist in the United States, two in Audubon sanctuaries in Florida and Texas, one on a private preserve in Louisiana, and a fourth at Stone Harbor, New Jersey, less than a hundred miles from New York City, once the capital of the plumage trade. This New Jersey colony, in a sanctuary maintained by the town of Stone Harbor, has been repeatedly threatened by real-estate promoters who want the property for another subdivision. Thus far, overwhelming public opinion has prevented its complete destruction, although recently the town fathers voted to subdivide a portion of the sanctuary area.

Plate 11
Common
egret

The common egret is the symbol of the National Audubon Society, and the living bird itself is a monument to the great work of that organization, which secured the passage of the bill that outlawed the trade in plumes and sent its people into the southern swamps and marshes to guard the surviving colonies. In 1903 hunters were offered thirty-two dollars an ounce for the plumes of these handsome birds and, law or no law, the "long white" was ruthlessly pursued and slaughtered. Today the big egret is safe, but—like its smaller counterpart, the snowy egret—will never return to its original glory. It gives us some idea of the tremendous numbers of these birds in early times to read the records of the auction rooms. One source alone, the London Commercial Sales Rooms, sold 1608 packages of egret plumes in 1902. It was estimated that the average weight of a "package" was thirty ounces, which makes a total of 48,240 ounces. Since the plumes of four birds were required to make one ounce, on the average, this means that 192,960 egrets were killed to provide one year's supply of plumes for a single auction house. Added to this astounding total were several times that number of young birds and unhatched eggs. No small wonder the long road back has been such a difficult one.

The common egret is highly gregarious and usually nests in mixed colonies with other waders. The eggs number from three to four and are a pale bluish-green. When the young hatch, after twenty-three or twenty-four days of incubation, they are ugly ducklings like those of other herons. They generally remain in the nest, which is often high off the ground, until they are able to fly.

Almost ethereal in its pure white plumage, the common egret has a typical heron voice, which can only be described as a croak, low-pitched, hoarse, and decidedly unpleasant. But considering its undeniable poise and beauty, and the long history of its persecution, the common egret can be forgiven almost anything.

Plate 12
Black-crowned
night-heron

When autumn brings a nip to the northern air and the leaves turn red and gold, those of us who live in the subtropical climate of southern Florida feel and see none of these things, but we hear, sounding across the clear night sky, the *woc-woc-woc* of migrating night-herons. Night after night they pass overhead, in unknown numbers, their destination the sunny isles of the West Indies and Caribbean. For the black-crowned night-heron is another avian tourist, a dedicated wanderer, footloose if not fancy-free—it returns with remarkable regularity each spring to nest. But, like certain other birds, these herons are cosmopolitan enough to make their home in every conceivable environment, building their loose platforms of sticks in groves of spruce on Maine coastal islands, in mixed stands of maple, bayberry, and alders on the rim of a Massachusetts marsh, in the cattails of a Colorado slough, or near the top of a 160-foot fir in Oregon.

Birds like the black-crown have long since solved some of the international problems that beset man. They care not what flag flies over them or in what state they build their home. Once I banded a young night-heron in a white-cedar swamp on Long Island, New York. A year later it was discovered nesting in Duval County, Florida, happily mated to a fellow spirit it had apparently met en route.

Night-herons find that life can be reduced to a few very simple principles. I have no doubt that if a healthy male member of the great clan *Nycticorax* could be transported from far-off Borneo and dropped in the midst of a night-heron colony in New York State, he would be perfectly at home in a few minutes. For one thing, all night-herons the world over speak the same lingo. And for another, come spring, when our Borneo bird's legs turned red and he began to sing the soft *snap-hiss* roundelay of his kind, every pink-legged female night-heron in New York State would know exactly what was meant.

The incubating night-heron in the color plate could be either a male or a female. They have a mutual interest in their homelife and take turns not only in warming the family eggs, but, later on, in feeding and looking after their young.

Nycticorax, meaning "night raven", is the fanciful name given the clan in 1817 by the eminent British ornithologist, T. Forster. The birds themselves seem to have a less romantic, but thoroughly practical name for themselves, as befits their nature. If you have ever been near when one or more night-herons were gathered together, you've heard them announcing who they were: *Woc-woc-woc!*

We swung away from the littered dock on the Port of Spain waterfront, glad to escape from the smell of dead fish and the sight of swarms of bold, rapacious black vultures—the corbeaux of the local people. Our destination was the Caroni River swamp, where I hoped to see my first scarlet ibis colony, but from the condition of our boat and the sputtering of the ancient outboard motor, I wasn't at all sure we would make it. Rain was beginning to fall, and the boat leaked. Somehow the motor kept going. I didn't know about the motor, although it would have taken a great deal to discourage me at that point, for of all the wonders of the Caribbean that I had seen, or ever would see, this was bound to be the ultimate. "Jets of flame," William Beebe had called them, and Antoine Léotaud, the virtually unsung Trinidadian ornithologist, physician, and scholar of a century past, painted a true French Impressionist picture of them when he wrote: "beautiful red stains on the green background." So I was prepared for almost anything.

As we rounded the last stretch of mangrove and headed into the Caroni River, we saw several caymans, and a little way upstream one about five feet long slid and wriggled his way off the bank as we drew near. Close by, a dark object moved in the dim light beneath some red mangrove roots, and I found myself staring at the grim visage of a greater ani (*Crotophaga major*), with its pale greenish-yellow eyes and the huge, misshapen keel on its upper mandible. It is much larger than the common ani and more brilliant of plumage.

Overhead, seemingly endless flights of fork-tailed flycatchers (*Muscivora tyrannus*) were moving up river to roost in the mangroves, a lively sight that con-

Plate 13
Scarlet
ibis

tinued until sunset. It was still overcast and rain sputtered down on us intermittently.

As the motor coughed to a standstill and Cecil Brown, the warden, patiently tinkered, a scarlet ibis shot by overhead, so rich, so solid, and so splendid in color that I was entirely speechless. My Port of Spain cab driver, Kelly, who had never been in the swamp before, was standing up in the boat yelling "Flamingo! Flamingo!" at the top of his voice, and it was a moment or so before I could collect myself and shut him up.

In almost every way the scarlet ibis is a white ibis (*Eudocimus albus*) that has radically changed its color. It lives in the same habitat, eats the same food, is similar in its behavior, and is only slightly smaller. Like the white ibis in Florida, scarlet ibises are prized by the natives as food and are still killed for this reason in many districts of their range. Fortunately, some protection is now afforded them in Venezuela, and the Caroni Swamp Sanctuary in Trinidad has been in operation since 1953. At that time R. Hernandez estimated that the Caroni colony contained at least three thousand pairs.

When we reached the nesting place that rainy August evening, we found that most of the corocoros had long since hatched their young, which were well grown and on the point of flying. The brown, white, and pale rose chicks were bunched in the mangroves beneath a fluttering, vivid canopy of adult birds. Other adults were coming and going, their plumage a deep, satisfying richness. Several species of herons, among them the cattle egret, share the safety of this protected nesting place. Let us hope that this valuable sanctuary will remain inviolate for all time. The living beauty of the scarlet ibis is a tribute to any land in which it dwells, and its continued security is a tribute to those who preserve it.

Plate 14
Roseate
spoonbill

Most of the sixteenth-century adventurers who set forth to seek wealth and fame in the New World found only bitterness and frustration. The fountain of youth was an elusive conceit, while gold and precious stones fell into the hands of only a few minions of Church and state. But beauty was there in this new land, if it could be seen, and there was wealth undreamed of, if it could be discovered. The beauty was of many kinds, and in many ways it exceeded that of the Old World from which these restless men had come. Somehow, it seems appropriate that a world unknown to civilized man for endless eons of time should finally greet him with a radiance of excessive, extravagant color and form.

There are six species of spoonbills in the world, all rather plain and relatively unadorned except the brilliant roseate spoonbill of the New World. Those inhabiting Europe, Asia, Africa, and Australasia are mainly white in plumage, with small areas of buff or black here and there. The short crests they wear during the breeding season are their only claim to elegance. But the spoonbill of America is dazzling in its color patterns. Picture these pinks and crimsons and rose-tinted whites, these flashes of saffron and orange and golden buff in the person of one bird. And place it against the dark, heavily shadowed green of a mangrove bush, or suspend it momentarily in a sky of warm, sparkling blue. Where could nature have dared such a wild fling at beauty except in this brash, exuberant New World!

Even yet we are scarcely able to cope with such loveliness. Roseate spoonbills are not overly abundant except in remote corners of South America, where they are seldom seen and consequently not often disturbed. In the United States their history has been of persecution and senseless destruction. Thanks to the efforts of the Audubon Society and other conservation agencies, most of the surviving colonies are now protected. In spite of this, however, the future of these birds is anything but assured. The greatest threat today is from real-estate developments that have pushed them out of traditional nesting sites and appropriated their feeding places, which have been leveled and filled and turned into subdivisions. Thus the acquisitiveness of the sixteenth-century adventurers is not entirely dead, and whatever these modern prototypes are searching for it is not beauty, or they could not possibly overlook the roseate spoonbill.

These birds are not abundant anywhere in the Caribbean, but I have seen them, in small numbers, in the Bahamas, Cuba, and the Dominican Republic. They also appear more or less frequently in such locations as the Caroni River Swamp in Trinidad. Wherever they occur they deserve to be guarded as if they were the crown jewels.

The West Indian flamingo is the national bird of the Bahamas, and in former times was a truly representative Caribbean species, with a large population that encircled this incomparably beautiful sea, from Yucatán, Cuba, Hispaniola, and Islote Ave to the offshore islands and isolated mainland shores of South America, from Colombia to the Guianas. Today this strange and lovely creature is not only sadly reduced in numbers, but in grave danger of ultimate extinction. How has this come about? The flamingo in a wild state is more efficient and better able to look after itself than you might imagine. It is a strong flier, capable of long over-water journeys; it survives quite happily in salt-encrusted, desert-like environments where most birds would soon perish, and if not disturbed it will manage to rear its sturdy little chicks in large numbers year after year.

Plate 15
West
Indian
flamingo

The chief trouble is man. Even before the pickled tongues of flamingos were eaten as a delicacy at Roman banquets, the birds were slaughtered for their feathers, for food, and even for sport. They have been killed in every conceivable way, wherever they came in contact with men and the sons of men. In many areas this slaughter continues to this day. I have seen salt rakers on the Cuban coast spend an idle Sunday afternoon stalking and shooting a flamingo, which they cooked and ate with obvious relish that evening, tossing the dismembered head to their dogs. In the Bahamas I examined two flamingos that had been killed by some native boys who weren't even hungry enough to clean and cook them. Elsewhere in the Caribbean, in the recent past, eggs, young birds, and adults have been taken by people who were actually food-gathering, that most ancient of human occupations. W. H. Phelps, of Caracas, sent me photographs of the naked footprints of Venezuelan fishermen in the mud around the flamingo nest mounds which they had robbed of their eggs. As disturbing as these examples undoubtedly are, we must realize that it is difficult for hungry people to appreciate beauty or to worry very much about the possible extinction of a species. Nevertheless, such slaughter must be stopped. All important breeding colonies are now protected by special wardens, employed in widely separated regions by the Society for the Protection of the Flamingo in the Bahamas, the Bahamas National Trust, the Netherlands Antilles government, and the National Audubon Society.

Despite these efforts, the big story about the West Indian flamingo today is its present danger and struggle for survival. A great deal is being done, but an even greater effort will have to be made if these incredibly beautiful red-coated flocks are to be saved from oblivion.

Plate 16
Horned
screamer

We are told that the name "screamer" was applied to birds of this family in 1773 by Thomas Pennant, the British naturalist, antiquarian, and traveler, because of "the violent noise it makes." It is doubtful if Pennant ever saw a live screamer, or heard its voice, so you can believe that its trumpeting is loud enough to carry great distances—at least by reputation. There are now thought to be only three species of screamers, of which the horned screamer comes nearest to meeting the geographical restrictions of this book. Its normal habitat is in fresh-water marshes, swamps, and wet prairies or grasslands, and for all its size (up to three feet in total length and seven pounds in weight) and big turkey-like body, it is equipped with very large feet, elongated toes, and partial webs, so that it scrambles about over floating vegetation like a gallinule.

Alexander Wetmore, who knew the chaja or crested screamer in the Chaco country of South America, has given us a most informative picture of them (1926): "The screamer was found in the Chaco in remote regions where settlements were few, and was common in the pampas on large estancias, where the birds were given more or less protection. Though formerly distributed throughout this entire region they have been killed or driven away throughout extensive areas. Occasional screamers were noted from the train in crossing the marshy region in northern Santa Fe on July 5. At the Riacho Pilaga, in the interior of Formosa, single birds were observed about lagoons from August 10 to 21, and on August 16 an adult male was taken. Near Puerto Pinasco, Paraguay, they were common from September 6 to 30, and were found in the interior Chaco to the westward as far as I penetrated (to Kilometer 200). One was observed on the Rio Paraguay itself on September 30.

"Screamers ranged usually in pairs, but at times congregated in some numbers. On one occasion I saw 14 in a flock, circling in the air like vultures, 18 gathered in a band at the border of a lagoon and others scattered about near by, until in all I had 40 of the great birds under observation at one time. They were found ordinarily on floating masses of vegetation over deep water or in damp meadows where marshy growth was not too luxuriant. When alarmed or suspicious they flew up to perch in the low tops of near-by trees, where they were able to view the country. On alighting on the *camalote*, as the masses of water hyacinth and other vegetation that formed floating mats in the water were called, they frequently extended the wings for a few seconds, until they had tested the footing, but their long toes enabled them to walk over these insecure masses without trouble. The approach of any suspicious object was the occasion of loud trumpeting calls, rather gooselike in nature, that resembled the syllables *chah hah*, given slowly and with equal emphasis. These calls were loud, so that they carried for long distances, and had a certain stirring quality that was more or less pleasing, but were repeated so incessantly that in time they tended to become irritating, particularly when more desirable game was put on the alert by the alarms sounded by these efficient sentinels. These loud calls were often followed by a curious rattling, rumbling sound, audible only for a short distance, that resembled the noise produced by rubbing and compressing a dried, distended bladder. This sound was wholly internal and seemed to be produced when air was forced from the large air sacs into the smaller cells that lie between the skin and the body. At times the forepart of the body was slightly elevated as it was produced."

Of their flying ability, which is considerable, Wetmore wrote: "In the vicinity of Lavalle, Buenos Aires, screamers were common from October 27 to November 9, and after my experience with them in the Chaco it seemed strange to find them walking about in marshy spots among scattered bands of sheep. The flight of screamers is strong, and they rise heavily with loud swishing wings. I saw them occasionally soaring in circles high in the air. At the Estancia Los Yngleses I was told that 50 had gathered to feed in a small tract of alfalfa and that it had been necessary to drive them away to prevent damage. On November 6, after a severe storm, an immature bird washed ashore on the beach below Cape San Antonio. I suppose that it had been blown out to sea during a heavy gale and drowned.

"In Uruguay screamers were seen at the Laguna Castillos, near San Vicente, on January 31, and the Arroyo Sarandi (Paso Alamo) February 2. A few were noted near Lazcano on February 6 and 8. The birds were very wary here and were much hunted. Their flesh is dark and coarse fibered, but I found it palatable. The species is known universally as *Chaja*, a name given in imitation of the common call."

The horned screamer is now extirpated, or nearly so, from Trinidad, where it formerly lived in the Narvina Swamp, the Everglades-like region near the eastern coast of the island. In Surinam, François Haverschmidt reported in 1955 that it is "apparently very rare in fresh-water swamps along the coast." With the expansion of human populations, it is increasingly difficult for large, loud-voiced, and otherwise conspicuous birds to survive, unless special measures are taken for their protection.

Plate 17
Black-bellied
tree-duck

Many North American waterfowl winter in the West Indies and throughout the Caribbean generally (James Bond includes fourteen species), but there are in addition six species of ducks that are West Indian residents, and at least three more South American species that breed on the Caribbean slopes of northern South America. A prominent member of this resident group, breeding in both Central and South America, and a visitor to the Lesser Antilles, is the black-bellied tree-duck. A closely related form, the West Indian tree-duck (*Dendrocygna arborea*) is resident in the Bahamas, Greater Antilles, and northern Lesser Antilles.

Tree-ducks are generally placed in the systematic order between the geese (Anserinae) and the surface-feeding ducks (Anatinae), which seems reasonable enough when one considers that they are very gooselike. This is especially true of their manner of flight, which is often in single file, and with a slower wingbeat than in the ducks. They stretch their long necks like geese when alarmed. And the black-bellied and West Indian varieties actually roost in trees, and even nest in trees, a habit not shared by all so-called tree-ducks.

As a result of the unrestricted shooting of these ducks throughout their Caribbean range they are growing scarce in many areas. Conservationists believe that there is a great need for a co-ordinated effort on the part of all Caribbean countries to set up a co-operative nature-preservation program. Such a program might be implemented through a Caribbean National Trust for the preservation of places of historic interest and natural beauty, along much the same lines as the British National Trust. "Places of natural beauty" would be certain to include swamps, marshes, lagoons, and other areas where these and other interesting forms of wildlife could find a safe haven.

Plate 18
Bahama
pintail

One morning in spring a group of us climbed Conch Shell Hill, on the south face of Great Inagua in the Bahamas, to have a look at the tropicbird colony in the rocks of the sloping cliff that dips gently into the sea. From the crest we turned to gaze out across the wild, uninhabited interior of that extraordinary island, with its flocks of flamingos, roseate spoonbills, white-phase reddish egrets, its wild jackasses, limestone caves, and other natural treasures. And there, just below us, partly hidden in the shadows of surrounding tropical buttonwoods, lay the *café con leche* waters of Conch Shell Pond. We decided at once to make this our next stop and were soon standing on its muddy shores. Almost at once someone spotted a Bahama pintail swimming along under the far shore. As we moved closer to get a better look, there was a sudden stirring and splashing almost at our feet, and we had flushed the mother "white-jaw" and her downy brood. The adults were in their best plumage, their dark cinnamon backs, fawn-

PLATE 1. WHITE-TAILED TROPICBIRD (*Phaethon lepturus*)

PLATE 2. BROWN PELICAN (*Pelecanus occidentalis*)

PLATE 3. DOUBLE-CRESTED CORMORANT

(*Phalacrocorax auritus*)

PLATE 4. ANHINGA (*Anhinga anhinga*)

PLATE 5. MAGNIFICENT FRIGATEBIRD (*Fregata magnificens*)

PLATE 6. GREAT BLUE HERON (*Ardea herodias*)

PLATE 7. GREEN HERON (*Butorides virescens*)

PLATE 8. LITTLE BLUE HERON (*Florida caerulea*)

PLATE 9. CATTLE EGRET (*Bubulcus ibis*)

PLATE 10. SNOWY EGRET (*Leucophoyx thula*)

PLATE 11. COMMON EGRET (*Casmerodius albus*)

PLATE 12. BLACK-CROWNED NIGHT-HERON (*Nycticorax nycticorax*)

a

b

c

PLATE 13. SCARLET IBIS (*Eudocimus ruber*)

a

b

c

d

PLATE 14. ROSEATE SPOONBILL (*Ajaia ajaja*)

a

b

PLATE 15. WEST INDIAN FLAMINGO (*Phoenicopterus ruber*)

C

PLATE 16. HORNED SCREAMER (*Anhima cornuta*)

PLATE 17. BLACK-BELLIED TREE-DUCK (*Dendrocygna autumnalis*)

PLATE 18. BAHAMA PINTAIL (*Anas bahamensis*)

colored tails, and the bright red on their bills shining brilliantly against the sun-flecked shadows. We thought them among the loveliest little waterfowl we had ever seen.

All ducks seem to be fair game in the West Indies and Caribbean, and the Bahama pintails, which are resident breeding, and always available, have been sadly reduced in numbers. Even the eggs are taken. They are easily killed, and a flock will circle back over their disabled comrades after a first volley, so that they receive the second load. Dr. James McCandless, writing of their status in Puerto Rico, said: "Permanent resident, formerly common, now very rare. Nests in grass where cattle, mongoose and eggers have destroyed many. Many experienced Puerto Rican hunters have never seen this duck." Yet in 1927 Alexander Wetmore had written: "This duck is the most common of the resident ducks of the island." We can hope that present efforts to establish refuges and improve protective measures will be successful.

You might see a king vulture by chance, and should know it by its contrasting black-and-white pattern. Of course, it is not really a common species anywhere and, in any event, you would have to look for it in humid forest regions of tropical America. In its habitat it may be fairly numerous, often in company with the commoner members of its family—*zopilote* and *zopilote negro*, the turkey and black vultures. It does not occur in the West Indies, where the scavenger job is taken care of by "John Crow," the turkey vulture (known on Spanish-speaking islands as aura).

Plate 19
King
vulture

Some years ago in Panama, Dr. Frank M. Chapman, at that time the illustrious head of the Bird Department of the American Museum of Natural History, was conducting his famous experiments in answer to the question (as he put it): "Does the buzzard follow his nose?" A century before, the great Audubon, then a struggling neophyte seeking recognition, read his first scientific paper before a learned society in Edinburgh, where he was trying to raise subscriptions to publish his monumental work on the birds of America. As he wrote later, it was his "maiden speech," and he added: "Well do I remember the uneasy feeling which I experienced." And no small wonder, for the topic he had chosen was "Account of the Habits of the Turkey Buzzard (*Vultur aura*) particularly with a view of Exploding the Opinion generally entertained of its extraordinary power of Smelling."

One hundred years later, in Panama, Dr. Chapman decided to carry out his own tests. Had Audubon been right in deriding the vulture's sense of smell? After many experiments, Chapman found the answer to be yes *and* no—the vulture depended on both sight and smell. What gave him the greatest thrill, however, was the wholly unexpected appearance one morning of a king vulture, a bird rarely seen on the Gatun Lake islands. The "lure" was a small package containing fish entrails, and Dr. Chapman was delighted that "so small a lure in so inconspicuous a place should attract so rare a bird as the King Vulture."

So, if you have an uncontrollable urge to see a king vulture, and there isn't one in your local zoo, you now know where you must go and what you can do to attract one.

Plate 20
Snail
kite

There are many people in Florida and elsewhere in the United States who will object, some of them vehemently, to calling this bird snail kite rather than Everglade kite. For this species is to them a symbol of the over-all conservation problems of Florida, just as the whooping crane is a symbol of similar problems throughout the United States and Canada. While we understand and sympathize wholeheartedly with such feelings, the snail kite is not restricted to Florida and, in addition, this is a book about Caribbean birds. We therefore believe that we should use the name that is applicable and generally used throughout most of its range.

In Florida the snail kite is close to extirpation as a result of the widespread drainage of fresh-water marshes, shooting by waterfowl hunters, and disturbance during the nesting season, even on those unspoiled marshes that remain, by an overflowing human population bent on recreation and more interested in large-mouth bass than kites. But this isn't the whole story. The snail kite is one of those species that seems unable to change with the times. In this case it's a question of food habits. *Rostrhamus sociabilis* feeds on the green snail (*Pomacea caliginosa*) and nothing else. It's just as if you were unable, physically and psychologically, to eat anything but pork. If all the pigs in your part of the world became scarce, or disappeared entirely, you would be in trouble. As Florida, and now Cuban, fresh-water marshes have been drained, the pearly clusters of *Pomacea* eggs, and finally the snails themselves, have gradually disappeared. Exit the snail kite.

Fortunately, there are plenty of these birds elsewhere in their extensive range and, perhaps, if kite enthusiasts could learn to set up and manage a fresh-water marsh with exactly the right environmental conditions, both *Pomacea* snails and kites could be introduced therein successfully. Such a "kite farm" would be an interesting conservation experiment.

Plate 21
Roadside
hawk

One of the most common tropical birds of prey, the roadside hawk is aptly named. Like northern broad-wings, which they resemble, these hawks frequently perch on fenceposts or trees close to roads. Since they are rather tame, they are easily approached. Their favorite habitat seems to be cultivated areas, clearings, second growth, and scrub, and this doubtless reflects a preference for a daily menu of small rodents, insects, and reptiles that usually abound in such locations.

Ornithologists are regaled by the polymorphic character (literally: many forms) of this little hawk, and while authors of most field guides, for obvious reasons, advise the amateur bird-watcher to forget about subspecies, there are interesting exceptions. After telling his readers not to concern themselves with subspecies, Roger Tory Peterson states: "It is a challenge, however, to be able to identify some of the more well-marked races." But perhaps the experts are right and only advanced students should be concerned with such matters.

To us, the real challenge would be to try working out the differences in climate, food, and other factors that result in a roadside hawk from a dry, scrubby area in northern Yucatán being paler and less heavily streaked on the tail than a bird of the same species from Campeche or Guatemala, where conditions are more humid or the elevation a few hundred feet greater. One ornithologist, who has kept many different kinds of hawks and eagles in captivity, claims that he can control the shading of the plumage in these birds, from very pale to very dark, by deliberately withholding or increasing certain basic ingredients in their normal diet, such as proteins and B-complex vitamins. In this way he has taken a "normal" red-tailed hawk from the eastern United States and by controlled diet has literally produced a geographic race, known as Krider's hawk, usually found in the prairie provinces and states—a *very* pale, sometimes almost white, "red-tail" with a pinkish tail.

We see then that it isn't simply a question of climate or humidity, as was once supposed, but a combination of these and other factors with the whole ecological complex of an environment, including the nutritional constituents of the prey.

In spite of differences in their environment and diet, and therefore in plumage coloration, all roadside hawks probably have much the same voice. I haven't heard enough of them to be certain, but in coastal Panama (which is quite humid) Dr. Chapman described their call as a loud *wack*, *wack*, *wack*, *kíe*.

Tropical America, with its wealth of diverse environments and rich variety of animal life, has a grand array of interesting and colorful birds of prey. The ornate hawk-eagle is not the least colorful of these, although it has some stiff competition. In Mexico alone there are twenty-one species of kites, hawks, and eagles that are tropical in distribution and do not occur north of Mexico. Many of them are big, spectacular birds.

The hawk-eagles are placed between the large "buzzard" type or *Buteo* hawks and true eagles such as the golden eagle and bald eagle. Thus, in a sense, they are something of both, but not entirely one or the other. Some authorities use the name "eagle-hawk" rather than the reverse, which would appear to lean in the direction of their more eagle-like proclivities. Eugene Eisenmann prefers "hawk-eagle," since it conforms with the older usage and that applied in the Old World for birds of the same group.

There are two other hawk-eagles in Middle and South America, the black-and-white and the black. As its name signifies, the present species is the most colorful. Emmet Blake says that it is retiring and not likely to be seen soaring over open country. Raymond Paynter considers it the most common of the very large

Plate 22
Ornate
hawk-eagle

hawks in Quintana Roo, though not abundant by any standard. He collected one that had been feeding on a skunk, but its choice of food is doubtless quite varied and impersonal. When Dr. Chapman was studying a large colony of oropéndolas on Barro Colorado in Panama, he saw a hawk-eagle plummet out of the sky, strike an oropéndola at work on its nest, and carry it off into the forest. He wrote (in 1929): "This event caused tremendous excitement among the oropéndolas, their united cries of alarm producing the effect of a loud chorus. They all left the tree and for the remainder of the day the colony was completely disorganized."

Plate 23
Osprey

Sandy sprunt and I were returning one day from a visit to Union Creek on Great Inagua, in the Bahamas, when I spotted a big, white-headed eagle-like bird perched in a tall tree a couple of hundred yards away. It was an osprey, but it was the first time I had seen one of the resident Bahamian race at close range and it was some minutes before I could accept its identity. Although I have been familiar with ospreys since I was a boy, those I knew had dark brown feathers on the crown and hindneck and through the eye.

Some years ago I was cruising the shallow, turquoise waters of eastern Florida Bay in company with Frank M. Chapman. We had seen a number of ospreys, which nest in the winter months in that area, and Dr. Chapman remarked that he had often wondered if these resident ospreys might not be more closely related to the white-headed Bahamian or Cuban birds than to ospreys from farther north. We didn't see a white-headed individual that day, nor have I since come across one in Florida Bay.

But these winter-nesting ospreys are different in other ways. For one thing, when their kin from Ontario lakes or the tidewater country of Maryland are moving along the Florida Keys on their way to winter quarters farther south, these birds are building their bulky nests atop a dead mangrove stub or even incubating their eggs. And, unlike many of their northern cousins, these Florida Bay ospreys seem never to have heard that eagles are the king of birds. In this region they dominate the fishing grounds completely and without the slightest hesitation will attack and rob an eagle of its freshly caught prey.

As an example of the wide-ranging abilities of this species, there is a record of an osprey that was banded as a nestling in Cecil County, Maryland, in July and recovered the following September in western Mato Grosso, Brazil. Most of the ospreys seen in the Caribbean are migrants and wanderers from North America.

Plate 24
Limpkin

There is a certain air of mystery about the limpkin, conveyed in part by its mournful wail ("the voice of one crying in the wilderness," as Arthur Cleveland Bent described it) and also by the shadowy nature of its secluded retreats. But although you may feel this dark and mysterious sensation—perhaps just an uneasy tingling along your spine—it is my belief that this may be engendered as much by the atmosphere, the psychological miasma of the swamp, as by this alert, quick-moving, flesh-and-blood bird. Nevertheless, the voice is eerie. If you have never heard it before, this penetrating cry will shake you to the soles of your feet. It is remarkable how otherwise reasonable people react to this sound. Dr. Henry Bryant of Boston, who, a century ago, contributed so many valuable observations on natural history, thought the note of the limpkin "the most disagreeable of any of our native birds." And the venerable William Brewster, one of the fathers of American ornithology, wrote of it as "a hoarse rattling cry like the gasp of a person being strangled."

Like the snail kite, the limpkin feeds on the *Pomacea* snail. But, in addition, it eats fresh-water mussels, frogs, lizards, worms, aquatic insects, and a variety of similar fare. So while the drainage of marshes and swamps has reduced the limpkin population in many places, they are an adaptable species and have held their own very well.

The name "limpkin" has not been satisfactorily explained. Buffon gave it the French name "courlan" in 1781, and Audubon referred to it as "the scolopaceous courlan," implying that it is a worm-eating, snipe-like courlan. Limpkin, which has somehow survived, is supposed to be an early Floridian name that describes its gait, like that of a limping man, i.e., a "limpkin." Although this might be called a "country name," probably of illiterate origin, it is colorful enough to have survived all these years.

It is easy to grow ecstatic about the purple gallinule, and even in the concise, matter-of-fact pages of a field guide, Roger Tory Peterson calls it "one of the most beautiful of all water birds." I believe that its tameness is as outstanding as the brilliance of its color, and the two together are what make it so irresistible. There are a good many birds that have resplendent plumage, but are so retiring, or so disagreeable when you do see them, that the beauty is spoiled.

*Plate 25
Purple
gallinule*

The purple gallinule likes placid ponds grown up with water lilies, yellow lotus, spatter docks, or bonnets. With its extremely long toes it climbs around through the lush plant growth or runs easily across the broad leaf pads, as Audubon wrote, "with great speed, and dives with equal address, often moving off under water with nothing but the bill above."

For a bird that is supposed to be a weak flyer, the purple gallinule can cover amazing distances. In addition to its regular migrations, it wanders far from its normal paths—to Colorado, Wisconsin, southern Ontario, Newfoundland, Bermuda, Tristan da Cunha, and even the island of South Georgia on the very edge of Antarctica.

The sunbittern is semiaquatic and lives in solitary seclusion in dank tropical swamps and marshes. It is a strange bird in many ways and ornithologists have had a difficult time classifying it. The first specimens from Surinam evidently

*Plate 26
Sunbittern*

reached European museums in the eighteenth century. The general appearance of the bird, which does and yet does not resemble an off-beat heron, had the various systematists of the day rather confused for quite a while. Eventually, in 1811, it was given a place and a genus all its own, and there it has reposed ever since.

Apparently a great deal was learned about the habits and behavior of this secretive, seldom-observed bird from specimens living in captivity. A pair nested in the Zoological Gardens in London and their young, on hatching, were covered with mottled down. The adults walk with slow, precise steps and when excited or alarmed spread their magnificent wings and tails in a really spectacular display.

Emmet Blake considers them one of the most beautiful of Mexican birds. They are not only uncommon but so retiring that they are seldom seen.

It should be added that the sunbittern is not a bittern at all. It is a marsh bird with its own individual peculiarities and has been placed (along with the sungrebes, jacanas, and oystercatchers) between the rails and the plovers. From this we can assume that it exhibits some of the characteristics of both these well-known groups.

Plate 27 *American jacana* Years ago, on the banks of a resaca in the Rio Grande Delta country of south Texas, I spent several days—without any luck—looking for jacanas, which are sometimes seen there. Then, not long ago, I was searching for a flamingo colony in eastern Cuba, and there, in a lovely marsh somewhere along the lower course of the Río Cauto in Oriente Province, I came across a whole bevy of these delightful birds. Not only were they beautifully plumaged, but they skipped about over the surface mat of lily pads, bonnets, and other floating vegetation with a lively grace and zest that were a pleasure to watch, their elongated toes serving as highly efficient water skis. And all the time they kept up a noisy *yip-yip-yip* that is the characteristic sound of many a tropical marsh.

On another occasion, in Jamaica, I drove into the back country south of Montego Bay, intending to visit the wild Cockpit region to see the famous jabbering crows and perhaps a few parrots. It was August, the rainy season. Before the morning was over it was pouring, and instead of chancing the mud of uncertain side roads, I decided to stay on the Adelphi-Hampden road and put off the jabbering crows until later. It didn't matter a great deal in any case, for almost anywhere you go in Jamaica you are sure to find new and interesting birds. Somewhere near Hampden I turned into a well-surfaced lane and drove through fine open country with well-tended fields and meadows on all sides. Here and there I found a small pond and a few water birds. There were numbers of little blue herons, purple gallinules, least grebes, cattle egrets, and, on every pond, a pair or two of jacanas. One pair made such a fuss, raising their rounded wings and showing the "pure primrose-yellow," as Lady Taylor calls it, underneath, that I kept my eye on them. And, sure enough, hiding in the heavy vegetation were two gangling brown-and-white youngsters, not yet able to fly.

I couldn't decide whether the sharp spurs on the bend of each wing were yellow or orange. Some authors say one and some the other, and I imagine that, like the so-called soft parts of most birds, the color varies with the season and may turn from yellow to orange at pairing time. The function of these spurs is not understood.

May Jeffrey-Smith describes the nest as a rough platform of grass and bamboo leaves, partly supported by the twigs of fallen bamboos and partly submerged. Sometimes the eggs may lie right in the water. In Jamaica the nesting season may extend from early April through August.

If you have ever had occasion to seek the peace and quiet of a warm, sunny shore and found it already claimed by the black-necked stilt, you will know what I mean when I say that these can be the most exasperating of birds. They will not give up. The sharp, penetrating *ip-ip-ip*, the constant flying about, the fluttering of the wings, the agitated running this way and that, will soon force you to retreat to a less "stilted" locality.

Plate 28
Black-necked
stilt

I recall with mixed emotions a hot day on the shore of a salt pond in the Upper Lakes region of Great Inagua in the Bahamas. My friends and I had gone there in the half-light of early morning to set up an observation blind from which to watch the expected hatching of the sprawling flamingo colony located close by in the shallows of the pond. When I was fixed comfortably in the blind and my friends had withdrawn to the shade of some tropical buttonwoods some distance away, the light began to improve and with it the visibility. Shortly the sun came up. The flamingos were flying in and out of the colony at a furious clip, and the thin, piping cries of the newly hatched chicks could be heard everywhere. Just as I was getting absorbed in the drama before me, a group of stilts, which had been flitting about nearby, moved closer and spotted my movements inside the burlap blind. The flamingos never even suspected my presence. The stilts, however, not only saw me, but set up such a hue and cry that my morning was ruined. There was nothing I could do except retreat. With stilts it is always like that.

The length and thinness of their legs in relation to the rest of their body struck Buffon as an "enormous defect" of nature, but he had the grace to admit that he did not know much about them. The neck of the stilt is highly flexible and, as Elliott Coues noted, the legs can be bent backward, with an acute angle at the heel joint to bring the body lower when feeding. Actually, except when disturbed by flamingo-watchers or people seeking quiet, they are poised and graceful birds, walking along with careful, measured steps and flying with easy skill.

Stilts feed on small snails, small fishes, aquatic beetles, flies, and other insects, including grasshoppers. On occasion they have been known to eat the seeds of widgeongrass (*Ruppia*).

Before the shooting of shore-birds was prohibited by law in the United States, the black-necked stilt was seriously reduced in numbers, notably along the

Atlantic Coast, where it formerly nested as far north as New Jersey. Today it is once more an abundant species, but shooting in all seasons still occurs at many locations in the West Indies.

Plate 29
Laughing
gull
With a party of friends I was crossing Florida Bay in a boat and someone had just asked what kind of bird was soaring over the boat's wake, when the bird itself replied with a raucous *ha-ha-ha!* As it continued this unseemly mirth, the notes became higher-pitched and more piercing. It seemed a simple matter to explain that this was a laughing gull, but oddly enough the name is so appropriate and so obvious that people hesitate to believe you.

You can scarcely fail to see this species in the Caribbean, although there are gaps in its distribution, both seasonal and ecological. I have not seen a breeding colony in the area, but there are a number of them. In fact, it is the only breeding gull of this region. Laughing gulls are a coastal species and build their nests on the ground out of whatever material is handy—grasses and seaweeds in some locations, stones, coral debris, and shells in others. In the Netherlands Antilles, Wagenaar Hummelinck reports, they have built nests on low stony walls separating deserted salt pans. Invariably they nest in colonies, some of them quite large.

Audubon was probably the first tourist to observe the laughing gull stealing a fish from the brown pelican. This is a common practice of these gulls, grabbing the fish right out of the larger bird's pouch, and the pelican never seems to know how it happened.

Plate 30
Sooty
tern
Once I rode out the edge of a hurricane, drifting helplessly with two Andros natives in a small baremasted sloop in the deep waters between Andros and New Providence in the Bahamas. When dawn came there was some sense of relief in just being able to see the mountainous waves and the roaring waterspouts that threatened us, but the only really cheerful note was the appearance of a small flock of seabirds, which mewed and fluttered over the foaming crests of the tumbling seas all around us. Most of them were sooty terns, and I watched them with gratitude. Somehow their matter-of-fact search for food and their ability to withstand the towering gusts of wind and stinging spray with such obvious equanimity dispelled the nightmares we had been through in the darkness and restored our hope.

The sooty tern has been a prime favorite of mine ever since, although I had known the bird long before and had previously admired its many outstanding qualities. The sooty is one of the great oceanic wanderers. We know the location of many of their colonies, some of them containing immense numbers of birds, but large flocks of sooty terns are seldom encountered at sea in the off season. Where do they go between breeding periods? One of the most famous colonies is that in the Dry Tortugas, off Florida, where today more than eighty thousand sooty and noddy terns nest each spring. This is one of the oldest-known bird

PLATE 19. KING VULTURE (*Sarcoramphus papa*)

PLATE 20. SNAIL KITE (*Rostrhamus sociabilis*)

PLATE 21. ROADSIDE HAWK (*Buteo magnirostris*)

PLATE 22. ORNATE HAWK-EAGLE (*Spizaetus ornatus*)

PLATE 23. OSPREY (*Pandion haliaetus*)

PLATE 24. LIMPKIN (*Aramus guarauna*)

PLATE 28. BLACK-NECKED STILT (*Himantopus mexicanus*)

PLATE 29. LAUGHING GULL (*Larus atricilla*)

PLATE 30. SOOTY TERN (*Sterna fuscata*)

PLATE 31. ROYAL TERN (*Thalasseus maximus*)

PLATE 32. BLACK SKIMMER (*Rynchops nigra*)

PLATE 33. WHITE-TIPPED DOVE (*Leptotila verreauxi*)

colonies in the New World, having been described in 1516 by Ponce de Leon's historian. A half century ago it was regularly "egged" by visiting fishermen and commercial eggers from Florida and Cuba. Soon after the turn of the century, the Audubon Society began a protection program, and today the islands, along with historic Fort Jefferson on Garden Key, are a national monument under the protective wing of the National Park Service. Thousands of tourists and bird-watchers visit it each year, making the sixty-eight-mile sea voyage by boat or chartered plane. Ostensibly this is the Fort Jefferson National Monument, but the big attraction is really the tern colony.

It was in the Tortugas colony that John Watson made his now classic studies of the homing ability of sooty and noddy terns. Both individual nests and the birds themselves were marked so that they could be recognized later. The birds were then carried in passing steamers to such distant points as Havana, Cape Hatteras, and Galveston, Texas, where they were released. The Havana birds were back on their nests the next day, those from Hatteras returned in five days, and two of the six released at Galveston were back in six and seven days.

As with all birds that perform long migrations, a compass, a radar set, and a special understanding of magnetic forces seem to be built in, but the sooty tern appears to be especially gifted in the navigation department. For this and other reasons the sooty tern is a bird worth knowing and worth protecting wherever it is found.

If the royal tern were less numerous and less ubiquitous than it is, we would probably make a tremendous fuss over it and declare it one of the most beautiful, most superb, most excellent of birds. But alas, the fate of the commonplace is otherwise. In season, the royal tern is an everyday sight along many familiar stretches of coastline, and during the winter months in the West Indies and Caribbean the royal tern is seen everywhere. *Plate 31 Royal tern*

Actually, this is an exceedingly handsome bird by any standard. The pale orange of the bill and the abbreviated little crest that stands out, like a misplaced Van Dyke beard, on the back of its head are not to be overlooked. The Caspian tern may have a redder bill; it may be a larger bird and have the extra glamour of being less than common in the region, but the royal tern is equally entrancing and has the distinct advantage of being ever-present.

These birds are highly gregarious, and you will seldom see one by itself. In their breeding colonies, where they lay their eggs on the ground, they crowd together in unbelievable numbers, so close-packed that the ground between birds is scarcely visible. They lay one or two eggs, sometimes three.

You will not see many black skimmers in the West Indies, although they may occur offshore or on isolated beaches on some of the islands in winter. But these unusual birds are common enough in other parts of the Caribbean. There are large *Plate 32 Black skimmer* breeding colonies along the Atlantic and Gulf coasts, from New England all the way around to Mexico, and with the first cold weather these birds move south in hurrying bands. Skimmers are graceful, effortless fliers and extremely gregarious, so that they travel in big flocks, often made up of several hundred individuals. With their sharply contrasting black-and-white plumage pattern they make a grand sight, wheeling in close formations just above the surface of the water, turning this way and that, so that they seem dark and indistinct at one moment and gleaming white the next.

When you approach a flock of skimmers resting on a mudbank, their heads and rather outlandish bills will be turned directly into the wind, their posture hunched and streamlined, the long wings folded across the rump. As you get nearer they shuffle about on their short legs and begin "talking" in a low, uncertain tone, so that all you hear is a kind of chattering sound. But this grows in volume and as their wings unfold and they take off, the chattering is replaced by a sharp, steady "barking." They actually sound like a pack of hounds, and we can understand why the vernacular name "seadog" has been given them in some areas.

The skimmer's unique method of feeding apparently requires them to take most of their meals at night, when the water temperature has dropped and small fishes and other animal life have risen to the surface. One school of thought has suggested that skimmers make a preliminary run across a stretch of water to stir up these aquatic creatures, which are then picked up on the return run over exactly the same course. At any rate, no other bird feeds in this manner—the lower mandible barely breaking the surface of the water. I knew a professional trapper who was always figuring out new ways to capture animals alive. As he watched a skimmer moving steadily across the smooth waters of a small pond, he said, in all seriousness, "If you were to stretch a thin wire just under the surface..." I doubt if he ever tried it. How in the world would you go about feeding a captive skimmer?

Plate 33
White-tipped
dove

There are so many large, handsome doves and pigeons in the Caribbean region that it would be difficult to pick one as most representative or most ornamental. The white-tipped dove is common and widely distributed, and although it does not occur in the West Indies it is well represented there by a close relation, the white-bellied dove (*Leptotila jamaicensis*). They not only look alike, but have the same shy, retiring habits and may be heard long before they are seen. In her colorful style, May Jeffrey-Smith writes that in Jamaica "Its sobbing notes have been translated as: 'Rain come wet me, sun come burn me.' You should then ask it, 'Why don't you build a house?' It will reply, 'What's that to you?' " She also says that these doves will come out into the open if you learn to imitate their call, and will feed around your home if you lay out corn or naseberry seeds. At the Westwood High School a pair regularly landed on the steps when the great bell rang for prayers and often came to the school garden during singing periods.

In Mexico the white-tipped dove ranges from sea level to an elevation of seven thousand feet, being more common in rain forest than in coastal scrub. But on dry islands such as Curaçao and Bonaire, Wagenaar Hummelinck says, it inhabits the dense undergrowth of fruit plantations, manchineel thickets (which are numerous), thorny scrub "and all other kinds of well-shaded bush and scrub vegetation, particularly along roadsides and often in dense opuntia vegetation." Charles Belcher and G. D. Smooker found it most abundant in "monsoonal bush" on the islands of the Dragon's Mouths, at the extreme northwest tip of Trinidad, especially on Patos, farthest west. Inland on Trinidad, around Tacarigua and else-where, it is one of the most common doves, according to G. C. A. Junge and G. F. Mees, inhabiting high secondary growths, bamboo in particular, and if found in true forest will not be far from the edge. François Haverschmidt found a similar preference in Surinam.

The nest may be quite large and well made for a dove, which usually builds a fragile platform of sticks and plant fibers. It is most often placed in a tree or shrub, from five to nearly twenty feet above the ground. The two eggs are white with a greenish cast.

Doves and pigeons are considered year-around game birds throughout the West Indies and Caribbean, and many forms are gravely reduced in numbers locally. Although easily killed, the white-tipped dove and its relative, the white-bellied dove, seem to be generally abundant.

The blue-headed quail-dove is neither widely distributed nor abundant, and these are two good reasons why it has been included in this volume. A third reason is its beauty, which is outstanding. A bird species whose normal distribution is limited to a single island is obviously more vulnerable than other members of its family with whole continents in which to spread themselves. The blue-headed quail-dove is found only in Cuba, where it has become increasingly rare. In many respects it is typical of other insular pigeons and doves, some of which are already extinct or locally extirpated, while the survival of others is in doubt.

Plate 34
Blue-headed
quail-dove

James C. Greenway lists twelve birds that have become extinct in the West Indies since the late seventeenth century. Of the causes of such extinction, he says: "A rail, two owls, and two night-hawks, five of the twelve, nested on the ground; quite probably they were victims of the rats and mongooses introduced by man. A sixth, the small finch of St. Christopher (St. Kitts), is thought to have been too much disturbed at nesting time by a large band of monkeys...also imported by man...A single dove and two parrots probably were shot and trapped too long and incessantly to allow them to survive on islands so heavily populated by human beings as Puerto Rico. The Cuban macaw, never recorded as numerous, probably suffered the same fate in spite of the fact that the human population of Cuba is relatively not as large as Puerto Rico."

The "dove" mentioned is the Puerto Rican plain pigeon (*Columba inornata wetmorei*), last recorded in the hills near Añasco in November, 1926. In addition to overshooting, Greenway adds "its extinction in Puerto Rico came concurrently with the almost total destruction of forests."

Other pigeons have been wiped out locally. The red-necked pigeon (*Columba squamosa*) has disappeared from Barbados and is on the verge of extirpation on Aruba, St. Martin, and St. Eustatius, according to Karel Voous. In Jamaica, the local race of the plain pigeon, there called the "blue pigeon," was not uncommon a century ago, but is now rare and seldom observed. The white-crowned pigeon (*Columba leucocephala*) is reduced by shooting in many parts of its range, particularly in the Bahamas, where it has been slaughtered at its breeding places by so-called "sportsmen," as well as for the market—a deadly combination. The Grenada dove (*Leptotila wellsi*) has been reported by James Bond as being exceedingly rare. There are many other examples.

We can only hope that human affairs in the Caribbean will someday reach a state where the various governments will have an opportunity to give full attention to the proper management and preservation of all non-renewable resources. Once they are gone, these handsome doves and pigeons can never be replaced.

Plate 35
Scarlet
macaw

One of the largest and most brilliant members of its illustrious family, the scarlet macaw is fairly common and highly conspicuous in certain parts of its extensive range. In Mexico, the smaller, green-plumaged military macaw (*Ara militaris*) lives in both arid coastal areas and mountains, where Emmet Blake says it reaches eight thousand feet altitude. But the scarlet macaw is more a bird of the lowland forests, except that in the Guianas of South America it seems to prefer the hill forests of the interior.

It is good to know that a number of the macaws are abundant and widely distributed. In discussing these "large, gay, noisy birds," as he very aptly describes them, James C. Greenway points out that records of their presence on West Indian islands began with Columbus in 1496, "and there can be little doubt that the birds were endemic on many islands." He suggests that the Cuban red macaw (*Ara tricolor*), extinct since about 1870, and perhaps closely allied and equally extinct forms on Jamaica, Guadeloupe, and other islands, were clearly representative of *Ara macao*, the scarlet macaw of Mexico and South America.

But there are intriguing shadows in the background of this situation. It was evidently on the second voyage of Columbus (1493-1496) that his party saw red parrots "as big as chickens," which were called guacamayos by the Carib Indians. This was at Guadeloupe in April 1496. It appears that these Caribs were better acquainted with the local geography than the Governor and Admiral of the Ocean Sea was at that time and they even told Columbus about the mainland and pointed out its direction. No doubt the "red parrots" were pets of the Indians and could very easily have been brought by them from the then unknown mainland. We know that Columbus was so impressed by the big birds that he carried several back to Spain with him (along with five shiploads of Indian slaves) and exhibited them during his triumphal processions.

That these were actually red macaws we cannot doubt, but whether they were the same scarlet macaw we know today, or an endemic race belonging to the islands and now extinct, we can only guess. There is a distinguished and venerable literature in which these and other possibilities are discussed, but many of the sources—such works as Du Tertre's *Histoire Générale des Antilles Habitées par les Français* (1667) and Browne's *The Civil and Natural History of Jamaica* (1765)—are hard to come by and thus not easily referred to. For the reader interested in pursuing such matters further, I recommend James C. Greenway's more recent book, *Extinct and Vanishing Birds of the World*.

With their great size, flamboyant colors, and droll expression, the macaws might have stepped right out of an Alice-in-Wonderland world. Instead they are birds of the tropical forests, from humid lowlands to high mountain ranges. Because they are rather sluggish, and perhaps not very alert, they are easily killed, and a number of species are now extinct. The blue-and-yellow macaw seems to favor the coastal wooded areas in some regions, but elsewhere it is at home on forested mountain slopes. Late one August afternoon near the east coast of Trinidad, from the lofty platform of the new lighthouse on Brigand Hill which rises 678 feet, I watched eleven of these big *Aras* come sailing out of the treetops and go flapping off, high in the air, until they disappeared from view. They were calling loudly, their harsh, strident notes rising above the other forest sounds below, where the voices of toucans, Amazona parrots, and howler monkeys mingled with those of many birds unknown to me.

Plate 36
Blue-and-yellow
macaw

Nearly the whole expanse of Trinidad can be seen from this vantage point. Off to the south lies the Everglade-like Nariva Swamp, bordered for an unbroken stretch of fifteen miles by a magnificent plantation of coconut palms, said to have been fortuitously planted many years ago from the wreck of a ship bound for Brazil. On the open sea the sand of the narrow beach is black with the heavy sediments that come downstream in the nearby Orinoco. To the north one sees the heavily wooded ridges of the Northern Range (3085 feet) and, vague, misty, and alluring in the distance, the Robinson Crusoe island of Tobago.

François Haverschmidt believes that the blue-and-yellow macaw is the most numerous of its tribe in Surinam, where it is found in forests near the coast, but has disappeared from the vicinity of settlements. There it has been recorded nesting in February, and half-grown nestlings have been observed in March. The lightkeeper at Brigand Hill, Mr. Lewis, told me that macaws seem to be most active and abundant in that area in June and July.

James Bond (1950) listed eight species of macaws from the West Indies, all of which are extinct. There is some question about the validity of certain of these, since no specimens remain except of the Cuban macaw (*Ara tricolor*), and our knowledge of the others is derived chiefly from drawings and early literature. Other forms once occurred on St. Croix, Martinique, Guadeloupe, Dominica, and Jamaica. In fact, two species of macaws once inhabited Martinique and two others lived on Jamaica. Of the Jamaican species, an individual of one form was supposed to have been shot about 1765, while another survived until 1845. Their habitat, according to W. Rothschild, was in the mountains of Hanover Parish, about ten miles east of Lucea, and in the mountains of Trelawny and St. Ann parishes.

Bond has written of the macaw: "In habits it was sluggish and stupid and easily fell prey to native hunters who secured the adults for food and the young as pets to be sent to Europe." Many of the existing species can be seen in aviaries and zoological gardens. Emmet Blake lists two species for Mexico, the military macaw and the scarlet macaw. Eugene Eisenmann gives the ranges of six species of macaws for the region from Mexico to and including Panama (Middle America), and Phelps and Phelps (1958) outline the distribution of seven species for Venezuela and adjacent parts of South America. In Surinam, Haverschmidt lists six species. In this whole tropical region, from Mexico to Argentina, there are eight different species of macaws. It is to be hoped that modern concepts of conservation and of the values inherent in wild creatures as spectacular as the macaws will not come too late to save all these big, handsome birds from the same fate as their lost brethren.

Plate 37
St. Vincent
parrot
The undeniable fact that we are more or less bound to associate parrots with pirates is probably the fault of Robert Louis Stevenson. Who can forget Long John Silver, or Cap'n Flint, the parrot who would say, with great rapidity ("till you wondered that it was not out of breath"): "Pieces of eight! Pieces of eight! Pieces of eight!"?

Cap'n Flint was in all likelihood an Amazona parrot, although we cannot be certain. It would be nice to imagine him a St. Vincent parrot, for these birds are by all odds one of the most handsome of the lot, but unfortunately this seems doubtful. The species is found only on St. Vincent, an island eighteen miles long by eleven wide, and they may never have been very numerous. It is by no means abundant today, and thus typifies the plight of many of the parrot clan. In 1928 James Bond wrote of the St. Vincent parrot: "Locally distributed on St. Vincent, but not as rare as I had expected to find it. Probably several hundred still exist, though I am aware of the fact that one is inclined to overestimate the numbers of Amazon parrots.... [These] parrots are most numerous in the northern part of the island, but occasionally I heard them in the southern mountains, the report of a gun usually inducing them to give forth a loud, unmusical squawk. There is still a good deal of illicit gunning going on on these islands, which, if not stopped, will ultimately result in the extermination of the parrots."

Bond went on to point out the small size of the island and its relatively large human population, and added: "It would seem, therefore, that *A. guildingii* is in most danger of extinction."

More recently, in 1947, he wrote: "The bane of the conservationist in this region [the West Indies] is the open season on pigeons. These birds are prolific breeders, and the numbers of the common species are not seriously affected by shooting. However, the average West Indian native will not confine his attention to pigeons, but will shoot any other edible bird whether protected or not. I can vouch from personal experience that many a hunter's bag will include parrots and paroquets, even on the British islands where the game laws are fairly well enforced. Again, parrots are often kept in captivity in the West Indies. Among those I have seen in native houses were three of the four Lesser Antillean species, all of which are rare."

Parrots have been, in turn, admired and mistreated, cherished and destroyed, loved and loathed for centuries. We are told by Pliny that Nero had numerous parrots brought back to Rome from beyond the limits of Upper Egypt. They were kept in elaborate cages of ivory and tortoise-shell, with silver wires, and when the Emperor wearied of them they were eaten.

It may be difficult for many of us to realize that parrots are considered a table delicacy by many people even today. And not all these people are "meat hungry." Only a few years ago I talked with residents of one of the Bahamas where Amazona parrots still survive, and was told that they prize these birds as a special dish. This particular parrot is a subspecies of the Cuban variety known as *Amazona leucocephala bahamensis* and is now restricted to a few flocks on Great Inagua and perhaps Abaco and Acklins, although the last is very doubtful. They have long been extirpated from Long Island, Fortune Island, and Crooked Island. Unless the small numbers that remain are carefully protected, these splendid birds will eventually disappear from the Bahamas.

During the nineteenth century, land-clearing operations in Puerto Rico destroyed most of the original climax forest. There was little timber utilization; the land was simply cleared to provide room for raising coffee, sugar, and food crops to feed the rapidly growing human population. Not only was much valuable timber wasted, but erosion, disruption of stream flow, floods, droughts, and other evils followed. In recent years, sound conservation practices and modern farming concepts are gradually bringing about an improvement, but it is easier to destroy natural resources than to restore them. Only some 8500 acres of climax vegetation remained, most of it in the Caribbean National Forest in the Luquillo Mountains. Here, where it is protected, the Puerto Rican parrot is making its last stand. In 1959 José Rodriguez-Vidal estimated that not more than two hundred survive.

James Greenway is not optimistic. "They must still be considered to be in great danger," he writes, "for they are inclined to wander, and it is difficult to see how they can be kept in any restricted area." There are only some 5600 acres of climax forest in the National Forest, according to J. H. Westermann (1952).

Several Caribbean members of this family are already extinct, but this region is singularly blessed and is still the home of a wondrous variety of macaws, parrots, parrotlets, and parakeets. The West Indies has lost all its macaws, but has nine species of Amazonas, four parakeets, and an introduced parrotlet. Between them, Middle America (Mexico to Panama) and northern South America (Columbia, Venezuela, and the Guianas) have a large and colorful representation of these birds, something like sixty species or more. Many of the parrots will have to be given special protection if they are to survive, and this is especially true of the Lesser Antilles species, including the beautiful St. Vincent parrot and subspecies like the Bahamas race. A full-scale study of the status and needs of all the parrot family in the West Indies and Caribbean would be a step in the right direction.

Plate 38
Caribbean
parakeet

Although I had traveled to Bonaire in the Netherlands Antilles to see the flamingos, one of the highlights of the trip turned out to be the lively, noisy, and always exciting flocks of prikichis, the Caribbean parakeet that is so abundant on these islands. There are parrots on Bonaire also, big Amazonas with yellow heads and red patches on the wings, the Lora of the local patois, and, in more universal language, the yellow-winged parrot (*Amazona barbadensis*). But these larger birds are not as numerous as the parakeets and therefore not observed as frequently. The parakeets are everywhere, in desert-like areas atop giant tree cactuses, in low half-flooded stretches where the deadly manchineel grows in thick clumps, in plantations with their cactus fences, and even in scrubby goat pastures on the outskirts of Kralendijk.

One day on Bonaire I stopped at Onima, where the limestone cliffs are strangely ornamented with what are described as "Indian inscriptions." It is a beautiful spot, with towering organ-pipe cacti, inquisitive goats, half-wild jackasses, and a magnificent view of the Caribbean, which surges against the rocky shores half a mile away with great violence, sending long sheets of spray and froth high in the air, where it hangs suspended for an instant, dancing and sparkling in the sunlight. I stood there entranced, completely absorbed in the beauty around me, when a fearful screeching sound came hurtling out of nowhere, shot by overhead, and disappeared beyond the rim of the clifftop. I had only a glimpse of the birds themselves, but I knew at once that they were parakeets. Later, I was to see them to better advantage. They are one of the many delights of that attractive island.

Karel H. Voous has written charmingly of these islands and their birds. He points out that they are not inhabited by the "romantic animal species" found in many parts of the tropics. There are no jaguars as in Surinam, no giant snakes or kangaroos, but there is a varied and colorful bird life, with a great deal of special interest for the scientist and conservationist. One of the most interesting is certainly the prikichi with its classic demonstration of geographical or island variation. Each island exhibits an independent little animal kingdom all its own. Even the lizards and land snails are independent. On Aruba the parakeets have olive-green heads, on Curaçao their heads are yellow, and on Bonaire the color is more widely spread and more deeply orange than yellow. Yet all these parakeets belong to the same species, and although the distance never exceeds sixty miles, they keep to themselves and do not fly from one island to another or to the nearby mainland, where still other races are found. They are what Professor Voous calls "genuine island residents," and something of a contrast to bird species that think nothing of migrating several thousand miles each year from one continent to another.

There are many large termite nests in that part of the Caribbean, and the parakeets dig their nest holes in them. There they lay their plain white eggs, and the termites don't mind at all. They go on living their lives, and the parakeets do the same. It's a kind of good-neighbor policy that has been going on for maybe a million years or so. There ought to be a lesson here for somebody.

Although there are three species of anis in the Caribbean, the smooth-billed ani is the one most frequently seen. These birds are in reality members of the family Cuculidae—the cuckoos—but they are strange creatures and totally unlike their more retiring relatives in both appearance and habits. They are gregarious, traveling around cane fields and pasture lands in bands of a dozen or more individuals. They are loose-feathered, unkempt-looking birds, awkward on the ground and apparently inept on the wing. Yet in recent years they have spread to a number of new areas, including South Florida, where they first nested at Miami in 1938, and have been steadily increasing since, the largest colony being located at Clewiston on the south shore of Lake Okeechobee.

Plate 39
Smooth-billed
ani

These anis are commonly seen around cattle and the name "tick-bird" suggests that, like the cattle egret, they feed on ticks lifted from the hides of their bovine companions. However, Alexander Wetmore examined forty-one stomachs in Puerto Rico and found only one tick. Apparently they follow the cattle to feed on grasshoppers and other insects that are disturbed by the animals' feet. C.B. Williams, working in Trinidad, listed among their food the following: beetles, caterpillars, grasshoppers, spiders, froghoppers, and weed seeds. They are probably quite beneficial in an economic sense.

The nesting habits of the ani are of special interest. Several females band together in a co-operative nest-building project, all depositing their eggs in this common nest, which is placed in trees or bushes from three to thirty feet from the ground. James Bond (in 1960) wrote that as many as twenty-nine eggs have been found in a single nest. The eggs are deposited in layers, and many at the very bottom of the heap often fail to hatch. The number of male birds involved in such a community effort is apparently unknown.

Plate 40
Barn
owl

Despite its knock-knees and monkey's face, the barn owl is widespread and highly successful, with a tremendous range that entitles it to avian citizenship in both hemispheres, from the north of Scotland to Capetown, and from Vancouver Island to Punta Arenas. It is no stranger in the tower of a Hindu temple in Java or the cupola of an old barn in Ohio. The barn owl in the color plate was photographed by John Markham near the village of Ludham, in Norfolk, England. Mr. Markham tells us that it is standing in the "owl window" of a barn built around 1760, the opening having been left there to encourage owls to make themselves at home (this one was nesting inside) and, incidentally, to catch mice. As you can see, this particular owl is exhibiting evidence that his rent is paid.

When you consider the generations of barn owls that have lived in this one old barn during two centuries, and calculated the sum total of their rent payments, if this were possible, you can realize what a friend of man these owls must be. Yet they are totally unknown to most people, and are feared and even persecuted in many places. Few West Indian communities will hear the eerie, hissing note of this owl in the night without reviving the superstition that this is a bad omen.

Barn owls are highly migratory. Years ago I saw large numbers of them hiding out during the daylight hours in dense thickets near Cape May Point, at the southern tip of New Jersey. With the coming of night they would take to the air and continue their journey across Delaware Bay and along the Atlantic Coast. Perhaps these were the same owls that reached the Florida Keys in winter, roosting in uncut hardwood hammocks or abandoned lime-sorting sheds during the day and feeding along the highway at night. Unfortunately, since the number of automobiles has increased in recent years, a great many of these owls are killed by flying into the glaring headlights of passing cars. And as if that weren't bad enough, the hammocks are being cleared by bulldozers and the lime-sorting sheds are a thing of the past, so there's no place for a self-respecting owl to spend the day anyway. But all this is done under the banner of "progress" and there's nothing to worry about. The local authorities now employ a squad of men called the "rat detail" who go around spreading red squill and other artificial rat deterrents—at the taxpayer's expense, of course, for "progress" comes high. So, in this and similar communities, it looks as if we are heading toward an owlless if not a ratless world. It might be better, and even more progressive, if we simply built a few sturdy barns with "owl windows" under the gables.

Plate 41
Ferruginous
pygmy-owl

The ferruginous pygmy-owl is a very common little bird within its range, which is extensive, although restricted in the West Indies to Cuba and the Isle of Pines. Lawrence Walkinshaw and Bernard Baker observed the pygmy-owl daily at Rancho Rockyford and Los Indios on the Isle of Pines. They heard it calling at dawn and at dusk—a shrill *tio-tio-tio-tio-tio*—and on occasion from the dense foliage in the top of a palm during the day, for these owls are largely diurnal. Actually, the Cuban bird is a separate species of pygmy-owl, but all are very much alike in every way.

C.B. Williams relates that in Trinidad late in May a pair of jumby birds, as these owls are called there, nested in a hole in a mango tree in Port of Spain. By early July four fully fledged young were flying around, and were fed lizards by their attentive parents. Father Raymund Devas writes in his poetic way that this little owl "is not afraid of subdued light. Not only when the sun has gone down, but on any dull day it may be in evidence. I saw two together at Tortuga [near the Montserrat Hills in west-central Trinidad]. They have one note. They can vary it a little it is true, and it is a low note and rather soothing, but that one note they go on and on repeating, as long as they choose. And there is more to it than that, for when this owl calls, little birds of all kinds gather round. Hence...the repetition of this very easily imitated note is a sure way in the country of summoning birds around you, if there are any in the vicinity. Boys told me that every now and then the pygmy will make a dart at one of these birds and devour it. But you must not believe all that you hear."

Undoubtedly Father Devas has a very special feeling for owls. The spectacled owl, he wrote "is as large as a cat, is as rare as a cat is common, with eyes that suggest orange-yellow, beautiful beyond words." Apparently it is quite rare in Trinidad, and all that C. B. Williams has to say about it is that one was shot in the Port of Spain Botanic Gardens and that it made a noise like "a Barn Owl with a sore throat." The comment of G. C. A. Junge and G. F. Mees is simply to the effect that it is resident on Trinidad and does not occur in Tobago. I did not see one in either place, but I had a good long look at a very fine specimen in the Port of Spain Zoo. It is an extremely handsome owl and quite large, nearly the size of a great horned owl. The natural dignity that is the hallmark of all owls (the "owlish" look) is wonderfully exaggerated by the black-and-white face pattern. But it is a mock profundity, of course, and I couldn't escape the impression that this bird was wearing very sporty sunglasses with white plastic rims.

Plate 42
Spectacled
owl

In Mexico it is common locally, according to Emmet Blake, but restricted to the heavy tropical lowland forests of Veracruz, Oaxaca, and Chiapas. Blake says that their usual call has been likened to "a prolonged, rapid tapping of a woodpecker." He adds that two of these birds sometimes perform a duet, the notes of each having a slightly different tone. In Venezuela they are found in wooded savannas and forests in the lowland tropical zone and the subtropical more elevated interior. François Haverschmidt also finds them "not rare" in forests and coffee plantations in the coastal area of Surinam and in the savanna belt farther inland.

When Dr. Frank Chapman was studying the habits of oropéndolas at Barro

Colorado in the Panama Canal Zone, he strongly suspected that a spectacled owl (known locally as el buho) was responsible for a night attack on an oropéndola nest. Apparently it clung to the long, sacklike structure with one foot and tore a hole in the bottom with the other. Chapman contributed still another version of the call of this owl. Writing of early morning sounds, he described two owls that were "also bidding their day 'good night' with a loud, resounding *woof-woof-woof* as though they struck the head of an empty barrel with a wooden mallet. They answer each other with perfect regularity, using different-sized barrels. I hear this note nearly every morning at daybreak but have never seen the birds that make it. I imagine them to be as large as Great Horned Owls with serious, solemn faces and a dignity of manner in keeping with their voices." A footnote says: "Probably the Spectacled Owl (*Pulsatrix perspicillata*)." I like this barrel-head version of their call the best, and I'd like to hear it myself someday.

Plate 43 Burrowing owl

The little burrowing owl is such a delightful creature that it has many friends and has been the recipient of special favors in many places. If you should be in the new Miami International Airport sometime be sure to look for the attractive signs (in English and in Spanish) that have on them a picture of the burrowing owl and call attention to the fact that the airport is a burrowing owl sanctuary, probably the only one of its kind in the world. This refreshingly novel arrangement, the result of a co-operative effort on the part of the airport authorities and the Florida Audubon Society, seems to be very sensible. The wide stretches of turf between runways are unsafe for human beings anyway, but excellent habitat for the owls, which have occupied them of their own free owlish will. And they evidently keep clear of the runways themselves, so they are not a hazard to the planes. Everyone concerned is happy with this arrangement, especially the owls, and the project is good conservation publicity.

At the golf links outside Nassau, burrowing owls dig their nesting holes in the fairways, or on the edge of a green, and sometimes the air is blue with the loud verbal protests of irate golfers. Holes have been filled in and, I fear, owls destroyed, but to no avail. They like the place and stubbornly insist on coming back. A few years ago the governor of the Bahamas was a retired major general of Royal Marines who happened to be interested in birds. He was likewise a golfer, but apparently there was no question as to which of these interests prevailed. One day I received a note from the A.D.C. at Government House asking me to supply His Excellency with a convincing argument, based on their value as mousers, that could be used to prevent the destruction of burrowing owls at the Nassau Country Club. I complied and, for a time at least, the owls were spared.

It is true that burrowing owls feed for the most part on insects and small rodents that are often harmful to man's interests. I suspect, however, that such arguments in their favor are no longer as important or as necessary as they once were, and that we want to have them around for their company alone.

When Alexander von Humboldt and his botanist companion, Aimée Bonpland, journeyed through South America (1799-1804) they made many new discoveries and added much to our knowledge of the physical universe. Among their lesser but nonetheless interesting discoveries was the guácharo or oil bird, previously unknown to science. In September 1799, the two travelers visited the monastery of Argonese Capuchins near Caripe, close to the northeast coast of Venezuela. There they were taken to a cave inhabited by some strange, undescribed birds. Their guides were a party of missionaries and a number of their Indian charges. They had to make their way up the mountain slopes through heavy tropical jungle and across raging torrents. Then, after reaching the entrance to the cave and marching a short way inside, the Indians balked. As Baron von Humbolt described it, "The natives attached mystical ideas to this cave inhabited by nocturnal birds. They believe that the souls of their ancestors reside at the bottom of the cavern. . . . To go to join the guácharos is to rejoin one's fathers, is to die." After penetrating a little farther, the party had to turn back. But specimens were obtained and in due course the strange guácharo was described to the scientific world.

In the years since Humboldt's discovery, other guácharo caves have been found and the natives, compromising with their fear of the souls of their ancestors, have learned to take the young birds and extract oil from their fat-laden carcasses. C. B. Williams, who visited the Oropuche cave in Trinidad in 1916, has given us an eyewitness account of the manner in which the young are obtained. "While we were at the cave," he wrote, "there was a man there collecting the young birds from the nests. It is a disgraceful proceeding in addition to being contrary to the law. A long pole with, at the upper end, a torch and a long hook bent downwards is the weapon used. The upper nests are scraped with the end of this hook until something falls out. It may be an egg (for the man cannot see what is in the nest), in which case it falls to the ground and breaks. It may be too old a bird, for only the very young are of value, in which case it is left to die. If however fortune favours the collector it is a nice plump youngster and then with a smile of pleasure he drops it into his bag, later to be boiled down to oil."

The grease from the young birds is melted over fires at the cave's mouth, stored in earthen vessels, and used for cooking and illumination. It is said that it will keep for a year without turning rancid, but this is a relative term under such circumstances. The young are also eaten, especially in Trinidad, but not by everyone, and Antoine Léotaud said they have the odor of a cockroach.

Needless to say, with the slaughter of thousands of young guácharos each year, the species soon became scarce, and in 1895 F. W. Urich reported that "a very limited number are now offered for sale on the market" in Port of Spain. Eventually legal protection was provided, though chiefly of a paper variety, but this situation has been improved somewhat today. The Caripe colony now not only is protected by the government, but is a tourist attraction, complete with a gravel

Plate 44
Guácharo

automobile road right to the cavern's mouth, a custodian, a crew of eager guides, and electric lights soon to be installed. In Trinidad, thanks chiefly to Mrs. Asa Wright, the Spring Hill colony is also protected and casual visitors are not encouraged.

The food of these singular birds, obtained during their nocturnal flights outside the home cave, consists of oily nuts and fruits. The seeds that are dropped to the floor of the cave germinate even in the semidarkness and pale yellow stalks with only rudimentary leaves grow from the mold to a height of as much as two feet.

The nest is also out of the ordinary, a mound or pillar of plant fibres some twelve or fourteen inches across the top, with a slight depression for the eggs and young. The height varies and it is probable that these mounds contain several layers, which are added from year to year. Two or three eggs are laid, white and very round, and singularly like those of owls.

Guácharos and their caves have been written about and visited by many scientists and travelers. Theodore Roosevelt was in the Oropuche cave in 1916 and wrote about it for *Scribner's Magazine* the following year. Frank Chapman of the American Museum visited the Huevos Island and the First Boca caves off the Trinidad coast in 1893 (and wrote about them for the Museum Bulletin). The status of these and numerous other caves, in Trinidad and elsewhere within the oil bird's limited range, is not clearly known, but it is unlikely that all of them have escaped repeated plundering and the extermination of their colonies.

In 1953 a Harvard professor, an expert on the acoustics of ultrasonic sounds and the sensory basis of bat movements, Dr. Ronald R. Griffin, followed Humboldt's trail to the Caripe cave and conducted some highly interesting experiments. After establishing that the guácharos fly in total darkness and yet avoid obstacles, he set up elaborate modern equipment for determining how they do it. A microphone was placed at the cave entrance, along with amplifiers, a variable electronic filter, a cathode-ray oscillograph, a tape recorder, a sixteen-mm. camera to photograph the cathode-ray traces, and a storage battery and vibrator to provide sixty-cycle power. As the guácharos came out of the cave at twilight they emitted a steady stream of very sharp *clicks*. Each click had a duration of only one to two thousandths of a second or, as Dr. Griffin points out, about the same length as the ultrasonic signals of bats. Thus, like bats, these birds use clicks to avoid obstacles in the dark by echo-location. Such experiments may add new knowledge of the mechanics of echo-location that will be helpful in developing latent abilities in blind human beings.

I'm sure that Alexander von Humboldt not only would be proud of this additional scientific contribution from his guácharo cave, but would be eager to take a personal hand in the experiments. Meanwhile, his guácharos have assumed a new stature and their preservation by the governments of Trinidad, Venezuela, and other South American countries takes on an entirely new meaning.

Except for slight plumage differences, the rufous nightjar, to all appearances, is the familiar chuck-will's-widow that is resident in parts of Central and South America and on the island of St. Lucia in the Lesser Antilles. Ornithologists have their reasons, of course, for considering this bird a distinct species rather than merely a geographic race, but these have to do with such details as a lack of lateral filaments in the rictal bristles and cannot possibly be of much concern to the ordinary observer. Actually, the rufous nightjar *is* a chuck-will's-widow in most other respects, although, according to James Bond, it speaks French in St. Lucia (*Jacques-pas-papá-ou* instead of *Chuck-will's widow*, for example), and we assume Spanish in the other portions of its range.

Plate 45
Rufous
nightjar

The fact that this species is found mainly in Central and South America, while an isolated population dwells on St. Lucia, is of special interest. All birds of this group—chucks, poor-wills, pauraques, and nighthawks—nest on the ground, or rarely in low tree stumps, and theoretically have been much depleted wherever the mongoose has been introduced. James C. Greenway lists a small Puerto Rican nighthawk (*Caprimulgus vociferus noctitherus*) as extinct. James Bond (in 1960) considers that it has been unreported since 1889, although Alexander Wetmore may have observed an individual of this race at Río Piedras in 1911. There are other examples. The mongoose was first brought to the West Indies from India in 1870 and was turned loose in Trinidad. In 1872 four males and five females were brought from Calcutta to Jamaica. They increased rapidly and were introduced to other islands. At first the purpose of this project, the control of rats, was amply fulfilled, but in time the mongoose, having disposed of the rats, started ravaging native animals, including ground-nesting birds. Many native forms were seriously reduced and several were exterminated. As indicated by J. H. Westermann (in 1953), the destruction of many insectivorous animals resulted in an increase of insect pests. Furthermore, the mongoose began killing young pigs, lambs, calves, and poultry. Twenty years after its initial introduction the mongoose came to be regarded as the greatest pest of all. Commissions were set up to study the problem, and at length the mongoose was blacklisted as an outlaw and enemy of society.

For many birds and other animals it was too late. On St. Lucia the rufous nightjar is rare and local. We can only surmise how it became isolated. It is only a little more than two hundred miles from this island to Trinidad, but the nightjar is not found on the islands in between (St. Vincent and the Grenadines). An intriguing sidelight is the presence on St. Lucia of the deadly fer-de-lance (*Bothrops atrox*), a snake that is wide-ranging in tropical America and may have been introduced to this island by man, although this possibility is not substantiated. From all reports, the mongoose is no match for a full-grown fer-de-lance, but the rufous nightjar and this fearful reptile get along very well together. If you want to see a rufous nightjar on St. Lucia, you will find them occupying the same territory as the fer-de-lance—which may be the reason they still survive there.

Plate 46
Pauraque

Far from its Caribbean haunts, and close to the northern limits of its range, I have frequently heard the hoarse voice of the pauraque on the coastal plains of south Texas. Although one of the commonest birds of its kind elsewhere, it is sufficiently unique in Texas to claim a special place among the "wanted items" on the list of every visiting bird-watcher. More than once I have joined Connie Hagar and a group of her guests on a brief twilight trip along a back road out of Rockport just to hear a pauraque calling.

As is usually the case, everyone seems to have a different version of the call, or a different way of expressing it. Roger Tory Peterson, who has one of the best ears for bird songs and calls that I know of, describes it as a hoarse whistle, *pur-we'-eeeeer*, sometimes with preliminary notes (*pup-pup-pur-we'eeeer*). He notes that from a distance only the last emphatic *we'eeeer* can be heard. Peterson has also said, "By no stretch of the imagination does it seem to say 'Pau-ra-que.' "

In Panama, according to Dr. Frank Chapman's testimony, the pauraque bids good-by to the night with a spirited *hip-hip, hip-hip, hip-hip horray!* "For a few minutes," Chapman wrote, "he will call and feed and then retire to his bed on the leaves at the edge of the forest to await the coming of that narrow margin between day and night which, in the tropics, reduces his time of activity to the minimum."

In Trinidad, and indeed wherever the same conditions prevail, pauraques are frequently seen on the asphalt roads at night, where they rise in the light beams of approaching motorcars. It nests on the ground, as do all of its kind, depositing its two eggs in a slight depression in the leaves. The eggs are said to show shades of salmon and reddish-brown, with a few gray marks or tracings toward the larger end.

The least pauraque (*Siphonorhis brewsteri*) of Hispaniola is little more than half the size of this species and belongs to another genus, which is endemic. It is not common. A larger and darker pauraque, also endemic (*Siphonorhis americanus*), was resident in Jamaica, but has not been seen since 1859. It is of interest that that was thirteen years before the introduction of the mongoose to that island.

Plate 47
Black-throated
mango

For all their diminutive size, hummingbirds are amazingly pugnacious. The black-throated mango is no exception. In his delightful account of a naturalist's view of the world around him, Frank Chapman learned a great deal about the character of this species. "On January 16, 1926," he wrote in *My Tropical Air Castle* "a Black-throated Hummingbird was discovered building her nest in the sandbox tree. She chose for a site the terminal portion of a long branch projecting to windward and with not a leaf nearer than twenty-five feet. It was, in fact, the most exposed situation in the tree.

"It is a very large tree, not less than 130 feet in height and widely branched. There is, therefore, abundant room for many birds to build in it without interfering with one another. On the westerly side, where they were more protected from the strong trade winds of the dry season, the Oropéndolas were weaving their long, pendent bags on the outer branches. Nearer the heart of the tree a pair of Blue Tanagers and of Colombian Flycatchers had made their homes. All were on excellent terms with one another and were doubtless quite willing to receive the Hummingbird into the circle of their community life.

"But the Hummingbird had ideas of her own. The aggressive pioneer spirit which has spread her kind from Magellan Strait to Alaska has not developed a feeling of sociability in her tiny body. She not only asked for the control of her corner of the sandbox tree, but she demanded dominion over the entire tree, and what is more, she got it! Woe to the Oropéndola that ventured near her home. The fact that he was as large as a Crow did not protect him. Like a winged terror she darted fearlessly at him, and evidently without thought of resistance, after dodging futilely once or twice, he would take to his wings. It was useless for him to retreat to his side of the tree. He was as helpless as a dirigible before a pursuit plane, and only the forest offered safety. Once on the warpath, the Hummer attacked any bird that she chanced to meet, and not infrequently she cleared the tree before her raid was ended. Then, like a bit of down, she returned to her nest.

"Fortunately for the other occupants of the tree, as the season advanced the Hummer's domestic affairs claimed an increasing share of her attention, and they were correspondingly free from attack. It was not possible for me to look into the nest a hundred or more feet from me, but it seemed apparent that by January 26 her eggs were laid, and she had begun to incubate. During this period nothing but her body stood between the eggs and destruction, one might say, by fire and water. Unshaded by leaf or branch, they might have been roasted if left exposed to the sun, and the nest cup would have been filled to overflowing by heavy tropical showers if it had not been tightly capped by the little mother.

"On February 9 it was evident that she had won her reward, for there were young in the nest. Within a week the tips of their bills could be seen above its felted rim. With a glass one could now watch the remarkable process by which a Hummingbird, after plunging her stiletto-like bill into the throat of her young, almost to the hilt, pumps predigested food well down its digestive tract.

"By February 20 the entire length of the young birds' still surprisingly short bills could be seen resting on the edge of the nest, and they turned their heads from side to side with an obvious awareness of their surroundings. Doubtless they left the nest within four or five days; but here, unfortunately, my observations for the season ended. Not once during the thirty-five days of my observation did I see the father of this family. True to the habits of his kind, he had apparently deserted his bride on their honeymoon. He had, I am sure, the sympathy of the Oropéndolas, and at the best there seemed to be no room for him in the family circle."

Plate 48
Ruby-topaz
hummingbird

A quiet August morning in the oasis-like grove at Fontein, on Bonaire, would have been disappointing if it had not been for the ruby-topaz hummingbirds. They were constantly buzzing around my head and flashing by, complaining angrily at my presence, in true hummingbird fashion, while other birds, especially the pearly-eyed thrashers I had come there to see, were either absent altogether or silent and hidden away in the thickets. But the lively and gemlike ruby-topaz made my trip worthwhile.

The emerald hummingbird (*Chlorostilbon mellisugus*) is said to be more abundant on the leeward islands of the Netherlands Antilles—Aruba, Curaçao, and Bonaire—but the ruby-topaz is by far the more spectacular. There is a certain mystery about its status. To quote Karel H. Voous (1955), it "is of a rather irregular occurrence, appearing extremely numerous at one moment and being almost absent a few months later." On these points, Wagenaar Hummelinck says of this species: "We found it common in all three islands, but it seemed less numerous than *Chlorostilbon mellisugus*. However, in some localities it was more abundant than the latter species (Arikok region in Aruba; Kralendijk in Bonaire). Its numbers seem to be subject to great fluctuations, which was not only apparent to us, but also well-known by local bird-observers. At a given time it appeared to be almost absent in Curaçao, only to be extremely numerous a short time afterwards. The same phenomenon was noticed by Dr. Ernst Schaefer in the Maracay district in northern Venezuela....It is, then, not impossible that this species wanders irregularly, disappearing for some time from a given place and turning up in large numbers in another. In this connection it seems worth while recording an observation on 17.XI.1951 of a solitary individual of this species flying straight into the sea at Lac, Bonaire, and disappearing out of sight in a southeasterly direction."

It is amusing to contemplate that this purposeful hummer could have been heading straight for Maiquetía Airport in Venezuela, a mere 140 miles or so directly southeast of the Lac. You learn to respect their abilities so that nothing seems too much for them.

Of its usual habitat Hummelinck says: "This species was found in all kinds of biotope, including mangroves, but it was much less common in gardens near houses than *Chlorostilbon mellisugus* and we did not observe it in the seasonal forest on the upper slopes and on the summit of Christoffel Mountain in Curaçao, where *Chlorostilbon mellisugus* did occur." On both Trinidad and Tobago, G. F. Mees found this species a common bird in more or less open country, "including gardens."

Hummelinck adds this additional note on the character of the ruby-topaz: "The thin, high-pitched notes of this species seemed very characteristic and were quite different from the more aggressive call notes of *Chlorostilbon mellisugus*. We never heard this species singing. Like all hummingbirds it was very pugnacious." He says that it was not unusual for two ruby-topaz hummers to engage in such furious combat that they would fall to the ground and continue fighting there, so absorbed in their fisticuffs that they could readily be picked up. Both males and females engage in these scraps. In their spare moments they chased other birds, including emerald hummingbirds, bananaquits, and even so-called birds of prey, notably the sparrow hawk and the caracara.

Two nests examined by Hummelinck were finely woven, cup-shaped structures of the buffish-white cotton which forms the basis of the inflorescence of *Melocactus*. In the outer lining these nests also contained several of the small, red flowers of this cactus, as well as small pieces of lichen.

Everyone has a blind spot or two. With Antoine Léotaud it was the motmot, and with Sir Charles Belcher the hummingbirds. In Commander C. E. Alford's *The Island of Tobago*, Belcher states: "Humming Birds are a bit disappointing when one first comes across them. It is high time someone 'debunked' the enthusiastic accounts of 'tiny-feathered jewels, scintillating iridescently in the glowing rays of the Caribbean sun, veritable living points of coloured flame,' and the rest of the patter which emanates from writers who would be hard put to it to recognise a Hummer from a Honey-creeper, and who usually suppose there is only one species, and that the Caribs were sufficiently poetical to call Trinidad after it."

Plate 49
Tufted
coquette

Apparently Sir Charles did not have the good fortune to lay eyes on a tufted coquette, which incidentally does not occur on Tobago. For this tiny hummer is indeed a feathered jewel.

But Sir Charles has more complaints. "In fact," he says, "of the five hundred species in North and South America, Trinidad has fifteen and Tobago probably seven. It is safe to say that not one of these would attract attention by its plumage unless the watcher were lucky enough to be standing within a couple of yards of a bird at rest. All, however, have the habit of hovering with a humming noise, which at once strikes anyone used to keeping his ears open for natural sounds."

More recent authorities have cut the number of species of hummingbirds to 319, but this has no real bearing on our present discussion. In *Fundamentals of Ornithology*, Josselyn Van Tyne and Andrew J. Berger, who *can* recognize a hummer from a honeycreeper, point out in purely factual language that birds of the hummingbird family are "mainly green, brown, or black.... Areas of brilliant iridescent green, red, blue, purple, or gold (on throat, crown, sides of head, back)." They go on to say that some species are crested and some have very long, racquet-tipped tails. A few even have downy "muffs" on their legs. Undoubtedly Sir Charles is a bit color-blind.

Father Raymund Devas, with his usual wit and good nature, takes this occasion to push forward one of his own favorites. In commenting on the Belcher outburst, he writes: "Now, the hummingbirds having been put in their place, there would be some sense and good reason indeed, for calling Trinidad the Land of the Kiskadee." However, the kiskadee, admirable bird that it is, graces the landscape in many locations other than Trinidad, and "Land of the Hummingbirds" really is quite poetic.

G. F. Mees found this species fairly common and widely distributed in Trinidad, "at least in the northern part of the island... inhabiting the edges of forest, and rich secondary growths, wherever there are flowers." He says also that it is particularly fond of pigeon peas, "and in the hills near Tacarigua it was hardly possible to miss the birds as they flew, like giant wasps, from flower to flower."

Plate 50
Cuban
emerald

The Cuban emerald is the common hummingbird of Cuba. Thomas Barbour wrote of this species: "An exceedingly common and very fine Hummer. One of the few birds peculiar to Cuba which the casual observer with but a few days at his disposal is sure to see. They occur wherever there are flowers, in parks, gardens and in the wild, open country. No more pugnacious bird is imaginable. They hector the little Owls and also other Hummers, and will even streak off after a Buzzard if one blunders too near their nest. The type of nest is very like that of our common Ruby-throat, and eggs may be found in any month. Many more males are seen than females, and the sexes associate but little. The story of Gundlach's famous little companion is familiar to many. She lost her nest in a hurricane, and by chance concluded to rebuild on the chandelier of Gundlach's study in Bemba. She raised four broods in this same nest, but never once was her mate seen. The same observer adds that the male does not get full plumage until the third year....

"The number of these Hummers at Soledad has greatly increased since the laying out of 'Arizona,' the arid area where we have gathered a great collection of succulents. Many of the species have red flowers which are especially attractive. Here a temporary shelter with red-tiled roof has been erected, so that visitors to this rather distant though very picturesque part of the garden would have a refuge against the sudden showers so characteristic of tropical climes. Here one may watch the Ricord's Hummers by the hour, as males dispute with one another their right to certain favorite flowers, and the aerial gymnastics of these apparently desperate battles are always amusing to behold. I have, however, never actually seen a feather fly."

On the Isle of Pines, Lawrence H. Walkinshaw and Bernard W. Baker observed "one or two on several days, feeding on flowers in the yards at Santa Barbara and Los Indios."

Hummingbirds of this same genus, *Chlorostilbon*—the emeralds—also occur in Hispaniola and Puerto Rico, as well as in Central and South America. The Hispaniolan emerald (*Chlorostilbon swainsonii*) is "found principally in the hills and mountains of the interior," according to Alexander Wetmore and Bradshaw H. Swales. It is a bird of the heavy forests and is most common in regions of considerable rainfall, in the darkest places. In early morning, when the air was damp it came out occasionally to feed in the open growths of pine. Wetmore found it on Morne La Selle above an elevation of 5700 feet and James Bond found nests of this species on Morne Tranchant at an elevation of 7220 feet. Apparently it is rarely seen in the lowlands, usually keeping above 1900 feet (500 meters).

The Puerto Rican variety (*Chlorostilbon maugaeus*) is less restricted in its vertical distribution. Bond (1960) says that it occurs from coastal mangroves to forested mountain summits, being most abundant in forested hills and in the coffee plantations. Wetmore (1927) found them "most abundant on the western end of the island beyond Aibonito. It was observed in the coastal region on the north side of the island only at Manatí, but on the south side was recorded from Salinas, Juana Diaz, Yauco, and Cobo Rojo.... On the eastern portion of the island I found the birds only on El Yunque, where they occurred sparingly up to 2500 feet elevation."

Hummingbirds are among the most attractive and exotic birds of the Caribbean, and the streamer-tail of Jamaica can hold its own with any of them. Many hummers are so small and fast-moving and comparatively rare that they are difficult to observe, but the streamer-tail, also known as the "doctor-bird," is not merely an excitingly beautiful creature—it seems to be everywhere, in and out of an open veranda 4000 feet up in the Blue Mountains, or hovering close to your head as you sit at lunch on the terrace of a hotel on the outskirts of Kingston. The whirring or humming noise made by its long, curving tailfeathers in flight, and the loud *tee-tee-tee* of its unabashed voice, are nothing short of startling. These streaming tailfeathers are six or seven inches in length, and scalloped along the inner edges, which may contribute to the whirring sound.

It is a completely fearless bird, and the males are even downright pugnacious. As one zooms suddenly by, you are presented with a flashing impression of emblazoned greens, emeralds, and purplish blacks, a ruby-red bill and glittering eyes smaller than a pinpoint that seem to be daring you to make an overt move. At other times one will perch within a few feet and calmly preen, just as if you were not even in sight. James Bond considers that the adult male of this species is the most spectacular West Indian hummingbird, and I will not disagree.

May Jeffrey-Smith writes that they are called "doctor-birds" because the black tufted feathers of the nape, which form a crest, recall the days when doctors were exceedingly smart and well groomed and wore top hats.

The same author describes the nest of the streamer-tail as purselike and beautifully compact, and made from silk cotton, the hairs from fern stipes, or the down of the asclepias seeds, the finished structure being crossed and recrossed with spider webs. Two eggs are laid, and the nest is the so-called "saddle" type, with the opening above the limb that passes through it.

Like other hummers, the doctor-bird seems to prefer any flower in the garden, just so long as it is red, but Miss Jeffrey-Smith has also seen them probing the flowers of less colorful blooms such as the Christian bush, search-me-heart,

Plate 51
Streamer-tail

and glass-eye berry. The early ornithologist P. H. Gosse (1810-1888) also observed their liking for this last-named flower, and in all of these blooms they are undoubtedly seeking the insects that have been deliciously marinated in the nectar.

It is interesting to note that the presence of a black-billed race of streamer-tails was first described in 1901, the original specimen coming from Preistman's River in Portland Parish, which is only a few miles southeast of Port Antonio, where so many visiting tourists enjoy rafting down the nearby Río Grande. The two forms apparently mix on occasion and "intermediates," presumably with bills that are red *and* black, have been taken at Hardwar Gap in the Blue Mountains and at Port Antonio.

The red-billed male in the color plate is hovering at the fount of an artificial feeder.

Plate 52
Copper-rumped
hummingbird
Within the confines of its rather restricted range, the copper-rumped hummingbird is one of the most common representatives of its family. It is a true Venezuelan hummer in a country that is the natural home of some ninety-seven species and fifty-five additional subspecies of these birds. It is not to be found outside the borders of Venezuela, except on the adjoining islands of Margarita, Trinidad, and Tobago. Margarita belongs to that country, while Trinidad is geologically and ornithologically a part of it, and might have strong political ties even today if Sir Ralph Abercromby and Admiral Harvey hadn't arrived at such an opportune time and claimed it for England. Tobago has much the same background, although the English took it from the French rather than from the Spanish.

All this probably makes no difference to this abundant hummer, now called (by French, Spanish, and English alike) *Amazilia tobaci*, for it is an identity all its own, and its busy, high-speed life is quite enough to keep up with without worrying about the political vagaries of *Homo sapiens*, even if it could. The Phelpses, incidentally, have described five races of the copper-rump. One is very generally distributed in the central part of Venezuela north of the Orinoco, where it occupies forests, thickets, and savannas in the Tropical and lower Subtropical zones. A second form is more locally distributed in the northern mountain regions of the states of Lara, Falcón, and Yaracuy, and yet another in the eastern Cordillera de la Costa from Anzoátegui to Monagas and the extreme eastern part of Sucre. A fourth is found only on Isla de Margarita, where it inhabits farms and brush country. The fifth and last race is generally distributed south of the Río Orinoco in Bolívar and northern Amazonas Territory. The copper-rumps on Trinidad and Tobago are evidently two additional forms.

Crawford Greenewalt says that this species was the most frequent visitor to the hummingbird feeders in the garden of Mr. Phelps in Caracas. And G. F. Mees found it the most common hummingbird in open country and near human habitations in Trinidad. "Also found in cacao estates and in light forest," he writes, "but not occurring in dark and heavy forest where this species is conspicuously replaced by the very similar-looking *Chlorestes notatus*." This last-named hummer is called verdecito in Venezuela, where it is widely distributed. It has a more extensive range than the copper-rump, occurring also in eastern Colombia, the Guianas, northeastern Brazil, and supposedly on both Trinidad and Tobago, although Mees does not agree with this last.

On Tobago the copper-rump was considered by Mees to be the most common hummingbird. He found it more of a forest bird on Tobago than in Trinidad. Mees also observed one of these birds bathing. "From its perch, about 2 m above a rivulet, the bird again and again flew fairly steeply down, hovered for a moment very close above the water surface, and plunged into the water, its head, however, remaining above the surface. Subsequently it would fly back to its perch and commence preening.

"A curious kind of behaviour was observed on 14 February in a cacao plantation at Back Hill. A *Saucerottia* was seen flying continually, like a pendulum with an amplitude of about four meters, to and fro, uttering a: 'tyeerr—tyeerr—tyeerr—,' evidently its alarm cry. Just like a pendulum it reached the lowest point in the middle of its flight, and soon I discovered that this strange behaviour meant an attack on a specimen of *Myiodynastes maculatus*, which was every time very closely approached by the humming-bird and, if I correctly interpreted the ticks that were audible, was hit also now and then. The flycatcher did not seem to be much distressed by the humming-birds' behaviour."

This is the streaked flycatcher, a large and widely distributed species whose life history has been written by Alexander Skutch (1960, vol. II).

A bird with the name glittering-throated emerald would almost have to be a hummingbird, for the words "glittering" and "emerald" are automatically associated in one's mind with these dashing, brilliantly colored little birds. And without question this species is every inch a hummer, or "hum-bird" as they were called by Sir Thomas Browne, the seventeenth-century physician, scholar, and prolific writer on many subjects. He spoke of their size as "not much exceeding a beetle," and it is true that one of these birds, the bee hummingbird (*Mellisuga helenae*) of Cuba and the Isle of Pines, is the smallest bird in the world—the male, that is. He measures only two and a half inches from the tip of his bill to the end of his gorgeous blue tail. Not as long as a regular-size cigarette.

This species is not as small as a bee hummingbird, but actually, it isn't much bigger—a mere inch or so. Foster Smith found it abundant throughout northeastern Venezuela, encountering it in all types of habitat except the lowland seasonal forest. He considered that it was most common in deciduous seasonal woods.

His remarks (in 1950) on the nesting habits suggest that the male is more

*Plate 53
Glittering-
throated
emerald*

attentive to his wife and offspring than is the case with some hummingbirds. "A nest of this hummer was found at Cantaura in January about 3 feet above ground in a small tree. It contained two white or light cream-colored eggs. While one bird brooded the other often hovered about the bush, occasionally coming in to inspect the observer when he approached the nest. The young uttered a weak chirp when hungry. Considering the small size of the bird, the collector was surprised to note that the young were fed at about 30-minute intervals, although, being fed by regurgitation, it may be that they received a large quantity of food at each feeding. One egg hatched late in the afternoon, the other early in the morning of the following day. The young left the nest 18 days after hatching. Two call notes were recorded, a sharp *chip* and a dry rattle."

Additional nesting observations were made by Smith in 1955, in the same general area. He wrote: "Six nests were found, two about 10 feet up, while the remainder were at less than 3 feet above the ground. Especially in January and February, groups of five and six birds could be seen chasing each other." This was apparently the breeding time. Smith noted that four species of hummingbirds were common in the deciduous woods habitat, the ruby-topaz, the copper-rumped, the common emerald, and the glittering-throated emerald. The first three feed typically at the flowers of high trees, while *Amazilia fimbriata* feeds close to the ground.

Plate 54
Belted
kingfisher

When I see a belted kingfisher, or hear its loud, rattling call, it brings to mind at once a vision of idle summer days of long ago, a quiet backwater shaded by overhanging willows and tall sycamores, and a small boy with a birch rod and a tin can half filled with "angleworms." I suppose that this same picture is shared by many others whose boyhood was lived in the country, almost anywhere in the United States or southern Canada. For this well-known member of a large, highly successful family seemed to be along every stream bank.

My friends and I had no idea, of course, that the kingfisher was such a widespread species for, in a typically boyish way, we were used to thinking of "our wild birds" as belonging just to that part of the country and to that part of the world that was familiar to us. Forty years ago, that usually meant an area within fifteen or twenty miles, at most, of our homes. Even though we considered the kingfisher as a rival fisherman, and envied it because it was so much more successful than we were, our over-all judgment was one of considerable admiration. If we had known that this aggressive, fiery-tempered little bird migrated each fall to winter quarters as far away as Trinidad and the coast of northern South America, I'm sure our regard for it would have more than doubled. But for years our only bird book was Chester Reed's little pocket-sized guide, and all it said about the kingfisher's migratory habits was that it winters "from southern United States southward." With our limited personal experience in geography, this didn't convey very much to us.

PLATE 34. BLUE-HEADED QUAIL-DOVE (*Starnoenas cyanocephala*)

PLATE 36. BLUE-AND-YELLOW MACAW (*Ara ararauna*)

PLATE 37. ST. VINCENT PARROT (*Amazona guildingii*)

PLATE 38. CARIBBEAN PARAKEET (*Aratinga pertinax*)

PLATE 39. SMOOTH-BILLED ANI (*Crotophaga ani*)

PLATE 40. BARN OWL (*Tyto alba*)

PLATE 41. FERRUGINOUS PYGMY-OWL

(*Glaucidium brasilianum*)

PLATE 43. BURROWING OWL

(*Speotyto cunicularia*)

PLATE 42. SPECTACLED OWL (*Pulsatrix perspicillata*)

103

PLATE 44. GUÁCHARO (*Steatornis caripensis*)

PLATE 45. RUFOUS NIGHTJAR (*Caprimulgus rufus*)

PLATE 46. PAURAQUE (*Nyctidromus albicollis*)

PLATE 47. BLACK-THROATED MANGO (*Anthracothorax nigricollis*)

PLATE 48. RUBY-TOPAZ HUMMINGBIRD (*Chrysolampis mosquitus*)

Opposite: PLATE 49. TUFTED COQUETTE (*Lophornis ornata*)

PLATE 50. CUBAN EMERALD (*Chlorostilbon ricordii*)

PLATE 51. STREAMER-TAIL (*Trochilus polytmus*)

Opposite: PLATE 52. COPPER-RUMPED

HUMMINGBIRD (*Amazilia tobaci*)

PLATE 53. GLITTERING-THROATED EMERALD (*Amazilia fimbriata*)

PLATE 54. BELTED KINGFISHER (*Ceryle alcyon*)

PLATE 55. BLUE-CROWNED MOTMOT (*Momotus momota*)

I remember one time when we dug out a nest cavity of these birds, a tunnel in the clay bank of a nearby stream, and decided that Mr. Reed could be wrong. His book said the tunnel was "two or three" feet in length, but ours was closer to four feet from end to end, with a sharp "dog leg" about halfway in. Also, instead of "five to eight glossy white eggs," we found four very lively young kingfishers that fought and snapped at us with so much vigor that we were glad to leave them where they were.

I was told by Dr. T. Gilbert Pearson that when he was a small boy in northern Florida many years ago, the only pictures of birds available to him were the small figures in Webster's Dictionary, most of which were somewhat lacking as identification aids. This dictionary belonged to a neighbor, and now and then he permitted the youthful ornithologist to have a look at it. There he saw a picture of a bird that seemed to him to resemble the crested, long-billed, and totally unknown bird that was so common along the stream banks and lakes of the neighborhood. And there, for the first time, he read its name, "Hoopoe." So for several years young Pearson went through life, as he expressed it, calling the kingfisher a hoopoe, a totally different species that dwells in Europe, Asia, and Africa.

There are some eighty-seven species of kingfishers in the world, three of which have been recorded in the United States—the belted kingfisher, the little green kingfisher which is an uncommon resident in Texas, and the large ringed kingfisher which has wandered up from Mexico a few times (Roger Tory Peterson says on at least seven occasions). Five species may be seen in Mexico—the three mentioned above, plus the large Amazon kingfisher and the tiny pygmy kingfisher. There are other species in Central and South America.

As you might suspect, the principal food of these birds is fish, but there are interesting exceptions. One of these is the pygmy kingfisher which subsists largely on insects and, according to Emmet Blake, are captured expertly "on the wing." There is also an old story of a belted kingfisher that fed on sour-gum berries when the water was too rough to fish in, but this may have been an individual peculiarity, for these birds are frequently seen diving for fish in the roughest surf.

The blue-crowned motmot is a kingfisher-like bird, and yet it isn't a kingfisher, although it is closely related and has been classified in the same suborder (Alcedines). In this respect it likewise has much in common with the jacamars with which it frequently associates. Apparently it was first described by the indefatigable Francisco Hernandez (*Historia Avium Novae Hispaniae*, 1651), who gave it the Mexican name it bears today: motmot. Early European ornithologists noted at once its resemblance to the bee-eater, which was on the right track, and it should be mentioned that, in addition to certain outward similarities, the kingfishers, todies, motmots, jacamars, rollers, and bee-eaters all dig nest holes in sand or clay banks.

Plate 55
Blue-crowned
motmot

The motmot is a very colorful, rather elegant neotropical bird that inhabits certain parts of Mexico, Central, and South America. Some species of motmots prefer humid lowland forests, others mountain rain forests, or arid lowlands and foothills. There are a number of species, with wide variation in the details of their plumage, but a common affinity for olive-green and rufous. All have longish tails and most of them have racket-tipped tails, including four of the six motmots found in Mexico.

The blue-crowned motmot is one of the more widely distributed and certainly one of the most attractive. G. C. A. Junge and G. F. Mees very properly complain that "it is not kind of Léotaud to write that: '...son port est lourd, sa forme peu gracieuse, et c'est en vain que sa parure emprunte l'éclat de quelques belles couleurs [...his carriage is awkward, his form has little grace, and it is in vain that he adorns himself with a few pretty colors...].'" The good M. Léotaud, for some unimaginable reason, must have had a grudge against the motmot.

Although only locally distributed in remote parts of Trinidad, this species is very common on Tobago, particularly in the cacao plantations. E. B. Williams tells us that it was much persecuted by cacao planters under the mistaken impression that it damaged their crops, but examination of stomach contents revealed 98 per cent insects, centipedes, and scorpions, and 2 per cent wild berries. In general they feed on insects, fruits, and small reptiles.

Mees describes a blue-crowned motmot in Trinidad that was perched in a dark place calling "*took-took terrook took took-took*." At the same time its tail, pointed diagonally upward, was swinging from side to side in a way that apparently is characteristic of these birds. The most curious habit of this and several other motmots is that of deliberately biting or picking the barbs from both sides of the two middle tailfeathers, near the end, thus producing the "racket-tipped" or "battledore" effect. Why they do this is a mystery.

Plate 56
Cuban
tody

I remember very well the first time I saw a tody. Even in so exciting a place as the wooded hills above the shores of Lago de Enriquillo in the Dominican Republic, with its view of high, cedar-covered ridges, its palm crows and winding donkey trails, a first meeting with this delightful little bird is not easily forgotten. We had been down along the lakeshore the previous day, below sea level, cutting our way through heavy barriers of cacti to reach a vantage point from which to get a clear view of the flamingos, roseate spoonbills, reddish egrets, and other birds out on the lake, and, later, up winding trails more than a thousand feet, through African villages of high-domed thatched roofs, to the green fringes of Lago del Limón, with its teeming birdlife. And now, from a hillside cut deeply by a dry gulch paved with rocks that were round and white and looked like cobblestones, we looked down on the whole expanse of this big salt lake, "the famous lake of Riquille, which belongs to the Spaniards," as M. le Chevalier Lefebvre-Deshayes described it in the seventeenth century.

Here and there the sides of the gulch rose to a respectable height, and in one of these cutbanks we saw our first tody. It was the broad-billed variety (*Todus subulatus*), fractionally bigger than the others of its kind, the bill broader and the underparts grayish-white generously washed along the sides with pink, and yellow on the belly and under tail coverts. It sat on a branch very close to us, its bill elevated jauntily and its manner friendly, curious, and totally unafraid. Its brilliant colors against the drab background of the gully were superb. A little jewel of a bird! Alexander Wetmore (in 1927) wrote of Puerto Rican todies that confidently shared the shelter of a banana plant with him during a sudden downpour, perching quietly almost within reach of his hand.

Later we saw other todies and found the tiny entrance to one of their nest tunnels, which may go back into a bank two feet or more. May Jeffrey-Smith writes that in Jamaica the male and female take turns at the excavation. "The one watches while the other digs. It is only when thus occupied that todies are seen close to the ground, the watching bird perching on a low twig near to the hole being dug." Wetmore has noted that in Hispaniola the narrow-billed tody captures insects on the wing, like the broad-billed, but "also hops about among the leaves and small branches, seeming more active in this way than its relative."

Not long ago Oliver Griswold of the University of Miami, after many failures, succeeded in keeping a Cuban tody alive in captivity, bringing it from Pinar del Río to Havana, then to Miami, and eventually to the Bronx Zoo in New York, the first of its kind ever to be exhibited alive. The major problem was feeding—not merely the correct nutritional balance, but a sufficient amount to keep pace with this tiny creature's high metabolism. It was found that a tody will devour forty to sixty mealworms each day, plus innumerable live insects. William G. Conway, curator of birds at the Bronx Zoo, estimates that a captive tody consumes 40 per cent of its own weight daily.

Their energy and liveliness is amazing. Oliver Griswold has described them very well: "Although the Tody is about the size of a House Wren, measuring only four to four and a half inches, it is blessed with extraordinary personality. Besides being beautiful, it is blithely active—does much flitting, much dainty head movement, frequent puffing out of the feathers and coy elevating of the top-knot. Very perky."

"Magnificent as is the Motmot," wrote Father Raymund Devas, "the Rufous-Tailed Jacamar is even more so. I do not think I am biased, but I must admit that the Jacamar is my first love. Before I had ever set foot in Tobago I was enraptured at the sight of a Jacamar beside the Hollis Dam at Valencia. And just imagine, I was still green to the birds of Trinidad and did not know what it was!...A bird to rave about indeed." When you meet your first jacamar, you may be inclined to agree.

Plate 57
Rufous-tailed
jacamar

One morning I was out along the Windward Road on Tobago, and at the bridge over Hillsborough River I stopped and walked for a short distance downstream. Three small boys, whose mothers were washing clothes nearby, followed along out of curiosity, for I was pausing now and then to look through my binoculars and this was a little out of the ordinary, even on such a famous birding island as Tobago. At that moment a pair of rufous-tailed jacamars flew across the stream and lit on a low-hanging branch. They were chattering away in their strange, energetic, jacamar language, and, although I had never seen the species before, I knew at once what they were from the picture in Kathleen Phelps' little book *Aves Venezolanas*. I then asked the wide-eyed little boys if they would like to look at them through my binoculars, and they did so with much wonder and soft-spoken expressions of obvious delight. Next I asked them if they knew the name of the bird, and at once the oldest boy, looking at me quite seriously, said, "Yessah, woodpecker!" I tried to explain that the correct name is jacamar, but it was no use. This was their island, and they knew a "woodpecker" when they saw one.

It is Sir Charles Belcher's recommendation, as quoted in Commander C. E. R. Alford's booklet on Tobago, that visitors to that charming island drive inland toward the Main Ridge. "It is not long," writes Sir Charles, "before one meets with two birds which one could not pass unnoticed. These are the Motmot and the Jacamar, and they are usually found in association, since like so many other birds of rich plumage they tunnel in earth banks to nest, and where such occur along the road-sides both species utilise them. The Jacamar...is the smaller and more common bird. It is often mistaken for a Kingfisher, and has in general the habits and poses of the European Bee-eater."

Emmet Blake remarks that these birds "customarily perch silently on exposed twigs from which passing insects may be captured by swift, darting flight." C. B. Williams, writing of them on Trinidad and Tobago, says that they lay three eggs, which are white and nearly round. He adds that the nest cavity is usually at the end of a long tunnel in an overhanging bank. Sometimes a few twigs are placed in the nest, but apparently there is no fixed rule about this so far as the jacamar is concerned.

In any case, with its splendid and even brilliant appearance, the jacamar is indeed "a bird to rave about." If you visit Tobago, look for them, among other suitable places, on Hillsborough River, at the Hillsborough Reservoir, and near roadside banks on the Roxborough-Parlatuvier Road. The larger green-and-rufous bird in the same habitat is the blue-crowned motmot (*Momotus momota*). It is blue and black on the crown, has a black mask under the eye, and the two longest tailfeathers have separate blobs of blue feathers and black tips.

Plate 58
Channel-billed
toucan

Dr. Frank Chapman (1929) tells of watching a pair of toucans behaving in a most amusing manner that provides a good illustration of what might be termed the charming side of their character. These two had landed in a nutmeg tree, and after picking off a ripe berry and dropping most of it the male offered what remained to the female. She promptly swallowed it. Without moving, the male, obviously pleased with himself, produced from somewhere in his capacious bill a berry from a mangabé tree. They had been in such a tree a little while before, but this performance smacked of sleight of hand, or sleight of mandible perhaps. Jumping gallantly to the other side of the entranced female, this droll avian Houdini now produced a second berry. She was so overcome that she dropped this one, but a third and fourth berry appeared and were gratefully accepted. The pair then flew off together.

Chapman remarks that such exchanges between birds are always pleasing to watch, but between toucans the pleasure is emphasized by the bigness of the birds themselves, their pronounced personality, and, above all, their "caricature of a bill."

But they are not always so charming. Alexander F. Skutch (1954 and 1960) found them to be among the most persistent predators in the forests of Costa Rica. He mentions Swainson's toucan (*Ramphastos swainsonii*) and the smaller fiery-billed araçari (*Pteroglossus frantzii*) in particular and cites repeated examples of these birds raiding the nests of yellow-green vireos, tropical kingbirds, vermilion-crowned flycatchers, Gray's thrush and other passerines and making off with their eggs or young. So there is no need to wonder about the utility of that big, oversized bill. At such a business as this it is doubtless quite efficient—a regular machete.

At Brigand Hill in eastern Trinidad, I watched the handsome channel-billed toucan moving about in the heavy foliage of big forest trees that grow on the slopes below the lighthouse. There were a considerable number of them, and toward evening they were calling constantly and flying from one branch to another as if feeding.

Toucans are found only in neotropical America. There are three species in Mexico and five additional species in Central America. In northern South America, on what we may conveniently term the Caribbean slopes, there are in the neighborhood of fifteen more.

Toucans are legally protected in Trinidad, but, according to G. C. A. Junge and G. F. Mees, are much hunted for food by native gunners. Incidentally, as you probably are aware, toucans, in spite of the noise they make, have long been kept as pets. In a recent issue of a well-known mail-order catalogue, toucans are offered for sale at a modest price. If you should decide to buy one someday, I think it might be a good idea if you don't allow it to get too chummy with your pet parakeet.

Woodpeckers comprise a large and widely distributed family and have a way of being either extremely common, like the Cuban green woodpecker, or among the rarest of birds, like the carpintero real or ivory-bill that is so close to

Plate 59
Cuban green
woodpecker

extinction in Cuba and may have already disappeared in the southeastern United States. Obviously, woodpeckers depend for their existence on certain kinds of forest habitat. When this is removed by cutting, or altered drastically in character, these birds may be in trouble, for the very practical reason that their natural food supply of insect larvae, fruits, and nuts is reduced below the subsistence level. Some species, however, are more adaptable than others and can adjust to such changes.

The Cuban green woodpecker, with its unusually beautiful but "complicated color-pattern," as James Bond calls it, is common and widespread. M. Rutten found it "rather common" in singles and pairs in Santa Clara and Camagüey, wherever there were trees and shrubs, but particularly in forests, as in the Trinidad Mountains and the Sierra de Cubitas. In the Organos Mountains of Pinar del Río it was equally abundant, although not seen in other parts of that province. It is common on the southern half of the Isle of Pines, and Lawrence Walkinshaw and Bernard Baker observed it near Santa Barbara, "along a semi-wooded highway border." In Oriente Province I saw these birds in extensive forests of tropical buttonwood (*Conocarpus*) near the north coast west of Puerto Padre.

The ivory-billed woodpecker, which is twice as big as the Cuban green woodpecker, can still be found in the northeastern part of Oriente Province, on the pine ridges of Mayari and farther east. Restricted to natural stands of pine and hardwoods, it has been reduced to a dangerously low population by the gradual decimation of such forests. Other members of this family are already extinct or extremely rare, the Guadalupe Island flicker being the best known. Their essential habitat on this island off Baja California was destroyed by goats that had been introduced there, and many of the birds themselves killed by roving house cats.

In general, however, the woodpecker tribe is well represented in the West Indies and Caribbean. On the island of Cuba alone there are no less than six species including two endemic forms, the Cuban green and Fernandina's flicker, the latter a large, extremely handsome bird with heavily barred plumage of yellow, cinnamon, buff, and black. In Hispaniola, including Gonave Island, there is the tiny, nuthatch-like Antillean piculet, another endemic form. Mexico has a remarkably varied and colorful array of native woodpeckers, the most outstanding example being the huge imperial woodpecker (*Campaphillus imperalis*), an endemic species, resembling the ivory-bill but even larger and more magnificent.

These big birds also require extensive stands of large trees and are now uncommon and of very local occurrence. According to Emmet Blake, "they probably face extinction unless steps are taken to preserve their habitat." Blake gives their range as the Sierra Madre in Sonora, Chihuahua, Durango, Zacatecas, Jalisco, and Michoacán.

The red-billed scythebill belongs to the neotropical woodcreeper family (Dendrocolaptidae), forest birds that range from lowland woods to the pinelands of high altitudes. One Mexican species, the ivory-billed woodcreeper, lives in dry open woodlands on both the Caribbean and Pacific slopes. Another, the spotted woodcreeper, prefers humid mountain forests. Most of them (but not all species) have tail spines that enable them to brace themselves on tree trunks woodpecker fashion, and as they search for food they fly from one tree to another, much in the manner of woodpeckers, starting at the base of the trunk and working their way upward.

Plate 60
Red-billed
scythebill

Of the present species, Foster Smith (1950) found it common locally in the wet woods around Caicara, in northeastern Venezuela. This was in the months of May, August, and December. Although the local name in that region means "anteater" (tanguero), Smith did not observe this bird eating ants. He did see it quite frequently using its long, curved bill to probe at the base of the pineapple-like leaves of the epiphytic plants commonly found on trees in wet forest. He thought the call note similar to that of another woodcreeper, the carpintero (*Dendroplex picirostris phalara*), whose notes are "a series of loud, whistled *chui's*, descending the scale and becoming more rapid at the end." The local people make no distinction between woodcreepers and woodpeckers, hence the significance of their name for these birds.

Another member of this same genus, the brown-billed scythebill (*Campylorhamphus pusillus*) ranges from Costa Rica and western Panama to Colombia and Ecuador. Of its distribution and habits in Costa Rica, M. A. Carricker wrote (in 1910): "This curious and easily recognized species is found over the whole of the Caribbean lowlands and up the eastern slopes to at least 4000 feet, in the southwestern Pacific lowlands in very small numbers (a single record), and occasionally a straggler in the central highlands (two records). It is most abundant in the northern part of the Caribbean lowlands, in the so-called Santa Clara Valley, and especially in the vicinity of Guácimo, El Hogar, Jiménez and Guápiles. It is found only in the heavy forest, and is almost always seen feeding on a certain species of palm, probing with its long curved bill between the clusters of nuts and between the bases of the leaf-stalks where they emerge from the crown of the tree, evidently in search of some insect. . . . It is a rare bird. . . ."

In addition to insects, woodcreepers feed on spiders and amphibians. Again like woodpeckers, their nests are made in tree cavities; unlike woodpeckers, however, they cannot dig these holes themselves, but must appropriate natural cavities or those dug by other birds (probably woodpeckers). They lay from two to three white or greenish-white, unmarked eggs.

The ovenbird family, to which the pale-breasted spinetail belongs, is best known for the curious oven-shaped mud nests built by certain members of this group, but other species make use of sticks, which they glue together in an elab-

Plate 61
Pale-breasted
spinetail

orate structure that is obviously designed to protect the eggs and young from predators. The nest of this wide-ranging spinetail is typical of its branch of the family, which has been appropriately labeled "firewood gatherers." These nests are veritable fortresses, with long tunnel-like entrances and rigid, built-in reinforcement to prevent them from being rent asunder and entered by force. The spinetail may be an inconspicuous, small, earth-brown bird of no great beauty, but as with man and his home, its nest is its castle. In fact, the noteworthy structures of these birds have earned them the additional name of "castle-builders."

Alexander Wetmore (in 1926) wrote of this species: "During the winter months, in the Chaco, this spine tail was abundant in saw grass and bunch grass at the borders of thickets, or in little openings among scattered trees and bushes on the savannas. On sharp frosty mornings comparatively few were encountered until about 11, when as the day became warmer these small birds appeared in numbers in brushy pastures where none had been visible two hours before. They flew out with quick, tilting flight to new cover or dodged in and out among the clumps of grass or low branches with quick scolding notes, but seldom paused to perch in the open."

Wetmore noted that in the Chaco their choice of habitat was fairly open, their pale plumage blending with the grass clumps, while other species of *Synallaxis* that live in the heavy cover of dense thickets are darker in the general tone of their plumage. However, in the Pampa, the pale-breasted variety was found in rather heavy scrub forest where it frequented bushes and low trees, although it kept well within the protective cover of the thorniest twigs and branches.

G. F. Mees found these birds in thick secondary growth in Trinidad. He describes their song as a rather unmusical double note, similar to that of the cinnamomeous spinetail, a closely related species that occurs in Colombia, Venezuela, Trinidad, and Tobago. This double note, which Mees disparagingly says "must probably be considered the song," he writes as "cheep—hooeuw, the first syllable short and loud, the second somewhat less loud, rather unmusical, and drawn-out."

In Venezuela, Foster Smith (1950) noted that the pale-breasted spinetail has a habit of continually jerking its tail up and down. He observed them carrying nesting material in the third week of July. His impression of the call was that it is "not unlike" the "phoebe" notes of the black-capped chickadee, but harsher.

Plate 62
Rufous-fronted
thornbird

I was driving toward Maracay in northern Venezuela, along a crowded modern highway through a wide and very beautiful valley. It is open country, with fields, meadows and pastures, and clumps of trees every now and then, some of the trees themselves quite large. I noted that many of these trees supported huge, ungainly clusters or masses of twigs and branches, some of them merely large round balls, others elongated, and hanging from swaying branches almost to the ground. Still others were smaller and placed high up near the very top of a tree. Paul Schwartz, who is something of an authority on these strange clusters and the birds that build them, told me that they were the nests of the rufous-fronted thornbird. Like the spinetail, this species is a member of the ovenbird family and an outstanding adherent of the "firewood-gathering" clan. From the size and weight of their nest structures I would suppose them to be the undisputed champions of this group.

Don Eckelberry wrote to me: "It would almost seem that the ovenbird family, realizing its lack of distinction in plumage or song, plunged into architecture by way of compensation and thus succeeded mightily in that art." I would add that they qualify also as engineers and builders. As Eckelberry describes their structures: "They are either built around drooping terminal branches or around small upright ones supported from a crotch. Most of the nests are two to three feet in height and a foot thick, but many are considerably larger and may weigh as much as 300 pounds! They are added to year by year until eventually they collapse, usually in the wet season from the added weight of water."

The construction of such huge nests by so small a bird is nothing short of astonishing, but actually several pairs co-operate in the venture and then occupy the separate apartments that honeycomb the bulky edifice.

Alexander Wetmore (in 1939) says that these nests of sticks, pendant at the end of a tree branch, caught his eye on the grounds of the Agricultural School near Maracay, on his first day afield in Venezuela, "and these same structures were seen constantly as I traveled through the country." Foster Smith (in 1950) describes the call notes as a loud harsh *chick-chick-chick* and a *chip-chip-chip-chip* that reminded him of the call of the chipmunk of the eastern United States. He saw them adding sticks to their nests in early January.

Classified between the better-known woodpeckers and tyrant flycatchers are a number of large and interesting families of tropical birds, including the woodcreepers, the spinetails, the antbirds, the manakins, and the cotingas. The abundant and widely distributed barred antshrike belongs with the antbirds (Formiciidae), of which there are a large number of genera and species, including such forms as the antthrush, antwren, and antpitta. They have not been given the name "antbird" without reason. It has been related that early travelers in the Amazon country depended on the twittering calls of the antthrushes to warn them that a train of foraging ants lay across their path, and to disregard this warning was to risk an attack by these ferocious insects.

In *My Tropical Air Castle*, Dr. Frank Chapman describes the hunting methods of these birds in Panama: "Anywhere on the trail one may chance to hear the low *chir-r-ing* of the Bicolored Antbird. Follow it and you will doubtless find army ants moving rapidly on broad fronts and narrow fronts, great masses and single columns. Viewed separately, each group, or detachment, seems to be acting independently, but as a whole they are guided by a common purpose that carries

Plate 63
Barred
antshrike

them forward without confusion. Silently, relentlessly, the black hordes flow over the leaves. Roaches leap from cover and frantically try to escape, but are soon a mass of devouring ants. Centipedes are no more immune than moths. One expects to hear the blare of trumpets and cries of agony but there is only a rustling in the leaves and the voices of birds. *Gymnopithys* (the Bicolored Antbird) never ceases his whining *chir-r*; McLeannan's Antbird [now the Ocellated Antthrush] utters a prolonged musical twittering; and the little Spotted Antbird of the white throat and black necklace, who seems to regard the whole affair as a joke, utters a quaint, humorous ditty singularly out of keeping with the grim spirit of death and destruction by which he is surrounded. These three birds always attend the army ants. The first two I never see elsewhere. *Eucometis*, the [Gray-headed] Tanager, I rarely see except with the ants. There are also other Antbirds, a few Woodcreepers, and, at times, even a Motmot. The ants act as spaniels, flushing hidden game which the birds promptly capture. I have seen ants running over a bird's toes while it was watching for other prey, but I have never seen a bird eat an ant. . . ."

In Mexico, while not especially shy, the barred antshrike frequents undergrowth and thickets and is likely to be known best by its repertoire of harsh, staccato calls and musical whistles. Raymond Paynter believes that it exists only in natural, uncut thickets in Yucatán, and does not utilize second growth unless it is immediately adjacent to natural habitats. In Trinidad, on the other hand, G. F. Mees found it most plentiful in thick secondary growths and gardens, but not in forests. Likewise, in Surinam it occurs in coffee plantations and gardens. Very likely the local distribution and abundance of ants in these various regions has something to do with where the antshrike will be found and can be observed by the interested visitor.

Plate 64
White-bearded
manakin
The manakins are noted above all for their "dances," and the white-bearded manakin, despite its demure appearance, is not to be denied its part in these terpsichorean orgies. While he was on Trinidad in 1953–1954, G. F. Mees observed such a dance, which he describes as follows: "I have on many occasions watched the remarkable performances which have given the Manakins their name. On one of these occasions I made the following description of their behaviour. The place was in a piece of fairly dark forest, it was overshadowed by a few large and heavy trees, and grown with a somewhat larger number of thin and very thin, though already fairly tall young trees. Ground covered with dead leaves. At least some ten, but probably more male Manakins were present, all of whom were dancing more or less intensively. The most intensive form apparently was excercised very close above the ground; these birds had their throats blown up and moreover their throat-feathers puffed up to such a degree that they even protruded beyond the bill; they continually jumped over distances of a half to one meter, often to and fro, from the basal part of the trunk of one thin tree to that of

another. During this performance hard and short notes were uttered: 'krr...
k-krr...' I did not observe the birds really on the ground, they always perched
on some place just above it.

"Another noise, 'rrrrt,' was heard mainly from the males perched somewhat
higher up; it was produced by the primaries; mostly it was made in flight but I
also saw a perched male produce it by quavering its slightly lifted but not widely
spread wings.

"Apart from the short loud note, there was a weaker note evidently expressing
a much slighter degree of agitation, which I described as 'kyerr...tyeeerr...'
Now and then two males would chase each other. Two females at least were
present, who proceeded to the intensively dancing males just above the ground.
Several times I noted how a male started courting a female with, of course, its
throat-feathers puffed to the extreme, and quivering its half-spread and partly
lifted wings.... On other places I sometimes saw dancing birds perch actually on
the ground, but even then usually on a root or a protruding piece of earth, not on
a flat bare place. I have never seen that a bird actually cleared away dead leaves
from its dancing place."

It has long been suspected that the "music" that accompanies this performance
of the manakins is produced by the wing feathers, which, along with certain of
the wing muscles, are highly specialized. The resulting sounds have been likened
by Josselyn Van Tyne and A. J. Berger to the "muffled rattling of dried peas
within their pod," "the crack of a whip," "a sharp explosive snap," and a "sharp
percussive crack." All this from a tiny bird not much more than four inches in
total length!

Its fellow manakins may dance and win much fame thereby, but the golden-
headed manakin prefers to gather well up in trees, not close to the ground like
others of its kind, and seems to enjoy flying from branch to branch, snapping
its wings, and making a lot of noise. It is abundant in Venezuela and common in
Surinam, but in Trinidad, according to G. C. A. Junge and G. F. Mees, it is
slightly less plentiful than the white-bearded species, though still a common
enough species in the right habitats.

Plate 65
Golden-headed
manakin

William G. Conway, curator of birds at the Bronx Zoo in New York, came
back from a live-bird collecting trip to Trinidad recently with two males of this
species, and his description of how they were captured is of considerable interest:
"Most of all, on this trip, we wished to capture Golden-headed Manakins:
wonderfully tiny, big-headed, short-tailed birds with carmine thighs, velvety
black bodies and startling golden heads set with bright white eyes. Manakins are
called 'stick men' by Peter [a local boy who helped the collecting party], referring to the habits of some species which display on a twig over a cleared courtship arena. Their fascinating habits are well entwined in Zoological Society
history, for Dr. Beebe began studying them in 1908 and David Snow is concen-

trating on them now. Peter spotted a Golden-head flying from perch to perch near one of the nets. Finally, it flew directly towards the net, then veered sharply and slipped below it, and we realized we had both been holding our breath. Suddenly, a flash of gold and black hit the net on our right and Manakin No. 1 was ours. I found I had achieved my first case of buck fever in a Trinidad jungle and my hands shook so badly that I slit the net to make sure the bird was not injured in removal.... A fascinating side issue which took my interest lay in the minute white spots in the eyes of certain of the leaf-green 'female' Golden-headed Manakins David Snow was banding, and to which he had called my attention. Zoo experience indicated that these birds might well be immature males. I was especially pleased, therefore, to trap a fine series that showed, as Will Beebe was quick to note, a strange asymmetrical distribution of tiny eye spots in some birds, larger blotches in others, and, in one specimen, a complete ring of spots encircling the iris in one eye but only small spots in the other. Thus we had a fine developmental sequence before us, leading from the brown iris of the female or immature male to maturation of the adult male with his completely white irises."

Incidentally, the golden-headed manakin in the color plate is one of those captured by Mr. Conway. The whiteness of the eyes tells us that he is an adult male.

Plate 66
Purple-throated
fruitcrow

The purple-throated fruitcrow is not a crow at all, and its throat may appear to be more red than purple, but it belongs to the large neotropical family of cotingas, which are capable of many rather curious eccentricities. Members of this family exhibit remarkable variations in size, vocal abilities, and color of plumage. Of the ninety species that have been described, the smaller forms measure only three and a half inches in total length, while the larger ones reach eighteen or twenty inches. Some cotingas are plain brown or gray, others a brilliant pattern of orange, red, green, or blue. While those of the *Cephalopterus* or umbrellabird group sport a huge, overhanging, umbrella-like crest, others exhibit heads that are barren of feathers or adorned with long, erectile caruncles.

Of their vocal range, Dr. Frank Chapman (1929) wrote: "The Manakins are instrumentalists rather than vocalists, but their relatives, the Cotingas, vary as much in voice as they do in size. At one extreme are the Bellbirds of Guiana and Brazil with their far-carrying, explosive, metallic notes, at the other, the nearly voiceless Tityras. A pair of these pearl-gray, black-headed birds, as large as a Robin, tries each year to find a nesting-hole in the upper branches of a dead tree near the clearing whence their low, husky *cack* is barely audible. I have heard a somewhat similar note from the female of Natterer's Cotinga. The *beat-it*, *beat-it*, *beat-it no-ó-w* of Sclater's Attila is a well-marked forest note, and the sharp, commanding whistle of the large Panama Lathria halts you in your tracks."

Dr. Chapman wrote of the present species: "The Purple-throated Fruit Crows are among the most common and willing performers of this family.... Heard in the distance, their loud *cher-káw*, *cherk-ków*, often repeated and on changing keys, even by the same bird, is strongly reminiscent of the latter part of the phrase with which a hen proudly announces the deposition of an egg. A long-drawn, upward sliding *coo* follows, and at shorter range one hears a note strongly like the throat-clearing scrape that precedes expectoration. As they alight they lower their head and shiver their tail violently from side to side as though they were shaking something out of it; then dart out at some berry or small fruit, which they take on the wing, and in a minute or two are off to some other feeding-place. An altogether unusual character is the Fruit Crow. The woods seem comparatively silent and deserted after he and his care-free band have passed."

The white bellbird is a good example of the wide virtuosity and extremist tendencies of the cotingas, for here is one so modest in outward appearance as to be almost lacking in interest, but with a tremendous voice that can be heard ringing through the forest ravines for nearly a mile. There are cotingas with incredible wattles, bare throat pouches, peculiarly shaped crests, and other improbable ornamentations, the function of many of which we do not even understand, and there are cotingas with outstanding vocal powers, but the bellbirds are far out in front when it comes to sheer detonating loudness.

Plate 67
White
bellbird

A closely related species, the mossy-throated bellbird (*Procnias averano*) is common in certain sections of Trinidad, where Frank Chapman studied them at Caparo in 1893. Of its song, which is much like that of the white bellbird, he wrote (in 1895) that it has "three distinct notes, the first *bok*, the second *tui*, the third *tang*. The *bok* is by far the loudest and for this reason the one most frequently heard, and is doubtless the call alluded to by previous writers. It can be heard in the flat forest at a distance of about 600 yards. . . . The *bok* is sometimes uttered with much regularity about every ten seconds; at other times longer or shorter intervals may elapse. At a distance of four or five hundred yards it resembles the stroke of an axe on hard, resonant wood. One would now imagine that the bird was within seventy-five yards, so deceptive is the nature of this note. As one approaches, the call does not seem to increase in volume and one is apt to imagine that the bird is retreating slowly from tree to tree. This impression, however, is dispelled when one comes within one hundred yards of the bird, for the sound then becomes much louder until, as one gets directly beneath the caller, its volume is simply tremendous. It now has a slightly rolling quality— *br-r-r-ock*— and is so abrupt and explosive in character that it is nearly as startling as the unexpected report of a gun. At each utterance of this note the bird opens his bill to its widest extent and throws his head forward and downward with a violent, convulsive jerk as if he were in a passion and striking viciously at some rival. This motion is so violent that the bird evidently has some difficulty in maintaining his footing during its delivery as well as in recovering his balance afterward."

William G. Conway of the Bronx Zoo has succeeded in capturing a mossy-throated bellbird for exhibit. While observing these birds in the forests of Trinidad, he was told the local legend of how the campañero had argued with a blacksmith over which could deal the strongest blow to an anvil. "The bellbird won and thus attained its voice! Actually, the voice of this species is not bell-like and the anvil-percussion simile is not a poor one."

*Plate 68
Guiana
cock-of-the-rock*
If the bellbird is well equipped to represent the highly gifted cotingas in the Loud Noise or Distant Early Warning departments, the cock-of-the-rock will be difficult to surpass in the field of sheer glamour. Whether you prefer the golden-orange plumage of the Guiana species, or the deep blood-red of the Peruvian bird, their form and appearance are striking beyond words. But there is more to these brilliant birds than meets the eye.

When my old friend and former colleague Ernest Holt journeyed into the Amazon-Orinoco region with the Venezuelan-Brazilian Boundary Commission field party in 1930, he observed this species in its natural habitat and became much enamored of it. He wrote: "It is a shy bird and has chosen for its haunts the occasional isolated hills and the lower mountain slopes of the Guiana highlands— a region little disturbed by white men and only thinly populated by Indians. We obtained several additional specimens, and found one nest, very much like a robin's, fastened to the bare face of a huge split boulder." The nest is of mud and sticks and usually contains two eggs.

In addition to their beauty, these birds are noted dancers, but the real significance of these performances is not understood, even though they were first observed and reported on by Sir Robert Hermann Schomburgk as early as 1841. This account suggests that these are social dances participated in by birds of both sexes, the males in all their regal splendor and the more demure females in modest olive-brown. Holt didn't see the dance of the *rupicolas*, but from Schomburgk's description, and other accounts, he wrote: "...a score of birds of both sexes gather on the bushes surrounding an open space while a male goes through an extraordinary performance on the ground. While the audience cheers approvingly, the bird, with lowered wings and outspread pumping tail, walks round and round, scratching the ground and springing into the air. When it tires, another male takes its place. There seem to be no data as to the duration of these marathons."

W. Frost went into this same general region to capture live specimens of these birds, and his picture of the dance is a little different. He said that the dancing went on for weeks, so the term "marathon" is well chosen. The dancing grounds, according to Frost, are cleared arenas two and a half to three feet across, placed under feeding trees close to running water. They are used most often between 8 and 10 a.m., but sometimes in the afternoons as well. At variance with the earlier accounts, Frost said that the dance is started by what he described as an old male bird, which jumps back and forth from a branch of the feeding tree to the arena, flicking his open wings and spreading his tail. The other birds are gathered in the feeding tree and one by one they drop down and watch. Finally it is all too much for them, and gradually several join in, jumping back and forth until there are seven or eight birds taking part.

Frost claimed that he saw no females at the dance, and from what has been learned since of the displays of a close relative, the manakins, it seems likely that the "females" observed by Schomburgk may have been immature males. Which, if true, suggests that this is a display by rival males, a contest and not a pleasant little social gathering or soirée.

But the matter is far from settled, and someone who is fully conversant with modern concepts of animal behavior will have to stuff himself with antibiotics and seek out *Rupicola rupicola* on its dancing grounds.

The black phoebe is a typical representative of this large New World family, the tyrant flycatchers, of which there are 365 species throughout North and South America. The present species is widely distributed, equally at home building its nest on the Pacific coast of California or on a rock above the turbulent Pejivalle River in Costa Rica, where Alexander Skutch found a pair completing their structure of fine grass and mud (1960). This particular nest was plastered securely to the almost vertical wall of rock, exactly forty-six inches above the rapidly flowing stream. The mud pellets that composed its thick walls were strengthened by bits of dead vegetation, "in the manner that men use chopped straw for binding the clay in construction of adobe and *bahareque*." The two immaculate white eggs had been deposited by April 26. Sometimes the eggs of the black phoebe are spotted and blotched with red or brown, and elsewhere clutches may contain as many as five or six eggs.

Plate 69 Black phoebe

In the course of watching this nesting pair, Skutch found that the female did all the incubating. Because there was no place for a blind, he had to make his observations from an exposed position some thirty-five feet away. The female didn't like this and would not stay on the eggs unless the male was close by, but his presence seemed to lend her the necessary confidence. The patient watcher was rewarded by some intimate glimpses of the home life of these birds. He writes: "The male phoebe would sometimes stand on the nest's rim, and then the female would go promptly to sit in it. When this occurred, I often heard a low, sweet trilling that sounded above the roar of the current as the female settled on her eggs in front of her mate. I could not tell, however, whether these notes were uttered by one member of the pair or by both of them. At other times, the male would hover momentarily in front of the nest, and this had the same effect of bringing the timid female promptly back to her eggs." Skutch admits that the behavior of this particular female, in gathering courage from the presence of her mate, was very "human-like." He adds: "But however we interpret the behavior of this pair of birds, it shows once more how inadequate our too mechanistic theories of animal conduct become when we confront them with the complex situations and delicately shaded motives that we actually observe in nature."

The food of the black phoebe consists almost entirely of insects. Its song is a strident *fee-bee*, repeated endlessly, for it is one of that small number of birds gracious enough to tell us their names.

Plate 70
Pied
water-tyrant

If you make the trip from Port of Spain to the Caroni River Swamp between early April and October (I was told), you will see the scarlet ibis. And that is not all, for there are many other colorful birds in that region, such as the pied water-tyrant. As it turned out I made the trip on the last day of August, which was a poor time, as the local birdlife was obviously less active and many species were apparently molting. But I did see the scarlet ibis *and* the pied water-tyrant.

My friends Whitney and Karen Eastman went there in late February, which is almost the beginning of spring, and had a much better day. They found the swamp "teeming with bird life. A Hindu boy poled our crude little skiff, whimsically named the 'Fairy Jet,' all day long without resting. In certain areas birds would fly up in front of us by the thousands, including several species of herons and the Jacana. Rarities like the White-shouldered Water Tyrant, the Yellow-throated Spinetail, whose coarse, teapot-shaped nests were in evidence in the shrubbery, the Gray Dacnis and the White-headed Marsh Tyrant were in great abundance" (1958).

Apparently, in the right season and in the proper locations, the white-shouldered or pied water-tyrant is quite numerous. C. B. Williams wrote: "This pretty little black and white bird is generally common, particularly in the more open parts of the country devoted to sugar growing, and is frequently seen settling on the telegraph wires along the main roads." Phillips Street wrote that it was "often noted from the road which borders the Caroni Swamp, and twenty were observed on May 24 on a boat trip through the swamp." However, G. F. Mees states that he failed to see this species or the white-headed water-tyrant (*Arundinicola leucocephala*)—locally known as "the widow"—"quite as often as indicated in former published notes about their abundance; a difference probably caused by the fact that I did not frequent suitable habitats."

Williams found its nest to be a small covered structure with the opening on one side near the top. It is made of grass stalks and cotton fluff and usually lined with feathers. He observed it in many sites: twenty feet from the ground in a large tree, at the end of a long branch of a fiddlewood tree overhanging a pond, in a bush next to a small stream and three feet from the ground, on a telegraph pole, and in many other locations. The nesting season in Trinidad is from June through September to October, the wet season. Three eggs seems to be the usual clutch.

In northern Venezuela, Alexander Wetmore (1939) saw a male of this species on a shaded perch in a little tree on the playa at Independencia. "With steadily

PLATE 56. CUBAN TODY (*Todus multicolor*)

PLATE 57. RUFOUS-TAILED JACAMAR (*Galbula ruficauda*)

Opposite: PLATE 58. CHANNEL-BILLED TOUCAN (*Ramphastos vitellinus*)

PLATE 59. CUBAN GREEN WOODPECKER (*Xiphidiopicus percussus*)

PLATE 60. RED-BILLED SCYTHEBILL (*Campylorhamphus trochilirostris*)

PLATE 61. PALE-BREASTED SPINETAIL (*Synallaxis albescens*)

PLATE 62. RUFOUS-FRONTED THORNBIRD

(*Phacellodomus rufifrons*)

Female

PLATE 63. BARRED ANTSHRIKE (*Thamnophilus doliatus*)

Male

PLATE 64. WHITE-BEARDED MANAKIN (*Manacus manacus*)

PLATE 65. GOLDEN-HEADED MANAKIN (*Pipra erythrocephala*)

PLATE 66. PURPLE-THROATED FRUITCROW (*Querula purpurata*)

PLATE 67. WHITE BELLBIRD (*Procnias alba*)

PLATE 68. GUIANA COCK-OF-THE-ROCK (*Rupicola rupicola*)

PLATE 69. BLACK PHOEBE (*Sayornis nigricans*)

PLATE 70. PIED WATER-TYRANT (*Fluvicola pica*)

twitching tail it moved actively near the ground. On October 29 I watched another for some time as it circled above the water of the lagoon, flapping and turning for minutes at a time and, after a rest on some projecting stub, continuing its flight. With its pointed wings it resembled a little swallow."

That classic among books on the Caribbean, Archie Carr's *The Windward Road*, has a chapter centered around the people, life, and dialects of Bocas del Toro—the Mouths of the Bulls—which is an isolated fishing village on the Caribbean coast of northern Panama. Above all, Carr discusses "Bocas Creole Spanish" and "Bocas English" with the relish and appreciation of the fine points that are known only to the connoisseur. As Carr writes, Bocas del Toro "was important to the buccaneers as a source of turtles and manatee for provisioning their ships, and in recent years it has served as a minor port for the Almirante Division of the United Fruit Company." Also, according to Eugene Eisenmann (1955), Bocas del Toro is the southern limit in Central America to the range of the great kiskadee.

Plate 71
Great
kiskadee

What I wouldn't give to go to the "jook" at the Hotel Miramar and, above the din of the *piccolo*, listen for the voice of the great kiskadee. There would be no point in listening for it anywhere else, because it is obvious from reading Archie Carr that this is the cultural center of Bocas del Toro and the place where one could expect to hear the purest Bocas creole. And what I really want to know is whether these particular kiskadees sound any different than they do elsewhere.

I was in my room at the Avila in Caracas when it struck me that wherever I went the words of the kiskadee were supposed to change, according to the local language. The Avila is on the edge of the city, and there are all kinds of birds on the lawn, around the swimming pool, in the shrubbery, and flying by overhead. Among them is the kiskadee, and in Venezuela it is said to call "cristofué," loud and clear. I listened to it, and in spite of my most attentive efforts it still sounded like "kis-ka-dee" to me.

Nor did I have any better luck in Trinidad—on the whole, even worse, I should say. In Trinidad I was told that this species is represented by a race that speaks French. As everyone knows, they said, this bird cries "Qu'est-ce-qu'il dit?" But not to my ear. The species is also resident in the lower Rio Grande Valley of Texas, but even though this brings it pretty close to home for most of us, it doesn't help much, for according to Roger Tory Peterson (1960), Irby Davis claims that its call is a loud "get-ter-heck." And Irby Davis is the acknowledged authority on the birds of that region.

The great kiskadee is an interesting bird for a variety of reasons. Within its extensive range it is abundant and highly adaptable, inhabiting both rural and urban localities. In Trinidad, V. C. Quesnel found that the population density in suitable habitat in the Port of Spain area was twenty pairs on forty-four acres. In addition to honeybees, moth borers, capsicum peppers, and lizards, the kiskadee is said to eat small fish, catching them much in the manner of kingfishers.

Alexander Skutch (1960) makes this interesting observation: "The great majority of the members of this family are among the mildest and least offensive of birds; and the kingbirds of the genus *Tyrannus* themselves, although admirably bold in the defense of their nests from large and dangerous predators, are not habitually domineering over smaller neighbors; they are tyrant-chasers rather than tyrants, as Benjamin Franklin long ago recognized when he proposed that the Eastern Kingbird rather than the Bald Eagle be chosen as the symbol of the newly created North American republic. Of the many species of American Flycatchers which I have studied intimately, the Kiskadee is the only one to which I am inclined to apply the epithet 'tyrant.' "

Plate 72
Common
tody-flycatcher The common tody-flycatcher, to quote one of its most ardent admirers, Alexander Skutch, "is well worth cultivating, for it has more character than most small birds, and indeed than many large ones. Its length is slightly over three and a half inches, more than half of which is taken up by its long, straight, flat bill and by its narrow, strongly graduated, uptilted tail" (1960). It is a bird of open country—"shady plantations, parks and gardens, roadside trees, pastures with scattered trees and bushes, and wherever shrubs and trees stand in open places," according to Skutch. It avoids all kinds of woodland and dense thickets, where it is replaced by the slate-headed tody-flycatcher (*Todirostrum sylvia*). It travels in pairs throughout most of the year, but Donald R. Dickey and A. J. Van Rossem say that after the young are on the wing, family parties of four or five birds stay together through the succeeding winter, "and to that extent it might be said that this species travels in small flocks."

These same authors, writing of the common tody-flycatcher in El Salvador, have given us a charming picture of the characteristic behavior of these tiny birds: "When one is walking through woodland in the lower country, he often hears the peculiar clicking notes of these little flycatchers. The first impression is that of a much louder call coming from a hundred yards or so away, but a glance around will usually show a tody perched within a few feet, its very smallness and lack of motion serving as concealment. At short intervals come the series of sharp clicks, accompanied by violent wigwagging of the short tail. The clicker's curiosity being finally satisfied, it resumes feeding, making short flights from some stand low in the underbrush or working through higher foliage in company with other small birds such as warblers and vireos."

Skutch (1960) describes the "dawn song" of this species. He says: "I had known the tody-flycatcher for many years before I became aware of its dawn song. Although the dawn songs of some of the larger flycatchers command attention by their loudness or their beauty, whereas those of a few of the small species are unforgettably quaint, that of the tody-flycatcher is so extremely simple that one may question whether it deserves this classification. But since this particular mode of vocal expression is rarely used except before sunrise and it is then, especially in the breeding season, continued for many minutes together, I believe that it is a true dawn song, comparable to the most elaborate twilight performances of the Tufted Flycatcher or the Streaked Flycatcher. The song consists merely of a slight, sharp *tic* repeated rapidly innumerable times, sometimes at a rate of 110 notes per minute. However, such rapid singing is rarely long continued.... Dawn singing begins in the last week of January or in some years not until late in February, and it may continue until the end of September.... Of the local flycatchers, only the Paltry Tyranniscus, which has a much longer breeding season, has a comparably long song period."

The common tody-flycatcher builds a pensile nest, attached to a twig or projecting limb where it swings free of other vegetation. Ludlow Griscom (1932) quotes A. W. Anthony as saying that such a nest, found in a thorny tree twenty feet from the ground at Hacienda California in Guatemala, "had the appearance of being a mere rag of dry grass hanging from a twig." This nest was two and a half inches in diameter by seven inches in length, "the entrance being a very small hole in one side, scarcely noticeable."

Skutch has noted that the female begins to sleep inside the nest in the evening of the first day on which she has laid her first egg. Two or three eggs are the rule, and the incubation period is seventeen to eighteen days. Skutch writes: "By night and by day, the tody-flycatchers rest in their snug chambers with their heads at the doorway." We can understand why this delightful little bird is such a favorite of those who have had the good fortune to know it intimately.

The most striking thing about this rather quiet, self-effacing little flycatcher, the Lesser Antillean elaenia, is its distribution. It completely encircles the Caribbean, from the farthest northwest point off the Yucatán Channel southeast to the island of Barbados beyond the Tobago Trough, and from Vieques Island east of Puerto Rico across more than one thousand miles of open sea to the small island of St. Andrew off Nicaragua. Yet, in all this expanse of water, and this profuse array of coral and volcanic and mangrove shores, this species will not be found on any of the larger islands or continental land masses. The biggest island inhabited by this particular Caribbean elaenia is Martinique, which measures only forty miles from end to end and little more than fifteen miles across.

Plate 73 Lesser Antillean elaenia

It will not be found on Puerto Rico proper, which has several flycatchers but no elaenia; nor does it occur on Jamaica or Hispaniola, which have a couple of elaenias of their own. This species prefers islands—the smaller the better.

On Vieques Island, Alexander Wetmore (1927) found this species in "thorny jungle on dry, hot slopes in the eastern and southern parts of the island, in areas where the scrub is almost impenetrable. Their habits differed decidedly from those usual in their family. At times they rested quietly and made sallies after passing insects like any ordinary flycatcher, and again were seen searching and climbing about among limbs like a vireo or titmouse." On Culebra, Wetmore came across these birds in dense and extensive growths of cactus and spiny shrubs on dry hillsides.

Of their behavior, he wrote: "They moved about very little, seldom flying more than a few feet at a time; so that at times I heard their sharply explosive, whistled call-notes for half an hour without being able to catch sight of them in the dense scrub. Twice I heard them singing a sweet, warbling song.... Natives have no special name for the bird, but recognize it as a small mockingbird (*Ruiseñor Pequeño*) because of its sweet song."

As would be expected, P. W. Hummelinck found this bird on Bonaire in thorny acacia and cactus scrub, *Croton* vegetation and manchineel thickets, as well as in scattered shade trees in the aloe-fields. This author remarks that the presence of this species on these islands in the South Caribbean rather than the elaenia found on the nearby mainland "makes this species a most interesting element of the avifauna of Aruba, Curaçao, and Bonaire which, for the present, cannot otherwise be indicated than as 'Caribbean.' "

Plate 74
Rough-winged
swallow

In spite of its plain appearance, the rough-winged swallow is of special interest in more ways than one. The roughened serration of the outer web of the outer primary gives the species its name. It is less pronounced in immatures and more evident in males than in females. All of which may be quite unique, but the ordinary observer will have to take this information on faith, as he is unlikely to see it for himself. More interesting to the layman is the fact that these little birds are so widespread, resident and breeding over a large part of the entire Western Hemisphere. There are many geographic races, often difficult to tell apart even by an expert.

Donald R. Dickey and A. J. Van Rossem, writing of this bird in Central America, have said: "The rough-winged swallow shares with the blue honey creeper, rufous and white wren, and raven the distinction of being one of the few species resident in El Salvador which has a vertical migration and which has different breeding and wintering ranges." Breeding in the high country of El Salvador, above two thousand feet, they arrive in March, flying up from their coastal wintering areas in swamp forests and mangroves. These same authors tell us that "Sites occupied included old nest holes of the Texas kingfisher and Nicaraguan green paroquet (the latter in a vertical bank of volcanic ash), natural crevices in lava cliffs, and chinks between roofing tiles in native houses. Bark strips, grass and feathers were the materials used...."

Although they spend the winter along the Pacific coast of El Salvador, Ludlow Griscom (1932) found these birds common in winter in Guatemala to an altitude of about eight thousand feet, but most of them were evidently passing through along with mixed flocks of cliff and barn swallows. However, some individuals remained in the higher altitudes all winter.

The rough-wing is an abundant species around the ancient ruins in Yucatán, according to Raymond Paynter, and it is very likely that they build their nests amid these ornamented relics of the past.

One of the best known and most cosmopolitan families among birds are the Corvidae, which includes in its distinguished membership the jays, magpies, crows, and ravens. Among the one hundred species known in the world is the green jay, a real gem in the color pattern of a group that ranges from the most somber blacks and grays to dazzling blues, yellows, and purples. This species, with the typical audacity of its kind, combines bright green with bright blue, green with black, and adds a bold dash of bright yellow.

Plate 75
Green jay

The green jay is common and widespread in much of Mexico in woodland habitats, chiefly lowland areas, but Emmet Blake says that it ranges to six thousand feet in the mountains. In Yucatán, according to Raymond Paynter, it occurs in "deciduous forest, heavy second growth, and lighter rain forest; rare in heavy rain forest."

There are recognizable differences in size, length of tail for example, and in the shading and distribution of colors in the plumage of these birds in different parts of their range. A number of subspecies, or geographic races, have been described. Ludlow Griscom (1932) found them "remarkably variable," green jays from eastern Guatemala being distinctly yellower underneath than birds from Mexico, with a tinge of green on the breast, but even this tinge showed geographical variations.

Of this species in Venezuela, Alexander Wetmore wrote (in 1939): "In the mountain forests at Rancho Grande (in the Cordillera de la Costa) this jay was fairly common and was seen to 3600 feet elevation. They ranged in heavy cover and were secretive but usually could be decoyed out into the open by an imitation of their notes. They were found here and elsewhere in little flocks of 6 to 10. One morning at sunrise such a band came into the lower garden at the house, where I could watch them from above as they worked through low bushes or came out to hop about on the ground, a beautiful and attractive sight. . . . Sometimes through curiosity they came within a few feet of me, and frequently two or three perched near together on the same branch. While some of their notes were peculiar other calls resembled those of the blue jay of the eastern United States." Wetmore wrote their call note as *kinkin*, which Herbert Friedmann and Foster Smith (in 1950) interpreted as *keen-keen*.

Roger Tory Peterson (1960) describes the voice of the green jay as follows: "*Cheh cheh cheh cheh*; also *cleep*, *cleep*, *cleep*, etc.; a dry throaty rattle like a cricket frog's; also other calls." In Texas, Peterson says, this species is resident only in the southern tip of the state, north to Norias and upriver to Laredo. There is a small colony of them at San Antonio and there have been occasional records at Beeville and Alice. They are more common in the mountains around Caracas in Venezuela.

Plate 76
Southern
house-wren

It is wise to be well prepared for a trip into brand-new birding territory. As a matter of fact, most of the birding fraternity are quite systematic and meticulous about such things. They wouldn't think of going into an unknown region without reading every scrap of pertinent literature they could get their hands on, besides talking personally with anyone who had been there and might have useful suggestions to impart. But when I made a somewhat hurried trip to Trinidad on my first visit, I was not prepared for some of the surprises that came my way. One of these was hearing the familiar song of the house-wren as I stood with David Snow on the front steps of Dr. William Beebe's house at Simla. I should have known that this common species was represented here and that the song of a house-wren in the Arima Valley of Trinidad sounds the same as it does back home.

Alexander Wetmore met this species at the southernmost extremity of its range, in Paraguay, Uruguay, and Argentina. He wrote (in 1926): "The southern house wren, of whatever race, in action and general appearance is the same busy bird, full of life and energy, that greets us in our northern dooryards, and is one of the first species to be recognized on arrival in unfamiliar southern scenes. Notes and actions are unmistakably those of a house wren, and even the bubbling song is not noticeably different."

Again, in Costa Rica, Wetmore wrote (in 1944): "On November 4 I heard one singing in early morning in the town of Liberia. At the Hacienda Santa María a male lived secretively around the house throughout my stay, taking care to keep out of reach of the collecting gun and finally, on the morning of my departure, coming out to chatter familiarly at me as I mounted my mule for the ride down to the lowlands." And he wrote of this species (in 1941): "One scolded me from the vines over a pergola in the main plaza of Guatemala City. They were known to the natives as *churrita*."

In Venezuela, however, Wetmore found the song, though generally similar, "sharper in tone and more emphatic" than that of the northern house-wren, and some of the scolding notes "distinctly different" (1939).

In both Trinidad and Tobago, G. F. Mees observed the house-wren near houses as well as in open country.

Only two species of wrens occur in the West Indies, the house-wren and the rare Zapata wren, which is the sole member of the endemic genus *Ferminia*. It is the only wren in the Greater Antilles, and is limited to the Santo Tomás region of the Zapata Swamp in southern Cuba where it inhabits dense shrubbery. Six races of house-wrens have been described from the Lesser Antilles, two of which are apparently extinct. It is believed that they were destroyed by the mongoose in Martinique and Guadeloupe.

Detailed information on the life and habits of the southern house-wren will be found in two papers by Alexander Skutch, one in the *Condor* (1953, 55: 121–149) and another (a résumé of the *Condor* article) in Volume II of his recent *Life Histories of Central American Birds*.

If you see a robin-like bird wearing large, yellow-rimmed spectacles, it will be the bare-eyed thrush—provided, of course, that you and the bird are in the right location. The French names, as usual, are highly descriptive meaning literally "the thrush with the yellow eyelids" and "the thrush with the spectacles." And the Spanish ojo de candil ("lamp eye") is equally fitting.

Plate 77
Bare-eyed
thrush

In Trinidad, according to G. C. A. Junge and G. F. Mees, it is common in second growth, bamboo clusters, and small isolated patches of forest. In large cacao plantations you will find thrushes, but not this one, and the same applies to the uncut forest primeval. C. B. Williams considered it "by far the commonest of the Trinidad thrushes," and widely distributed, often being found in gardens in Port of Spain. As an example of their abundance, at Carlsen Field, on the Southern Main Road about midway between Port of Spain and San Fernando, Phillips Street counted nineteen of these birds on May 21. On May 26 he found a nest containing young. Williams recorded active nests on June 20, July 3, July 7, and August 26, all with eggs. Mees noted an adult carrying food on July 6, and "on 28 July a nest was found, about 2 m. from the ground in a very young forest tree near Tacarigua." It contained one egg and a second egg two days later. A fledgling just out of the nest was seen on August 14. Williams describes the nest as deep cup-shaped and made "of various materials." He adds: "I was informed by Mr. Shannon that the bird frequently places a large leaf of prickly Solanum in the middle of the nest, but have not been able to confirm this."

In Venezuela this species inhabits woodland clearings, stubble, groves, and open fields, chiefly below 1500 meters (Phelps and Phelps, 1950). I found it common in the Botanic Gardens in Caracas in early September.

Herbert Friedmann and Foster Smith (1950) tell us that "This thrush was common in the lowland seasonal forest at Caicara [Venezuela]; it was present, but rare, in the deciduous seasonal woods at Cantaura and then always near water.... A nest of mud mixed with a few fine twigs was found at Caicara the first week of July, about 6 feet up in a crotch formed by a big branch; it was so covered with moss as to be most inconspicuous. It contained four blue-green eggs, heavily blotched with russet."

We usually think of thrushes as gifted songsters, and this is generally the case, though some species of this world-wide family are more gifted than others. Few can match the nightingale of Europe, the hermit thrush of North America, or the solitaires. But these are real artists and set a high standard. James Bond (1960) says of the vocal abilities of the bare-eyed thrush: "Song a clear *turé-too-too*, repeated indefinitely and much like that of the American Robin. Also utters a whining *pe-ou-wa*, and a variety of shorter call-notes." In Venezuela, according to Friedmann and Smith (1950), this bird "has a variety of calls, some quite thrush-like and some decidedly not. Among the common calls was a catlike *meow* and a rising *cha-ray-rah* (charera)." The authors add that the song was melodious and thrushlike.

Plate 78
Orange-billed
nightingale-
thrush

It is our good fortune that there is a complete little monograph of the orange-billed nightingale-thrush in Volume II of Alexander F. Skutch's excellent *Life Histories of Central American Birds.* For this is one of the shyest, most elusive of birds, not readily observed even in its favored haunts. Of its presence in the Northern Range of Trinidad, G. F. Mees has written: "This is one of the few—or perhaps the only—species of Trinidad birds that is strictly confined, by habitat preference, to the greater altitudes; I did not observe it below about 500 m. altitude...." He goes on to say that in the forest near the summit of Morne Bleu (2761 feet), as in similar environments, it is nonetheless a characteristic species. He adds: "This restricted habitat evidently is the reason that comparatively few of the earlier collectors obtained the species. The birds live solitary or in pairs and give the impression of being definitely territorial."

We can speculate at once whether or not this is true of them throughout their range, for it is a long way from Morne Bleu to, let us say, the western slope of the Sierra Madre in Mexico. Emmet Blake, however, says of this same species in Mexico: "Except when singing, nightingale-thrushes are likely to be overlooked in the heavy forest growth that forms their usual habitat."

But Skutch, who has probably observed more of these birds than anyone else, seems to settle the question when he writes: "At all times most difficult to see, their presence was usually revealed by their notes issuing from the depths of the tangled vegetation. I was unable to discover whether these secretive birds live singly or in pairs during the portion of the year when they are not engaged in nesting. At least, they do not flock. Such birds as these must be constantly changing their area of residence; when the thickets where they live are cut and burned for the purposes of agriculture, they find fresh havens in neighboring fields which meanwhile have been overgrown with bushes and vines."

If we are ever to get acquainted with the nightingale-thrush, even on the briefest and most casual terms, it should be obvious that the first step will be to learn its song. One of the penalties of getting to know a great deal about almost anything is the risk you run of unearthing, at the same time, little particles and fragments and scraps of disillusionment. In this case, the price we must pay for Skutch's admirable life-history sketch of this species is revealed by his statement that "the name 'nightingale-thrush' appears to have been applied to these birds because a few of them, including the Orange-billed Nightingale-Thrush, resemble in *appearance* the renowned nocturnal minstrel of the Old World and not because of their qualities as songsters."

All that Skutch can add is that it "compensates for the plainness of its song by the regularity with which it utters it." He describes the song as "short, simple, prosaic, decidedly un-thrush-like, and pleasant but not inspiring." The only faintly happy thing about all this are the paraphrases that its song suggests to him— *Thanks very much, that's very nice,* and *Will Shakespeare.*

And one thing more. It is among the few birds that continue to sing during "the wet and gloomy months of September and October, the nadir of the songbirds' year...."

The great family of thrushes, comprising 305 species, is of world-wide distribution except for New Zealand and some of the oceanic islands. They are abundantly represented in tropical America, especially in forested mountain country. In the West Indies, where the red-legged thrush is the most widespread and abundant member of the family, there are thrushes such as the handsome La Selle (*Turdus swalesi*) and the forest thrush (*Cichlherminia l'herminieri*) that are restricted to heavy woodland cover and mountain slopes. But the red-legged thrush is more adaptable. Although in some regions it is rather shy and retiring, in what is perhaps typical thrushlike fashion, elsewhere it has altered its habits in the direction of more open country and less bashful behavior. In very early times it was probably a characteristic forest thrush on New Providence, perhaps even confined to the gentle slopes of Blue Mountain, but today it can be seen hopping about well-tended lawns in the city of Nassau. This is much the same change that was made many years ago by the American robin, which began life as a forest thrush.

Plate 79
Red-legged
thrush

In 1927, Alexander Wetmore was in Hispaniola and found this species "shy and retiring so that it is not easily observed" (Wetmore and Swales, 1931). But in Cuba, Thomas Barbour observed that the same bird "is seen everywhere... hopping about or scratching diligently in the dry leaves of garden thickets and wilder coppices." In the Exuma Cays, a lovely chain of small islands in the central Bahamas, I landed with a party of naturalists one morning in late January on Warderick Wells. As we went ashore on a wide spit of sand on the west side of the island, we were immediately greeted by the loud *wet-wet* of the red-legged thrush (in Haiti they would say *ouète-ouète*). Here we were, right on the rim of the sea, surrounded by salt water, with hills that rose less than one hundred feet in elevation, and here also was the red-legged thrush. The scenery was charming, with thickets of sea grape, Joe-wood, thatch palm, sabal palmetto, buccaneer palm, and gumbo-limbo, but it was scarcely our conception of thrush habitat. There was a great deal of sand, a wonderful population of exceedingly tame curl-tailed lizards, vast stretches of blue water all around, but one expected mockingbirds, not thrushes.

Still, they were there, and it is possible that this species, for some reason or other, like the pearly-eyed thrasher, is extending its range, or reclaiming former range, or branching out just because it feels like it. This is all the more interesting, as a subject for speculation, when we consider that on the tiny Caribbean island of Cayman Brac this same bird was extremely abundant in 1911 and apparently rare in 1930. Its more recent status is not known.

It is also of interest that the La Selle thrush is known only from the La Selle ridge in southeastern Haiti, being most abundant at the summit of the ridge, from six thousand feet upward, and meets the red-legged thrush at a slightly lower altitude on what James Bond has called the La Selle Plateau. Below five thousand feet, in the Jardins Bois Pin, where much of the forest has been cleared, only the red-legged thrush is found.

Incidentally, for a thrush, caleçon rouge isn't a notable singer. But it is an abundant, thriving, and extremely handsome creature.

Plate 80
Rufous-browed
peppershrike

Although the peppershrike has a harsh, scolding note, like any bird so closely related to the vireos, it is one of the sweet singers. "One chattered harshly from concealment among leaves in the grounds of the American Legation at Caracas," wrote Alexander Wetmore in 1926, but at another time (1939) and place he remarked: "The song...was a pleasant warble, somewhat accented, so that it did not seem monotonous though constantly repeated. From its tone I had supposed that it came from some finch and was astonished to trace it to a pepper shrike."

In Panama, he found this species fairly common: "...but on my arrival at the beginning of the dry season their songs had become infrequent, and without these notes as a guide they are difficult to find. While they are robust in body, they move about behind leafy cover in such leisurely manner, resting for minutes with only slight movements of the head, that it is only casually that one is seen. They are birds of the high forest crown, but come also about clearings, even into the low second growth called rastrojo, or to the borders of mangrove swamps. At the Maria work camp I found one feeding in mango trees and cocoanut palms standing isolated in the extensive clearing.

"The song is loud with strongly accented notes, and ends abruptly, when there is a pause of varying length, often of several minutes, before it is repeated. The first two or three syllables are uttered rather slowly, followed by a rapidly given louder phrase. The notes carry for several hundred yards, and, if the song is continued, eventually the bird may be located, though the process of finding one may require half an hour. The three males that I collected represent many hours of search, since, as already stated, during January the birds were not singing steadily." (1957).

Another description is contributed by Don Eckelberry, who writes in a letter: "The rich, rollicking and varied song of the peppershrike reminds me, in its cadence and quality, of the vigorous notes of the white-eyed Vireo but is louder and more emphatic. So emphatically delivered is it in fact, that in its upright singing stance its stubby, hanging tail vibrates with the effort. It looks and acts rather like a grossly built vireo, too, though the bright red-orange irides bordered with rust red gives it a peculiar sore-eyed appearance.

"Peppershrikes are birds of the forest edge, second growth and shrubby openings of the tropical lowlands from Mexico to Argentina. They are not particularly shy but their habitat preference and their slow, deliberate movements would, were they silent, make them difficult to find."

A male from Panama, described by Wetmore, had the iris "wax yellow," upper mandible (maxilla) "mouse brown," lower mandible "neutral gray." In Trinidad the bill color was given by G. C. A. Junge and G. F. Mees as "maxilla pinkish, mandible bluish grey."

In Mexico, according to Emmet Blake, these birds "frequent thickets and forest edge from sea-level to an altitude of about 4,000 feet. They usually prefer good cover within a few feet of the ground, but often select an exposed perch for singing. The song is rather weak, but fairly varied and musical." On the Yucatán Peninsula, Raymond Paynter found peppershrikes "particularly numerous in thinned forest in the vicinity of towns, principally in the zone of deciduous forest." Their apparent liking for the vicinity of human habitations was noted also by Wetmore, who observed them in southern Veracruz, "in leafy cover, sometimes in tree tops projecting above the surrounding growth, and sometimes along thicket lined trails, or in more open trees near the village [Tres Zapotes]. They moved along rather quickly and kept under shelter" (1943).

In his guide book, *Finding Birds in Mexico*, Ernest Edwards lists the rufous-browed peppershrike as occurring on the hillsides below Jalapa (Veracruz), north of Tamazunchale (San Luis Potosi), on the grounds of the Hotel Mi Ranchito at Villa Juarez (Puebla), in river-edge woodland in Chiapas, and in overgrown fields, forest edge, and low deciduous woodland on the Yucatán Peninsula.

The bananaquit has a fascination that is as widespread as its distribution. It is of more than casual interest to the ornithologist because of the many distinct races that can be described among individuals of this species that have been isolated in different island groups or widely separated continental regions. And to the layman, the "non-birder" who knows it only by one of its many local names—the sucrier or reinita or John Croppie, depending on where he is and what language he speaks—it is an attractive, ever present little bird that lifts his spirits on a dull morning by landing boldly on his breakfast table and cheerfully filching sweets from the sugar bowl.

Plate 81
Bananaquit

The ornithologists may argue about the number of geographic races that can be described, and about the way in which these have developed, but all seem to agree as to the bird's habits. May Jeffrey-Smith tells of a bananaquit in Jamaica that "regularly joined us at tea in the afternoons. We would leave moistened sugar in the teacup and the bird would perch on the rim of the cup and leisurely sip the syrup." Virgilio Biaggi, Jr., writing of the Puerto Rican variety says that they have become so accustomed to people and the trappings of civilization that it is not uncommon to find them building a nest inside a house. One pair "built their laying nest on the hanging lamp of the main room of a house. The female laid three eggs and they all hatched. She used to retire to the nest early in the evening and leave it when the doors were opened in the morning." At the hotel on Bonaire a pair had built their nest under the ceiling of an open veranda next to the bathing beach, and as the guests sat at their meals on the hotel porch nearby, the tiny suikerdiefje flitted back and forth and from table to table, watching for a chance to dip into a cup or sugar bowl.

Biaggi says that its food (aside from sugar) consists principally of "flower nectar and small invertebrates. It obtains nectar of the flowers by introducing its de-curved bill and bifid (i.e., forked) tongue into the opening of the flowers." It also secures insects from the undersides of leaves, and spiders seem to be a favorite item. Also, according to Alexander Wetmore (1927), it eats lantern flies, small beetles, caterpillars, bees, wasps, and ants. Often when feeding bananaquits hang upside down from a twig or branch. Wetmore notes that a favorite flowering plant is the molinillo (*Leonotis*), likewise the muñeco (*Cordia collococca*), and the bucare (*Erythrina*). It eats many kinds of fruit, including ripe bananas, but, as Wetmore points out, this is not a destructive habit since the bunches are cut for human consumption while still green. May Jeffrey-Smith lists several plants that are especially attractive to the little "beany bird" in Jamaica, among them the soldier's tassel, Chinese hat, hibiscus, moringa, and bauhinia.

The bananaquit appears to nest throughout the year over most of its range, and it may raise several broods. The globe-shaped nests have the entrance hole at the side and are loosely made of leaves, grasses, and plant fibers and lined with a variety of finer materials, including threads, bits of paper, chicken feathers, spider webbing, wild cotton, and similar items. The nest is suspended or semi-pendant, usually near the tips of limbs, from five to thirty feet above the ground. There may be two types of nests, one unlined which is used for roosting or sleeping only.

From one to three eggs are laid. They are white or light creamy in general color, some varying to pinkish buff, with brown- or salmon-colored spots that may be sparsely distributed or heavily mottled and quite dark.

The song of the bananaquit is an incessant, insect-like trill, expressed as *zee-e-e-e-swees-se-te* or *zee-e-e-e swee-stee*. It differs somewhat over the range.

Father Raymund Devas has written: "These sucriers have an entertaining pro-gramme of courtship, which so often takes place indoors, even in church. Facing one another at close range, they bow and scrape, turning their heads this way and that in unison, and then flying off, they start the whole performance over again a couple of pews away. I have not noticed authors call attention to this." Not everyone has had the good friar's opportunities to watch these charming little birds inside a church. From what I have seen of them there seems little reason to doubt that this same performance takes place in open-air cafés and cantinas as well. The bananaquit is nothing if not thoroughly ubiquitous.

Plate 82
Yellow-legged
honeycreeper

You will probably meet with the little sugar-thief, the sucrier or bananaquit, as your introduction to the honeycreepers, because this species is so extremely common and widespread. The yellow-legged honeycreeper has a more limited

PLATE 71. GREAT KISKADEE (*Pitangus sulphuratus*)

PLATE 72. COMMON TODY-FLYCATCHER (*Todirostrum cinereum*)

PLATE 73. LESSER ANTILLEAN ELAEN

(*Elaenia martinica*)

PLATE 74. ROUGH-WINGED SWALLOW (*Stelgidopteryx ruficollis*)

PLATE 75. GREEN JAY (*Cyanocorax yncas*)

PLATE 76. SOUTHERN HOUSE-WREN

(*Troglodytes musculus*)

PLATE 78. ORANGE-BILLED NIGHTINGALE-THRUSH (*Catharus aurantiirostris*)

PLATE 77. BARE-EYED THRUSH (*Turdus nudigenis*)

PLATE 79. RED-LEGGED THRUSH (*Mimocichla plumbea*)

PLATE 80. RUFOUS-BROWED PEPPERSHRIKE (*Cyclarhis gujanensis*)

range, but you will come across it in Trinidad, certainly, and nearly everywhere along the coast of Venezuela, from the Caracas region eastward. In Trinidad, aside from the omnipresent bananaquit, there is some question as to which of the honeycreepers is most abundant, the yellow-legged or the red-legged (*Cyanerpes cyaneus*). Antoine Léotaud, a century ago, considered that the red-legged was "*très commune*" and the yellow-legged "*moins commune*," while more recent observers either disagree entirely or feel that one form is seen about as often as the other. G. F. Mees (who was in Trinidad from late June 1953 until February 1954) found the red-legged honeycreeper "decidedly uncommon." He comments: "In view of the fact that I have been continually on the watch for the species, it seems hardly likely that this lack of observations is accidental." Mees quotes Dr. G. A. C. Herklots as having had a similar experience, and supposes that for some unknown reason the red-legged form "has become very much scarcer (perhaps only temporarily) during the last twenty years. Many species of birds, of course, are known to undergo strong fluctuations in numbers." He observed this bird in La Laja and in the Valencia Reserve.

The yellow-legged honeycreeper, on the other hand, according to Mees, was "a common and widely distributed species of forests, and perhaps particularly of the cacao and orange estates of the Northern Range." He observed that they feed on oranges, but adds that "it seems most unlikely that they are able to do any harm to sound fruit."

A shorter-billed variety, the green honeycreeper (*Chloraphanes spiza*), has been considered by some as uncommon in Trinidad, but Mees found it otherwise. It is "plumper and less elegant than the other honeycreepers."

It is an interesting distributional oddity that the red-legged honeycreeper also occurs in Cuba. James Bond (1950) states that it was fairly common in former times, "now rare but of widespread distribution, most numerous in the Province of Oriente." Thomas Barbour wrote of this species in Cuba: "The Blue Honey Creepers are very local. Ramsden showed them to me near Guantánamo in early March, 1915, feeding on the flowers of the cupery (*Clusea rosea*), a parasitic tree which towers far above its host. It also feeds in the majagua blossoms, but though this tree is widespread, the bird is very local. Their erratic appearance accounts for the name of *Aparecido de San Diego*, but *Azulito* is more generally used. Many are caught with bird-lime, and for a short while each spring scores are for sale in Santiago and at Panama. Bangs has described the Cuban birds as a local race, *ramsdeni*; yet, loath as I am to part with this friendly name, I must conclude that the Cuban birds are not separable from those of Panama and Nicaragua. If the bird was introduced into Cuba purposefully, this must have been done years ago, for it was well known during all Gundlach's sojourn. He found his first nest in 1844; then it was widespread. Today it certainly is rare, except in Oriente, where I have seen it near San Carlos de Guantánamo and near El Cobre. I have heard of it in San Carlos de Luis Lazo and San Diego de los Baños."

PLATE 81. BANANAQUIT (*Coereba flaveola*)

173

Plate 83
Chestnut-bellied
chlorophonia

The tanagers could win many prizes for their brilliant plumage, and these smaller members of this group, the chlorophonias, are no disgrace to the family tradition, with a very striking emphasis on green. All four species, including the chestnut-bellied chlorophonia, exhibit daring combinations of offbeat greens, blues, and yellows. The males are the more brilliant.

These birds live in high mountain regions and are not too well known, particularly the chestnut-bellied ones from the northern and northwestern highlands of South America, but the turquoise-naped or blue-crowned variety (*Chlorophonia occipitalis*) of Mexico and Central America has been studied by Alexander Skutch (1954) and is perhaps the best known of the group.

The unwieldy name has simply been taken from the generic appellation, for want of a more suitable handle, and mistletoe birds might be a better term were it not for the fact that the closely related euphonias are likewise strongly addicted to mistletoe berries. On the subject of nomenclature, Skutch has written: "The critical student of etymologies may well take exception to the name *Chlorophonia*; for it is not the voice of the bird that is green, but its plumage. But if we interpret it as a contraction of *chloro-euphonia*—green euphonia—the generic name is indeed happily chosen, for these highland birds are the green counterparts of the typically yellow and blue-black euphonias of lower altitudes."

Although the chlorophonias are mountain dwellers, and the present species perhaps more Andean than Caribbean, they have much in common with the colorful little euphonias, which are represented in the West Indies by the widespread blue-hooded euphonia and the Jamaican euphonia, the latter restricted to the island for which it is named. In many of their habits chlorophonias and euphonias are much alike, including nest-building.

Skutch located several nests of *Chlorophonia occipitalis* in Costa Rica and describes them as follows: "All six nests were placed high in trees standing in clearings in the cloud forest. The lowest was at an estimated 35 feet above the ground, the next about 60 feet up, the other three between 75 and 100 feet, in the tops of lofty trees. Five were placed among the moss and other epiphytes which in this humid region covered most of the trees in great profusion; and in such situations the mossy nests could be detected only by watching the activities of the birds which built and attended them. One of the nests, however, was situated conspicuously in the bare crotch formed by the bifurcation of a great trunk, naked and charred, standing in a pasture not far from the edge of the forest. All the nests were roofed structures, entered through a round doorway in the side facing outward from the tree. Euphonias of several species build nests of similar form; but most other tanagers construct cup-shaped nests open above."

Plate 84
Lesser Antillean
grackle

In the West Indies there are two species of grackles, the Lesser Antillean grackle, which also inhabits northern South America, and the similar though slightly larger Greater Antillean grackle (*Quiscalus niger*), which represents this group on the larger islands of Cuba, Jamaica, Hispaniola, Puerto Rico, and many smaller islands close by. In Mexico and Central America, besides the purple grackle and boat-tail, there are the slender-billed grackle (an endemic restricted to the marshes near Mexico City) and the Nicaraguan grackle, found on the shores of Lakes Nicaragua and Managua. Northern South America, where the Lesser Antillean grackle appears, has a variety—the Colombian mountain grackle, the red-bellied grackle, the Peruvian grackle, and the Amazonian velvety-fronted grackle. Apparently there is a satisfactory niche for each one of these forms.

James Bond (1950) describes several local races of Lesser Antillean grackles, the one on Barbados "probably introduced on St. Vincent, whence it now seems to have disappeared, presumably through interbreeding" with the local St. Vincent race, which is common on that small island. The Barbados grackle has also been introduced on Barbuda, Antigua, and St. Kitts. Another race is common on Grenada and the Grenadines, still another on St. Lucia. The most northerly form is common on the islands of Guadeloupe, Marie Galante, and Martinique, merely local on Montserrat, and accidental on Antigua.

In Trinidad, according to G. C. A. Junge and G. F. Mees, this species is "plentiful in open cultivated country, especially on artifical savannahs, where in general behavior the species is reminiscent of old world Starlings." Mees, who used the local name "boat-tail" for this species, observed the roosting habits and reported: "...on Orange Grove Estate I regularly saw how late in the after-noon small flocks of Boat-Tails flew at a rather great height in a W. to S.W. direction; often I watched such flocks through my field-glasses, and all the time they remained visible they steadily kept the same height and direction. The question where these birds went was solved on 1 October when towards the evening near the colony of Scarlet Ibises in the central part of the Caroni Swamp, we saw many small troups of Boat-Tails arrive from the East. The warden who accompanied us told that thousands came in every night for roosting in the man-groves. The savannah of Orange Grove Estate is in a straight line about nine to ten kilometers away from the roosting place and on the Estate I often saw flocks pass overhead, which came from even farther to the East, so that the roosting place apparently attracts birds from a very wide area."

Bond has pointed out that the notes of the Lesser Antillean grackle differ from island to island in some instances. Those on Barbados say "*betse-weee, sicker, sicker, sicker*," while on St. Lucia they say "*weee-tsi-ke-tsi-ke-tsi-ke*" (Bond, 1928). On St. Lucia they were nesting during the latter part of April, while in Venezuela Foster Smith (1950) found active nests in February, March, and September. "The nest was a well-built affair of twigs, fibres, string, and cotton and was often placed in the *Trinitaria* bushes growing against the houses." These birds are often quite tame, and Alexander Wetmore tells how they came into the patio of the hotel in Maracay after the noon meal and searched for food on the tables, "eying me sharply as I sat preparing specimens, but without fear" (1939).

Plate 85
Glossy
cowbird

The glossy cowbird is a bustling, burgeoning, successful species that is expanding its range. Originating in South America, it spread to the island of Carriacou in the Grenadines in 1899 and has now become well established as a resident breeding bird as far along the chain of the Lesser Antilles as Martinique. And it bids fair to continue this expansion.

The outstanding characteristic of the cowbirds is their habit of laying their eggs in the nests of other birds and permitting these unsuspecting dupes to have the doubtful privilege of rearing their young. This "brood-parasitic" habit is similar to that of the Old World cuckoo (Cuculidae) which has no other kinship to the cowbirds. The brown-headed cowbird of the United States is reported to parasitize at least twenty species. In Trinidad and British Guiana, according to François Haverschmidt, the glossy cowbird preys on the red-breasted blackbird, and in Surinam on the house-wren. In this last instance, the legitimate young are much smaller than the young of the larger cowbird, which often seems to be the pattern, and the interloper probably gets most of the food brought to the nest by the foster parents. However, in Venezuela, Foster Smith reported that this cowbird "parasitized the [Lesser Antillean] grackle *Quiscalus lugubris*. This is interesting because the parasitism reported is on a large scale, and apparently, at least locally, the *Quiscalus* seems to be the exclusive host. In this case the host is the slightly larger bird and belongs to the same family as the parasite" (1955). Smith went on to describe how the grackles came to the feeding station with their young, about 25 per cent of which were young cowbirds. Even before they leave their juvenal plumage, these young cowbirds forsake their foster parents and join flocks of their own kind.

Smith and his collaborator, Herbert Friedmann, make the interesting observation that in 1946 glossy cowbirds were not present in northeastern Venezuela in flocks of more than ten, but a few years later, in the same area, flocks of over a hundred were not rare. They attribute this increase to the recent abundance of water at the oil company camps that have sprung up in that region.

In Uruguay and Argentina, Alexander Wetmore (1926) found several local birds being parasitized by the glossy cowbird, including a tapaculo, a couple of finches, the honero or ovenbird, a flycatcher, and the rufous-bellied robin.

Glossy cowbirds have a bubbling, oriole-like song. Most of those who have heard it seem to consider it melodious, but G. P. Mees, who heard them in full song in the Laventille Swamp near Port of Spain in December, thought that it "perhaps stamps the species as the best songster found in the islands." One can imagine that with someone else to look after the children, they can well afford to sing.

Plate 86
Montezuma
oropéndola

We are indebted once again to Alexander Skutch for providing us with a complete life-history sketch, this time on the Montezuma oropéndola, in Volume I of his *Life Histories of Central American Birds*. Those especially interested in these unusual and striking birds will do well to consult this absorbing and highly informative account. For the purposes of this brief narrative, we cannot do better than to quote, in part, from Mr. Skutch's summary:

"The oropéndolas forage in the crowns of trees in the primary forest, where they seem to eat a great variety of soft fruits; but much of their nourishment is found in cultivated country with scattered trees. In banana plantations they feast on ripe fruit and drink nectar from the staminate flowers. In coffee plantations the shade trees, especially *Erythrina*, supply nectar and other food.

"The notes are amazingly varied. The song of the male, a long-drawn, far-carrying, liquid gurgle, is delivered as he bows forward into an inverted position, raising his wings above his back.

"In various parts of the Caribbean littoral, breeding continues from January to at least September. Oropéndolas nest socially, by preference in a great tree with a long, clean trunk and an ample crown isolated from other trees. When tall palm trees are used, the nests are attached to the fronds; and a number of palms standing close together may support the colony. The great, woven pouches are not distributed evenly over the crown of the nest tree but are often crowded in clusters so compact that contiguous nests are sewn together in the course of construction. A populous colony may contain nearly a hundred nests.

"In these colonies there are several females to each male. The latter, which are much bigger than the females, do not seem to be attached to particular females or groups of them. All the work of building, incubation, and feeding the young is performed by the females, with no help from the males. These, however, serve as watchmen for the community, sounding a strident note of alarm when danger seems to threaten. This note usually sends the birds diving into lower vegetation. The males accompany groups of females on long expeditions to gather building material or food....

"The hanging pouches, woven of slender vines and fibrous strips from palm or banana leaves, were usually from 2 to 4 feet in length, but in exceptional cases were $6\frac{1}{2}$ feet long. Replacement nests were woven in from 7 to 17 days, but the usual time was only 9 to 11 days.

"After the weaving was finished, the females remained away from the nests for a day or two, during which courtship and mating probably took place at a distance from the colony. Then they returned and devoted from three to six days to carrying fragments of dead or dying leaves into the pouch. This litter of loose material probably served to keep the eggs from knocking together and breaking when a strong wind swung the nests. Occasionally a female brought additional leaves while she incubated, or even while she attended nestlings.

"In fallen nests the maximum number of eggs was two, which seems to constitute the full set....

"The young are fed in the nest by the female for about 30 days. Much of the food is brought from a long distance. In this long period of occupancy, many of the nests are damaged by the female's repeated passage through the doorway.

Although some hang precariously and others fall, no attempt is made to repair them—an operation for which the bird has the skill, but not the insight, to perform.

"Two months or a little more elapse from the beginning of nest building to the emergence of the nestlings. The young, which resemble the adults in plumage, are fed by the females as they wander about in small flocks."

It is interesting to note the way in which the troupial and the yellow oriole complement each other with regard to habitat preference. The troupial avoids if possible the very dry or xerophytic types, such as thorny scrub and acacia or cactus growths, which are the special delight of the yellow oriole, and Wagenaar Hummelinck observes that the yellow oriole is found in mangroves while the troupial is not. It seems rather curious that a bird should show a penchant for hot, dry, desert-like places *and* mangroves. However, there is also a slight but interesting difference in the food habits of these two orioles. Both species partake of a varied diet of fruits and insects, but the yellow oriole is more of an insect-feeder than the troupial—which may explain, in part, why the latter is found more often in old fruit plantations, in close proximity to sapodillas, mangos, kenepas, and other edible fruits and vegetables.

In more detail, Hummelinck reports that the yellow oriole fed on small beetles, the larvae, pupae, and imagoes of *Diptera*, caterpillars, grasshoppers, cicadas, spiders, and (in one instance) a *Soliphuga* (a spider-like arachnid). Of fruits, it was seen feeding on the date palm and shimarucu (*Malpighia*). Most of the insects were caught in flowering trees and shrubs, including the tamarind and the brazil wood (*Haematoxylon brasiletto*).

The troupial fed regularly on many kinds of fruits, including various components of the flowers of the *Opuntia* cactus, but they also ate insects, especially beetles.

In the vocal department there seems to be no room for comparison between these two birds. The yellow oriole's call, to quote Karel H. Voous (1959), is "decidedly unmelodious and may best be described as an unpleasant kind of miaowing or screeching." He adds: "That is why the bird is called trupial cachó in Papiamento, which means dog troupial." Papiamento is the local patois of the Netherlands Antilles leeward group, a mixture of many tongues. I cannot help thinking that "cat" rather than "dog" is intended, or at least more appropriate here, but then I have had the experience of trying to get a native of the region to translate from Papiamento into English (in this instance, a rather complicated cocktail recipe) and—well, I will say no more!

In any case, the troupial is an outstanding singer, and its fluty song is heard throughout the day in all weathers. It is one of those delightful birds that speaks its name—*troo-pee-oo, troo-pee-oo*—but this isn't really necessary. You will know it by the bold orange-and-black plumage.

We have discussed a few members of the large avian family of the Icteridae but, with the limitations of space, and the need for including as many representative groups as possible, these have been restricted to a grackle, a cowbird, an oropéndola, a troupial (which is an oriole), and now a meadowlark. No blackbirds, no bobolink, no scarlet-rumped cacique! But it is a large family and we cannot include them all. The Icteridae, to quote Alexander Skutch (1954), is a "heterogeneous family of middle-sized or large passeriform birds containing, according to [Ernst] Mayr...88 species...." Josselyn Van Tyne and Andrew Berger maintain that there are ninety-four species, but this does not concern anything we have to say here. Two of them (or possibly only one) are meadowlarks.

Skutch points out that some members of the Icteridae clan are wholly black, often with a glossy iridescence, while the somberness in others is relieved by contrasting patterns of yellow, orange, chestnut, or red. Still others have brown-streaked plumage, with breasts of yellow or red, as in the meadowlarks and military starlings. Some species, like the oropéndolas and orioles, feed on fruit and insects which they seek in the trees; others forage on the ground, like the meadowlarks and cowbirds. And there is a great variety in the types of nests built by these birds.

"Voice is richly developed in the Icteridae," Skutch states, "and some of the most delightful songsters belong to this family. The Spotted-breasted Oriole, the Giraud Oriole, the Melodious Blackbird and many others are superb musicians. ...The Yellow-rumped Cacique and the Yellow-tailed Oriole are noteworthy for their varied repertoire and brilliant execution. The various liquid and harsh notes of the oropéndolas are among the unforgettable sounds of tropical America. The Troupial is an accomplished mimic. Flight-songs are regularly delivered by the Bobolink and the Red-breasted Marsh-bird of Argentina." With such an array of highly gifted and exotic vocalists to consider, the humble meadowlark is not even mentioned, but all who have thrilled to his sweetly sad, flutelike song will agree that it is one of the best and, to many people, one of the best-loved. There is a nostalgic quality to the song of the meadowlark that touches many of us.

Incidentally, the familiar song of this bird is made up of two clear notes, both slurred, the second note on a descending scale. The western meadowlark (which reaches Mexico, but not the Caribbean slopes) has a wholly different song, which Roger Tory Peterson (1960) describes as "seven to ten notes, flutelike, gurgling, and double-noted; very unlike clear slurred whistles of Eastern Meadowlark."

The song of the resident meadowlark in Cuba is described by Thomas Barbour as "a more prolonged whistle, and is less broken into several notes than with our birds." By which, I would think, is meant less slurred. Lawrence Walkinshaw and Bernard Baker thought the song of these birds on the Isle of Pines also differed from that of our meadowlark and, in northeastern Venezuela, Herbert Friedmann and Foster Smith (1950) say the song there is "similar to but more rapid" than that of our bird. However, of the same species in Costa Rica, Alex-

Plate 88
Common
meadowlark

ander Wetmore (1944) remarks: "Flight and other mannerisms were typical of meadowlarks everywhere, and the song and call notes are like those of the bird of the eastern United States."

Plate 89
Swallow-tanager
A tanager with a swallow-like bill, the aptly named swallow-tanager has the rare distinction of being the only species in the family Tersinidae. Ernst Schaefer, who studied these birds for several years in the Parque Nacional de Rancho Grande in northern Venezuela, considers them "one of the most fascinating South American birds." The park area "extends from the inland basin of Lake Valencia at an elevation of 450 meters, across the peaks of the Cordillera de la Costa (2400 meters high) to the rocky coast of the Caribbean Sea." Within this region one encounters tropical, subtropical and subtropical-temperate conditions, from an ecological viewpoint, and all three zones together are extremely rich in bird-life. More than 450 species have been counted, among them the highly interesting *Tersina viridis*, which breeds there.

Because of its uncertain taxonomic relations, and the lack of detailed knowledge of its habits, Schaefer undertook his careful study of swallow-tanagers which was published in *The Auk*. He found them breeding in forested areas at elevations of from 500 to at least 1100 meters (3600 feet), with a wide range of ecological tolerance. Schaefer's description of this species' niche is excellent: "*Tersina* is not found in the widely distributed secondary savannas which cover the lower slopes towards the great alluvial plains of Lake Valencia. It is strictly a woodland species. The lower limit of its range is in the deciduous forests characterized by dense evergreen underbrush and widely scattered, often thorny, trees (*Hura crepitans*) the majority of which shed their leaves during the dry season.

"At about 800 meters these deciduous seasonal forests merge insensibly into the semi-evergreen forests where only one-third of the trees shed their leaves during the dry season. The part-evergreen forest is characterized by an overwhelming growth of creepers and lianas, which cover nearly all the treetops in unbelievably thick masses. Here, between 800 and 900 meters, we found the optimum habitat for *Tersina viridis* in the Parque Nacional.

"At approximately 900 meters, the part-evergreen forest merges with the evergreen montane cloud forest of the subtropical belt. Here, close to the watershed, the Estación Biológica lies at 1090 meters above sea level. The half-ruined building lies in the middle of an ecological island of secondary growth, partly introduced and twenty years old. A high percentage of the bird population of this semi-xerophytic ecological island consists of aggressive invaders from the lower tropical belt. Only about half of the species belong to the sub-tropical cloud forest biocoenosis (rich in species but poor in numbers of individuals).

"This also explains why *Tersina viridis* has developed a rather large, isolated breeding community in and around the Rancho Grande building where human interference has changed the natural habitat.

"Possibly all newly formed ecological niches are first settled by younger birds which, through population pressure, are driven out of their home areas. Because of competition from old birds of both sexes, these younger birds are often forced to content themselves with inferior biotopes. Once settled, however, they soon develop a strong homing faculty. Therefore, *Tersina viridis* is rather evenly distributed along the road wherever adequate breeding conditions are found. The ecological extremes of open savanna and heavily wooded, humid gorges are always strictly avoided. After the road reaches the humid subtropical cloud forest, *Tersina viridis* is absent, except around a few human settlements and, of course, the ecological island of Rancho Grande itself. Here, however, it has found exceptionally favorable breeding conditions and is even more abundant than in the semi-evergreen forest. *Tersina* favors a broken landscape with not too dense secondary woods and many clearings. It is a bird of the high tree-tops and even while foraging seldom descends to the middle or lower strata."

The swallow-tanager is highly specialized in structure and habits, and the peculiar bill is particularly interesting. Ernst Schaefer says: "The flat, broad, swallow-like bill of *Tersina*, with its sharp edges and a pronounced hook on the maxilla, together with the proximally placed cone-shaped nostrils, is an ideal instrument not only for catching flying insects and holding, cutting, and swallowing big, pulpy fruit with hard peels, but also for excavating holes." Nests are built in holes in buildings, bridges, etc., or the birds may dig out their own holes in vertical banks. Sometimes they occupy abandoned nesting holes of jacamars or swallow-winged puffbirds. Three eggs are the usual clutch, and the incubation period lasts from thirteen to seventeen days. The young remain in the nest twenty-four days and, although only the female *Tersina* incubates the eggs and broods the young, both parents feed the nestlings.

In the course of his studies, Schaefer took two young *Tersinas* out of a nest shortly before fledging and kept them for observation. He writes: "I have never had more enjoyable pets among passerine birds." He found them very intelligent. "They recognize their master and greet him by stretching their wings and legs. They always like to 'play,' parrot-like using their bills." And, as in nature, he observed that they went to bed early and rose late! Quite remarkable little birds, and we can envy Schaefer his intimate contact with them.

The "mass ecstasy" of the so-called "curtsy reaction" is an unusual display that has its counterpart in no other passerine, and this performance is described and analyzed in a complete and most interesting way by Schaefer. It is possible that this display takes the place of an elaborate song performance, for song, as such, is little developed in these birds.

Of the copper-crowned tanager, in Venezuela, Kathleen Deery de Phelps has written: "La Monjita is one of the most abundant birds of the country and inhabits the forests. Their nests are well and cunningly constructed. They lay two oval eggs

Plate 90
Copper-crowned
tanager

of cream color, spotted heavily with maroon." Certainly, this species is one of the most beautiful examples of this very large and wonderfully endowed family. There are 222 species of tanagers according to Josselyn Van Tyne and Andrew Berger, a total that has been reduced to 197 by Ernst Mayr (1946). At any rate the tanagers, as Alexander Skutch has said, are "one of the most brilliant and varied of all avian families." They are a product of the Western World, restricted almost entirely to the tropical portion—Central America, South America, and the West Indies—only four species of the genus *Piranga* reaching the United States (western tanager, scarlet tanager, hepatic tanager, and summer tanager).

Song in the tanagers is not highly developed, many of the most strikingly beautiful species having only weak songs or none at all. But this lack is more than made up for by bright colors. Skutch writes: "The genus *Tangara* (including *Calospiza* and *Calliste*) alone would seem to exhaust the possibilities of color and color combinations in the plumage of a small bird. Black and white plumage is found in the well-named Magpie-Tanager. A few genera, as, for example, *Chlorospingus* and *Schistochlamys*, are dull-colored. In most species, including many of the most brilliant, the sexes are similar in coloration. The majority of such species are non-migratory and appear to remain in pairs throughout the year. Sexual differences in coloration are found chiefly in the migratory species (*Piranga*), and in those non-migratory species of which the male is brilliant and which flock during the non-breeding season (*Ramphocelus, Tangara, Chlorophonia, Piranga leucoptera*). Seasonal changes in plumage are exceptional, the Scarlet Tanager being the outstanding example of this in the family" (1954).

Copper-crowned tanagers collected by Ernest Holt along the Upper Orinoco showed interesting plumage variations, the edges of the tailfeathers and their upper coverts varying from "quite greenish" to "bluish," and the forehead and anterior portion of the crown showing a sprinkling of greenish feathers in some individuals, but not in others. The extent and intensity of the blue on the throat and breast also varied, according to Herbert Friedmann (1948). But if you are fortunate enough to see one of these birds, such details are not likely to deter you from the full enjoyment of their beauty. And, when all is said and done, it may not be unreasonable to suppose that such a fulfillment is the ultimate and highest mission of all the tanagers.

Plate 91
Blue-gray
tanager

In many parts of its range you will probably see this handsome tanager more frequently than any other member of its family. I first came across it along the Blanchisseuse Road in Trinidad, then close to the Windward Road in Tobago, and in the Botanic Gardens in Caracas. With its soft silver-blue plumage it is easily recognized.

Alexander Skutch has written a life-history sketch (1954) of the blue-gray tanager in which he tells us that it occurs in both humid and arid regions, "but in the drier types of country it is largely restricted to the more luxuriant vegetation along the watercourses, irrigated areas, and other spots where abundant ground water favors the growth of taller trees. I found Blue Tanagers among the palms and shade trees of the central plaza of Chiclayo, situated in an oasis amid the sandy wastes of the northern coast of Peru. In the surrounding deserts this tanager could not survive."

Although we think of tanagers as forest birds, Don Eckelberry has told me that it has been his observation that tanagers of this genus (*Thraupis*) prefer somewhat open situations, adapting well to cultivated conditions and coming readily to the feeding shelf for bananas and other fruits. Skutch says that blue-gray tanagers are especially fond of wild figs and bananas. They also eat the dry green fruits of the Cecropia tree and "they find many insects on the leaves and bark of trees. Often they bend down to examine the lower sides of a branch for the insects and spiders that harbor there, a habit common to many of the more arboreal tanagers. Or they hang head downward from the end of a twig to pick an insect or caterpillar from among the terminal leaves. Although they forage much in the manner of warblers, these larger and heavier birds are somewhat less spry in their movements. Often, too, they make quick aërial darts to snatch insects on the wing."

Eckelberry speaks of its voice as "an incredibly thin, wavering song, hardly deserving the name." And Skutch writes of it as "animated but lacking in force. The phrasing, varied and intricate, would do credit to any songster, but the tone is weak and a trifle squeaky. The bird seems to attempt a musical feat beyond its slight vocal powers."

At night these birds like to roost in orange or lemon trees, where they are protected by the heavy foliage and sharp thorns. Skutch describes how he discovered a pair sleeping in a lemon tree, feathers fluffed out and heads turned back and buried in the plumage of the back. "For a month this lemon tree was the Blue Tanagers' roosting place. But one evening at the end of November they arrived to find that most of the branches had been pruned off in the course of the day. The few that remained did not offer them sufficient shelter and concealment for the night. Confused, the tanagers flew back and forth many times between the shorn lemon tree and the neighboring trees, voicing low, questioning notes. Finally, when the light had grown very dim, both entered a sour orange tree where they had earlier nested, and here they passed the night.

"A week later, I found the pair sleeping in a smaller sweet orange tree close beside the sour orange. I sometimes stole out in the night to see them by flashlight. Each roosted upon one of the long, horizontal thorns in the center of the tree, in positions about a foot apart. They never slept pressed closely side by side, as mated birds of some kinds roost. After a fortnight, one of the pair returned to the sour orange tree to roost, leaving the other to sleep alone in the sweet orange close by, still on the same thorn. A few days later the second tanager deserted the sweet orange in favor of the taller and more densely leafy sour orange, where both were so well screened by the dark foliage that I never succeeded in seeing them while they slept. Usually they came together to their roost, but at times one bird would arrive a few minutes ahead of its mate. This was their nightly roosting place until about the middle of the following January, after which the pair shifted to another situation and I lost them."

Plate 92
Scarlet-rumped
tanager

The distribution of this strikingly colored tanager is limited to tall, lush forests on both sides of the lofty Cordillera, on the Caribbean slope from Tabasco south through Chiapas, Guatemala, Honduras, and Nicaragua, and on the Pacific slope, a distinct race found only in southern Costa Rica and just over the border in neighboring Panama. The interesting thing about these two races of the scarlet-rumped tanager is that the males on both sides of the divide are so alike that they cannot be distinguished in the field, while the females are quite different. Females on the Caribbean side are uniformally olive and buff, while those on the Pacific slope are bright orange on the breast and rump.

This greater geographic variation on the female rather than on the male side is a phenomenon known as "heterogynism." Ernst Mayr (1942) says that it is encountered most often in species where the male is black or otherwise strongly colored and the female drab. He considers that the male has gone to the limit so far as intense pigmentation is concerned, and that further geographic variations can be attained only by the female, whose plainness gives her more room for improvement.

There is also an interesting difference in the song of these two races. Alexander Skutch is of the opinion that this tanager, as a species, is more gifted as a songster than other tropical members of the family, while the race on the Pacific side produces a greater volume of song than any other Central American tanager that I know." He says that these Costa Rican birds are far more musical than their counterparts on the Caribbean side and he has given them the name "song tanager." It is a vireo-like performance, and they are "methodical rather than brilliant musicians. Their song has small range and lacks variety; it consists of the tireless repetition of a simple phrase of three or four notes. There is, however, considerable variation in the songs of different individuals, both in tone and phrasing. Some have rich, full voices; others sing in far slighter and weaker tones; an occasional individual sings with a nasal twang" (1954).

Anyone contemplating a detailed study of the life history of a bird, and particularly one of the passerine birds, should consult Skutch's "Outline for an Ecological Life History of a Bird," which has used the song tanager as a model. There is also a complete monograph of the species in the first volume of *Life Histories of Central American Birds*. The amount of information that Skutch has accumulated is remarkable. What time does the song tanager begin to sing in the morning? On a clear morning in March, the first notes were heard at 4.58 a.m., from a dawn singing post. Others joined in and then, at 5.12 a.m., all song tanagers became silent. What is the incubation pattern of this and other tanagers? You will find the answer to this and a hundred other questions in Skutch's book, for few birds have been observed with more assiduous devotion.

In Venezuela, the silver-beaked tanager is found widely distributed in open woods and plantations to 1500 meters, and over into the lower fringes of the Subtropical Zone at a little higher elevation. Alexander Wetmore found these birds at La Trilla, inland from Ocumare de la Costa in northern Venezuela. He found one little company of four, chattering away in the lower branches of the shade trees in a cacao plantation. He also saw them in the valley of the Río Cumboto, and at Rancho Grande they were observed about growths of dense brush along the open roadway. "One called loudly *whis whis* as it rested with jerking tail on an open perch" (1939).

Plate 93
Silver-beaked
tanager

As with the other brilliant *Ramphocelus*, the scarlet-rumped tanager, the females of this species may sometimes show greater geographic variation than the more gaudy males. Herbert Friedmann (1948) found the females of one race more reddish underneath than females from another region, something between chestnut and mahogany red in the one, the other more brownish, with the abdomen ferruginous. However, this species is not as consistent in this respect as the scarlet-rumped tanager, and some forms of the silver-beak exhibit distinguishing characters only in males from different geographic regions (Friedmann and Smith, 1950).

In Trinidad, C. B. Williams wrote in 1922, "this bird is not uncommon particularly in the less open districts. In the sugar cultivation I have only seen it when close to the edge of wooded land. I have noted its occurrence at Maracas, Harmony Hall and Palo Seco." Phillips Street noted it often throughout Trinidad. He saw a group of fifteen near Freeport in a bamboo thicket, "the greatest number observed in one gathering." G. F. Mees notes that this bird is a common inhabitant of "high second growths and light forests, where the beautiful red plumage readily draws attention."

Don Eckelberry has told me "Just as the Blue-gray Tanager works the upper story of the trees in tropical clearings, the Silver-beaked Tanager haunts the shrubbery below. Its name derives from the swollen blue-white base of the lower mandible. The smoldering red plumage makes the males very attractive. From a bird painter's point of view, this species and its near relatives have considerably more character than most tanagers in that they cock and droop their tails and assume, as my field notes say, 'sparrowy' attitudes."

Williams found these tanagers nesting in August, one nest in a croton bush four feet up, another in a similar bush about three feet from the ground. The nests were cup-shaped and lined with strips of dead banana leaves. The eggs, Williams writes, are "elongate ovate, light blue, spotted and wreathed black at the base."

Plate 94
Ruddy-breasted
seedeater
The large, well-known family of the finches (Fringillidae), numbering some 375 species around the world, is represented here by one of its most diminutive members, the ruddy-breasted seedeater. Perhaps its small size and over-all modesty has resulted in this little bird's being frequently overlooked, and Ludlow Griscom, of its presence in Guatemala, wrote (in 1932): "A pretty little species, which is now known to be far commoner than the scanty published records would indicate."

In some regions it is found in fresh-water marsh growth, and Donald Dickey and A. J. Van Rossem suggest the name "marsh seedeater" as appropriate, "for during the breeding season it was confined to mimosa, wild roses, and other low, thorny growth in the immediate vicinity of water. During the winter at Puerto del Triunfo (El Salvador) a good many were found in tall, head-high grass in a field near the town." But, the authors add, this was the only occasion on which they observed these birds away from the vicinity of a lake or pond.

Evidently two broods are raised each year. Van Rossem found them breeding at Lake Guija in late May and at Lake Olomega in late July, August, and early September. A nest at San Sebastián was placed in the triple crotch of a rose briar about two feet above the shallow water of an immense tule marsh. "It was tightly and compactly woven of fine grasses and weed stems, with a lining of still finer grass.... The very small and deep cup measured $1 \times 1\frac{1}{2}$ inches in diameter at the brim and was 1 inch deep. Only two eggs were in this nest, evidently a complete set, for the male was on the nest when it was discovered. They were white with a heavy sprinkling of minute, dark brown and purplish spots which decreased rapidly in number toward the smaller end."

In Trinidad, Phillips Street found these seedeaters a very common species and frequently encountered flocks of fifty to a hundred about the island in open and scrubby country. C. B. Williams referred to it as second only to the black-faced grassquit in abundance in the sugar-cane districts of Trinidad. G. F. Mees says: "Widely distributed in open country in Trinidad and very common in the waste sugar cane fields and on the savannah of Orange Grove Estate. My impression is that this species usually inhabits more open country and lower vegetation than its congeners. On 9 August an adult male was observed while catching insects. The bird was perched on an electric wire in our garden, and again and again made fluttering flights, often several meters away from its perch, catching insects on the wing like a flycatcher. The performance was repeated tens of times and, as far as could be ascertained, every time an insect was caught." This is especially interesting because most reports, as might be expected, state that the stomachs of these birds contain nothing but seeds.

Plate 95
Saffron
finch
If you are in the right place, the saffron finch will make itself known to you with little or no effort on your part. On my first visit to Jamaica, I landed in Montego Bay, and as I walked through the grounds of the hotel, saffron finches

rose from the lawn with a fine flurry of small chatter and bright colors. In close attendance was the usual bevy of young finches, so dark and greenish that I was puzzled at first by their identity. And there were also a number of black-faced grassquits and at least two mockingbirds, the "nightingales" of Jamaica. They were all very friendly birds, and constantly underfoot.

The saffron finch is a South American species, and has been kept as a cage bird in many places for many years. Its introduction to Jamaica is an interesting story. According to May Jeffrey-Smith, the gentleman responsible was a Rev. John Mure Shakespeare, who came to Jamaica in 1823 and settled on his own land, a property known as Hodges, in St. Elizabeth Parish. The story goes that Rev. Shakespeare brought with him, or had sent to him, canaries from the island of Madeira, which lies on the other side of the Atlantic, just north of the Canary Islands off the African coast. Philip Henry Gosse, the early Jamaican ornithologist of note, apparently believed that Portuguese sailors carried saffron finches from Brazil to Madeira, from whence they found their way back to the New World, but to the island of Jamaica and not to their original home. There "several pairs" were released "in the fields around the rectory at Black River," probably in 1823.

All this is quite possible, of course, although transporting "wild canaries" from Brazil, or anywhere else, to Madeira is rather in a class with carrying coals to Newcastle for, along with the Canary Islands, the Azores, and several other places, Madeira is the home of the serin (*Serinus canarius*), which may be the original wild stock from which the well-known caged canary was bred centuries ago. But anything is possible, and the saffron finch is a very pretty finch, although it is no great vocalist. Alexander Wetmore (1939) says it very well when he describes their song as "high-pitched and squeaky," but they make up for this with sheer rapture.

In Venezuela, Foster Smith found this species to be one of those that responded favorably to the presence of an increased supply of surface water in the vicinity of oil company camps. He wrote: "A flight song was recorded in March and again in November, once a single male and once two males together. The singing bird rose almost vertically to a height of perhaps 80 feet, and still singing, fluttered down to the top of a tree, where the song was continued, the bird standing very upright, bill pointed straight up, wings still fluttering" (1955).

I saw many of these birds in cages in Jamaica, Venezuela, and elsewhere, and it always occurred to me that although they seem quite content in captivity, they are denied a freedom that includes the ecstasy of a flight song that may carry them eighty feet or more into the air.

The long list of local names applied throughout its range to the black-faced grassquit indicates that it is abundant, popular, and widely distributed. In short, it is a bird that hops about dooryards and is known by everyone. They are "tame,

Plate 96
Black-faced
grassquit

unsuspicious little birds," writes Alexander Wetmore, "found in pairs or in small flocks, that fly out with a quick up and down flight to alight in plain sight or under cover in bushes. As one rides through the canefields at dusk, they continually flutter along ahead, so that the cane is full of their rustlings. Though common in the open fields, they are at home in dense second-growth forest. Here they work through the trees, searching the limbs like honey-creepers.... Males sing constantly all day long from a post, weed, telephone wire or some other open perch. Theirs is a harsh, emphatic little song that reminded me of that of a dickcissel. In flight they frequently changed to a slow, direct wing beat, with trembling wings and heads thrown back, and sang until another perch was reached. The call note is a low *tseet*" (1927).

These observations were made in Puerto Rico. On St. John, in the Virgin Islands, William Robertson (1960) found this species second only to the burgeoning pearly-eyed thrasher as the most abundant bird on the island (February 12 to March 10). In 1927 Wetmore found the present species less abundant in Hispaniola than the yellow-faced grassquit (*Tiaris olivacea*), but he added that it was "widely distributed through semi-arid and humid sections and like its relative thrives in canefields and pastures where there is the slightest cover to give it shelter. The heat of the coastal plain and the cold, bracing air of the high mountain slopes are equally agreeable to it, and it will probably increase in all situations as continued developments in agriculture clear away the land" (1931).

Wagenaar Hummelinck writes that the black-faced grassquit is "rather abundant in Curaçao and Bonaire, but decidely scarcer in Aruba. It is one of the species of birds which are most familiar among the native inhabitants of the islands and is usually considered to be the counterpart of the European sparrow." He adds: "Although these birds apparently occurred in every biotope, they were most abundant in dry acacia and cactus scrub with open sandy places and a rich vegetation of small herbs and dry grasses.... We had the impression that these birds often congregated into breeding companies of 20-30 individuals, but we have also found solitary nests. On the whole, however, they were rather social, and large flocks were observed sleeping together in the undergrowth of a big stand of mahogany at Rond Klip, Curaçao."

It is of special interest to consider that these successful little birds are common residents on St. Andrew and Old Providence in the southwest Caribbean off the coast of Nicaragua, where they are known as "grass birds." The species does not occur in Central America, and James Bond (1950) presumes that they must have reached these relatively isolated islands from Jamaica, which is about four hundred miles northeast of Old Providence.

Plate 97
Grayish
saltator

On the Yucatán Peninsula, Raymond Paynter found the grayish saltator primarily in second-growth deciduous forest and uncommon in rain forest. Emmet Blake says that in Mexico it occurs generally in the forested portions of both

PLATE 82. YELLOW-LEGGED HONEYCREEPER (*Cyanerpes caeruleus*)

PLATE 83. CHESTNUT-BELLIED CHLOROPHONIA (*Chlorophonia pyrrhophrys*)

PLATE 84. LESSER ANTILLEAN GRACKLE (*Quiscalus lugubris*)

PLATE 85. GLOSSY COWBIRD (*Molothrus bonariensis*)

PLATE 86. MONTEZUMA OROPÉNDOLA (*Gymnostinops montezuma*)

PLATE 87. COMMON TROUPIAL (*Icterus icterus*)

PLATE 88. COMMON MEADOWLARK (*Sturnella magna*)

PLATE 89. SWALLOW-TANAGER (*Tersina viridis*)

PLATE 90. COPPER-CROWNED TANAGER (*Tangara cayana*)

PLATE 91. BLUE-GRAY TANAGER (*Thraupis virens*)

PLATE 92. SCARLET-RUMPED TANAGER (*Ramphocelus passerinii*)

PLATE 93. SILVER-BEAKED TANAGER

(*Ramphocelus carbo*)

PLATE 94. RUDDY-BREASTED SEEDEATER (*Sporophila minuta*)

PLATE 95. SAFFRON FINCH (*Sicalis flaveola*)

PLATE 96. BLACK-FACED GRASSQUIT

(*Tiaris bicolor*)

PLATE 97. GRAYISH SALTATOR

(*Saltator coerulescens*)

PLATE 98. RUFOUS-COLLARED SPARROW (*Zonotrichia capensis*)

coastal slopes, from sea level up to about five thousand feet. Other saltators occupy the rain-forest niche, and, while all of them seem to be birds of the thickets, Alexander Skutch, in comparing the distribution of two Costa Rican forms, says: "Less tolerant of varied ecological conditions than the Buff-throated Saltator, the Streaked Saltator abandons the thickets if they remain undisturbed by agricultural operations until the swiftly growing trees form a closed canopy and exclude the sun's beams from the bushy undergrowth. Nor is this smaller saltator so commonly seen in plantations of coffee or bananas, in shady but clean pastures, or among dooryard shrubbery. The Buff-throated Saltator is a regular visitor to the feeding shelf in my yard; the Streaked Saltator, although sometimes heard at the house from not far distant thickets, rarely pass through the yard, and has never been seen eating the bananas put out for the birds on the shelf" (1954).

Walter W. Dalquest, in Veracruz, found the grayish saltator along the edges of sugar-cane fields, but it was most common in brushy places on the coastal plain. He agrees with other authors that it is one of the shyer, less noisy species of this group. In southern Veracruz Alexander Wetmore found it of wider distribution than other Mexican saltators, and observed it daily near his camp at Tres Zapotes, as well as in brush bordering old fields and in the scattered thickets about Tlacotalpam. He also noted its shy and retiring nature. As for their song, he wrote: "In March and early April I heard them singing clear, loud warble suggestive of a grosbeak, with occasional ringing notes that bring to mind the ecstasies of the northern bobolink" (1943).

In northeastern Venezuela, Foster Smith found these birds common at the edge of wet woods around Caicara, but "not present" around Cantaura (1950). Later, after oil-company camps had been established in the area, the grayish saltator also became common around Cantaura, possibly because of the increased supply of surface water. They had young out of the nest in August and again in early November and on both occasions "the two parent birds accompanied a single fledgling to the collector's feeding station where one or possibly both of the parents fed the young bird. The call of the fledgling is a single very characteristic loud *peeeep* quite similar to that of a lost chick" (1955).

It would seem to be remarkable enough that this mild, rather modest little sparrow inhabits high mountain ranges, building its nest and rearing its young at elevations up to twelve thousand feet, and doing so with marked success over a vast region extending from Chiapas in southern Mexico all the way south to Tierra del Fuego. But this is only a small part of the story of the rufous-collared sparrow. It is a bird that had been known for some years from the highlands of Guatemala, Costa Rica, and elsewhere, always from mountain country. Then it turned up in bird lists, and later in collections, from the arid tropical islands of Curaçao and Aruba, where it was a common resident. It was first reported from Curaçao by Ernst Peters, a German clergyman who was working in Venezuela

Plate 98
Rufous-collared
sparrow

and who went to the islands in August 1890 and eventually sent his bird skins and lists to Hans von Berlepsch. Afterward it was also found by Ernst Hartert on Aruba, but it is not as common there as on Curaçao. It has never been recorded on nearby Bonaire.

It is true that there are mountains on both Curaçao and Bonaire, not Andean in their ruggedness and elevation, but mountains all the same. Cristoffel on Curaçao is something over 1200 feet, and Brandaris on Bonaire about 800 feet. But this seems to mean little to the sparrows, for although they are more common "in the least visited valleys in the Arikok hills" than elsewhere on Aruba, according to Wagenaar Hummelinck, they also come into the towns and can be observed right at sea level. Hummelinck says: "We found this species in open bush and thorny scrub, in fruit plantations, in farm yards and around human dwellings, in the gardens of Willemstad and Oranjestad, and even in the streets close to busy traffic."

Some years after Ernst Peters found this species on dry islands in the southern Caribbean, at sea level, Dr. William L. Abbot sent to the Smithsonian Institution in Washington a collection of bird skins from Hispaniola. That was in the autumn of 1916. Among these skins were specimens of a sparrow that had never before been reported from the West Indies and was wholly unsuspected there. It turned out to be this same species, which came from a small area in the high portion of the Cordillera Central of the Dominican Republic, in the general area about the great Valley of Constanza. The geographic race—*Zonotrichia capensis antillarum*—is also known as the Constanza song sparrow.

Alexander Wetmore tells us that he observed it, in 1927, on the great hill known as El Barrero, where the Constanza trail climbs from the Río Jimenoa, near Jarabacoa, to El Río and Constanza. He writes that it is found "in thickets along little streams in open valleys, at the borders of the deciduous forests, or less commonly, scattered through growths of bracken in the pine lands, where it lives a secluded life, being shy and retiring in habit" (Wetmore and Swales, 1931). This hardly seems like the same species in the busy streets of Willemstad or Oranjestad!

How do we account for the amazing distribution of this bird? James Bond (1942) believes that the rufous-collared sparrow reached Hispaniola from Central America by way of "what is now the Mosquito Bank and Jamaica at a time when the former was above sea level, at least to a considerable extent, perhaps during the last glacial period." He says that evidently it did not thrive in the Antilles, and points out that even today, in Hispaniola, it has a more circumscribed range than any other bird species on the island except the La Selle thrush.

But it *is* in the mountains of Hispaniola, and from what we have learned about this hardy and adaptable sparrow, it will probably be there for a long time to come.

Identification Guide

PLATE 1
WHITE-TAILED TROPICBIRD (*Phaethon lepturus*)

Other names: Yellow-billed tropicbird; gannet (*Haiti*); chirre, chirre de altura, gaviote caracolera (*Puerto Rico*); rabijunco (*Cuba, Dominican Republic*); contramaestre (*Cuba*); paille-en-queue, truphit, tropic, long-tail, boatswain bird.

Description: A large white seabird, with strongly contrasting black patches in the wings (primaries and tertials), a black line through the eye, and a yellow or coral-red bill. The two central tail-feathers may extend as much as 15 inches beyond rest of tail, like a graceful white streamer. Flight rapid and wingbeat similar to that of pigeon. Immature birds have finely barred black-and-white pattern on back, yellow bill.

Range: Throughout the tropical Atlantic, central Pacific, and Indian Oceans. Widespread in the Caribbean, but most often seen in vicinity of Greater Antilles and Leeward Islands. Breeds locally in rocky crevices on steep slopes or cliffs of islands in both Greater and Lesser Antilles, the Bahamas, and reportedly off Tobago. Said to nest on the ground in Bermuda. Colonies have been recorded on Great Inagua (Bahamas); the north coast of Jamaica; (near) Quebradillas, Mona Island, and Louis Peña (Puerto Rico); Congo Cay and Virgin Gorda (Virgin Islands); also probably breeds on Great Abaco (Bahamas) and on Île à Vache and elsewhere in Haiti. Observed off Caribbean Guatemala near Puerto Barrios.

PLATE 2
BROWN PELICAN (*Pelecanus occidentalis*)

Other names: Alcatraz, grand gosier, pélican (*West Indies*); ganshi (*Aruba, Curaçao, Bonaire*); alcatraz (*Mexico, Puerto Rico, Venezuela*); old Joe (*St. Catherine Parish, Jamaica*); booby (*Barbados*); pelícano moreno, pontoj (*Yucatán*); blue pelican, common pelican, piliken (*Florida*). "pelican of America" of George Edwards (1743-1751) and "le pelican brun" of Mathurin Jacques Brisson (1760).

Description: A large bird of the seacoasts and harbors. Big and bulky, with large head, long pouched bill, short legs, and a wingspread of 6 to 7 feet. Slow, dignified, and deliberate in flight, but extremely able on the wing. Often seen in long lines, close to the water, each bird flapping and sailing more or less in unison. The adult has upper parts silvery gray streaked with brown, sides and flanks whitish. Head of adult white, the crown tinged with yellow. White of head extends down neck in narrow band that borders the large throat pouch. Rest of neck a rich chestnut brown. Immatures brownish or drab gray on head, neck, and back, white underneath. Nestlings covered with white down.

Range: A familiar and widely distributed species along the shores and in the harbors of North and South America, on both the Atlantic and Pacific coasts. It occurs from North Carolina to Florida (breeding from North Carolina southward), along the Gulf Coast to southernmost Texas and Mexico (with immense breeding colonies on mud banks off the Mississippi Delta); in the Bahamas (Grand Bahama, Abaco, Bimini, Berry Islands, Andros, Inagua); throughout the Greater and Lesser Antilles, nesting in many locations, including southern Cuba (Oriente Province) and on numerous islands and keys off both the north and south coasts; on Trinidad and Tobago and on many islands in the southern Caribbean, including Los Roques, Chimana Grande, and Morro de Esmerarda off Venezuela (where it nests), and on Bonaire, Curaçao, and Aruba. It also breeds on Pelican Key off the southeast coast of St. Martin and is suspected of breeding on the Reef of Aruba. Occurs likewise, and breeds, around the Central American rim of the Caribbean and on the coast of South America to British Guiana and Surinam, where, however, it is only a migrant. On the Pacific side, it is observed from southern British Columbia southward, and on many coastal islands (breeding on islands from the Santa Barbara group to the Tres Marías) to Peru and Chile as far as Chiloé Island. There is at least one record for Tierra del Fuego (Isla Picton, Ushuaia).

Several geographic races have been described, differing chiefly in comparative size from one region to another, and less so in coloration, the "California brown pelican" being larger and darker on the back of the neck than individuals from the Atlantic and Gulf of Mexico, and West Indian birds being smaller and darker underneath. On the Pacific side of South America individuals are decidedly larger and have longer and heavier bills, but they are all brown pelicans.

PLATE 3
DOUBLE-CRESTED CORMORANT (*Phalacrocorax auritus*)

Other names: Cormoril, corúa corúa de mar (*West Indies*); pato negro, cuervo marino, camacho (*Yucatán*); shag (*New England*); nigger goose, crow duck, water-turkey, lawyer (*southern U.S.*). Also, but referring to the Brazilian cormorant: duikelaar, duikla, dekla, patu morèkè (*Netherlands Antilles*); bubi bulau (*Curaçao*); cotúa (*Venezuela*). The Dutch name is Zuid-Amerikaanse aalscholver.

Description: Large, black, ducklike water birds with slender bill, sharply hooked at tip, long neck, and long stiff tail. Perch in an alert, bolt-upright posture, fly with very rapid wingbeat. Expert underwater swimmers. Adults are a glossy greenish black, back and wings mottled with coppery gray and black. The curly black tufts or crests on each side of head not always apparent. Throat pouch at breeding time is orange. Immatures are brown on back, whitish underneath. Nestlings when newly hatched are naked with coal-black skin and "look like rubber toys" (Pough). It is very difficult to tell the different races, and even different species, of cormorants apart in the field (*see* Peterson, 1960, p. 10).

Range: Widespread distribution across the entire width of North America, from the Alaska Peninsula and Kodiak Island to central Saskatchewan, northern Ontario, and Newfoundland south to California, Panama, southern Mexico, British Honduras, the Bahamas, and Cuba. Several geographic races are met with in such a vast and diverse territory, and those that reach the Caribbean are almost certain to be the Florida variety (*P. a. floridanus*), which breeds in the southeastern U.S. from North Carolina to Florida and Louisiana and also in Cuba, the Isle of Pines, and the Bahamas. The larger double-crest that nests in Canada and on the New England coast occurs in Florida in winter, large flocks of several thousand individuals sometimes being seen in shallow open waters in the Lower Florida Keys. There is one record of this northern form from Cuba, a bird banded in Quebec and shot at Guanabacoa in January (Bond, 1950).

Cormorants observed elsewhere in the Caribbean are either the Mexican (also called the olivaceous) or the Brazilian, which are smaller cormorants of a species that is widely distributed from southwest Louisiana and Texas south through Mexico and Central and South America to Argentina, Tierra del Fuego, and the region of Cape Horn. This cormorant also occurs in Cuba, the Isle of Pines, and the Bahamas, where it has been found breeding on Watling's Island (San Salvador). Other breeding sites include Cayo Culebra and Isla Contoy (Yucatán). Hummelinck says that it is a regular inhabitant of the coastal lagoons of Colombia and Venezuela. Phelps and Phelps (1958) mention that it is found on Isla de Margarita off Venezuela and also on Bonaire and Trinidad. Voous (1955) states that it is a regular visitor to shallow coastal seas (Paardenbaai, Aruba) and inland bays (Schottegat,

Curaçao). I observed a single individual, probably of this species, at the Lac on Bonaire (August 28), but they do not breed in this area and usually occur as flocks of immature birds (middle of December to July—Voous). In Surinam, Haverschmidt finds these cormorants rather common on most of the forest-fringed rivers (Nickerie, Corantijn, Wayombo, Surinam, Cottica, Marowijne, Nanni Kreek, Blackawattra Kreek).

PLATE 4
ANHINGA (*Anhinga anhinga*)

Other names: Corúa real, marbella (*West Indies*); camacho (*Yucatán*); cotúa agujita (*Venezuela*); water-turkey, snakebird, darter (*U.S.*).

Description: Superficially the anhinga resembles the cormorant, but is longer-necked, longer-billed, and longer-tailed. Bill sharp-pointed, without a hook at the tip. Tail fan-shaped and when spread in flight looks like that of the turkey (hence "water-turkey"). The adult male is a glossy, greenish-black, the tail tipped with white or pale brown. He also has a wide silver-gray band across the wings, and the shoulders spotted and striped with silver gray. At breeding time the male displays long black feathers and slender brownish-white plumes on the back of his neck. The head, neck, and breast are light buffy brown in the female. Immature birds are generally brownish, lighter underneath. The male anhinga in the color plate is drying his wings in a characteristic pose.

Range: It inhabits streams, lakes, and swamps from western Mexico (Sinaloa), east and south-central Texas (*see* Peterson, 1960), Tennessee, Alabama, southern Georgia, and central North Carolina south to Cuba, the Isle of Pines, and Central and South America. It formerly nested as far north as southern Illinois, and fossil remains have been discovered in the Pleistocene of Florida, where it is today an abundant breeding species, particularly in the southern part. Paynter observed few anhingas in Yucatán, presumably because there is little suitable habitat, but recorded it at Celestún on the coast and at Laguna Chacanbacab, inland in Quintana Roo. Anhingas banded as nestlings in Mississippi have been recovered at Palizada and Champotón in Campeche (Coffey). In South America it ranges through Colombia, Venezuela, Trinidad, Tobago, and the Guianas south, east of the Andes, to southern Brazil and northern Argen-

tina. According to Phelps and Phelps (1958) it is generally distributed in the Orinoco basin, and has been recorded in northwest Venezuela (Rio Socuy and Lago de Maracaibo) and at Lago de Valencia and Turiamo in Aragua. On the island of Trinidad it occurs in the Caroni River Swamp (Junge and Mees). Although usually found in fresh-water sites, the anhinga may be observed in brackish or salt-water situations. Rutten noted it in the mangroves along Cienfuegos Bay, Cuba, and I saw large numbers of this species in the open bay, close to shore, off the delta of the Río Cauto in Oriente Province, Cuba.

Other forms inhabit Asia, Africa, New Guinea, and Australia.

PLATE 5
MAGNIFICENT FRIGATEBIRD (*Fregata magnificens*)

Other names: Rabijorcado (*Cuba*); tijereta (*Dominican Republic*); rabijunco, tijerilla, tijereta (*Puerto Rico*); frégate, queue-en-ciseaux (*Haiti*); mansfeny (*Guadeloupe*); cobbler (*Barbados*); skerchi, macuacu, maniwa (*Bonaire*); weather bird (*St. Eustatius, St. Croix*); tijereta de mar (*Venezuela*); man-o'-war bird, man-o'-war hawk, hurricane bird, scissor-tail.

Description: A large, dark, extremely long-winged seabird. Wingspread 7 to 8 feet. Soars for long periods without flapping. Deeply forked tail which it opens and closes in flight. Bill long, heavy, and strongly hooked at tip. The adult male is brownish-black throughout, with a scarlet throat pouch or gular sac that can be inflated like a balloon. Feathers of head and shoulders show purplish or greenish reflections and are elongated and lance shaped. The female is browner and generally less brilliant than the male, and her lower neck, breast, and sides are white. Immature birds of both sexes are similar to the female, but the entire head is white (*see color plate*). Nestlings are covered with thick white down.

Range: Found in subtropical and tropical seas of both hemispheres, in the North and South Atlantic and Caribbean, as well as in the Pacific and Indian Oceans. The magnificent frigatebird occurs on the Pacific side from Lower California to the coasts of Ecuador and Peru and on the Galápagos Islands. It wanders north to the California coast. In the Atlantic and Caribbean area it is found from Texas, Louisiana, and Florida (where it is a non-breeder) south through the Bahamas and West Indies to Santos and Fernando de Noronha,

Brazil. It has been recorded also at the Cape Verde Islands and off the coast of Gambia on the western bulge of Africa.

It occurs throughout the West Indies, breeding in the Bahamas, according to Bond (1950) on Cay Verde, Atwood Cay, Seal Cay, and other small islands. Also reported as breeding at Puerto Escondido (Cuba), Siguanea Bay (Isle of Pines), Samaná Bay (Dominican Republic), Gonave Island (Haiti), Tobago Island, George Dog, and Dutch Cap (Virgin Islands), Barbuda, Navassa, Little Swan, Little Cayman, Mona, and Desecheo Island. Also on Battowia in the Grenadines.

Other breeding sites have included: Tête à l'Anglais, off Guadeloupe (Noble), and a small islet off Parguera, Puerto Rico (Wetmore, 1927). Large colonies have been described by Paynter for the coasts of the Yucatán Peninsula—at Cayos Arcas, Isla Desterrada, Isla Contoy, and Cayo Culebra. Additional breeding sites may exist on Banco Chinchorro, Isla Holbox, and Isla Cozumel. Phelps and Phelps (1958) list Los Hermanos and Los Testigos as nesting places off the Venezuelan coast, but definite breeding locations in the vicinity of Aruba, Curaçao, and Bonaire are unknown.

This species also breeds on Man-o'-war Cays, British Honduras, and on several sites off the Brazilian coast.

PLATE 6
GREAT BLUE HERON (*Ardea herodias*)

Other names: Gray gaulin, gaulding, arsenicker, morgan, garcilote, guardacosta, garzón cenizo, gironde, crabier noir (*West Indies*); garza moreno (*Yucatán*); garzón ceniciento (*Puerto Rico, Virgin Islands*); garzón cenizo (*Venezuela*); Amerikaanse blauwe reiger (*Netherlands Antilles*); calotte blanche (*Trinidad*); blue crane, poor Joe.

Description: A tall, heavy-billed, long-legged heron. General color blue-gray. Stands 4 feet in height. Wingspread to 6 feet. Adults white on head except band along sides of crown which is usually black. Neck pale cinnamon streaked in front with black. Thighs cinnamon, legs black. There is a white phase with gray and white intermediate examples, both usually with yellow legs (orange to scarlet in breeding adults). Immatures normally grayer, less white on head, generally paler including bill and legs. Nestlings grayish on back, whitish underneath.

Range: Widely distributed across North America

from southeastern Alaska in the northwest to Nova Scotia in the northeast, south to southern Mexico, the Galápagos Islands, the West Indies, and southern Caribbean to northern South America. Probably individuals of this species that normally breed on the U.S. mainland or Florida Keys occur in the West Indies and Caribbean merely as winter migrants. Herons of this species breeding in the West Indies are generally considered as resident birds, but this situation needs clarification. In any case, the several geographic races are not readily distinguishable in the field.

Bond (1950) considers that great blue herons breeding in Cuba, the Isle of Pines, Jamaica, St. Thomas, Anegada, and perhaps those in Yucatán (*see* Paynter) are the indigenous race of those regions (i.e., *A. h. repens*).

Great blue herons nesting on El Gran Roque, off Venezuela, are considered by Phelps and Phelps (1958) to belong to the West Indian variety (*repens*). Another species, the cocoi heron or aileronne (*Ardea cocoi*), which is somewhat like the great blue in appearance, occurs over the greater part of South America from Colombia, Venezuela, Trinidad, and the Guianas south to Chiloé Island, Chile, and Chubut, Patagonia. It is a large blue heron with a black crown and crest, white neck, underparts white and black, and thighs white rather than cinnamon as in *herodias*.

PLATE 7
GREEN HERON (*Butorides virescens*)

Other names: Little gaulin, Lees Pond gaulin, water witch, poor Joe, bitlin, aguaita, Caimán, martinete, caga-leche, cagón, cuaco, kio, cra-cra, rac-rac, valet de Caïman, caäli, crabier (*West Indies*); green gaulin, garling, martín pescador (*Puerto Rico, Virgin Islands*); qui-o, crabier vert tacheté (*Guadeloupe*); garcita (*Yucatán*); chicuaco, cuello rojo (*Venezuela*); galinja di awa, galiña di awa, groene reiger (*Netherlands Antilles*); gaulin (*St. Martin, Saba*); crab-catcher (*Jamaica*); skeow, shite-poke, fly-up-the-creek, chalk-line (*U.S.*).

Description: The smallest of the herons. Usually has neck drawn in or hunched, even in flight, but when alarmed stretches neck, raises crest, and wags tail. Appears quite dark, almost black. Adults are dark green above, dark brown below. In adult and juvenal males, crown solid greenish-black, neck solid chestnut. Adult and juvenal females show chestnut streaks in crown, sides of head and neck streaked with chestnut or buff. Meyerriecks considers the female plumage generally duller than that of male (the green heron in the color plate is an adult male). Back plumes vary from bluish-green to gray. Legs short for a heron and yellow to orange-red at breeding time. The harsh, penetrating call note is characteristic and is usually written *skow*, *skeow*, or *skyow*.

Range: Across North America from the Columbia River country in southwestern Washington in the West to southern New Brunswick in the East, south through almost the entire U.S., into Mexico, Central America (including Panama and the Pearl Islands), the West Indies, northern Colombia (Río Baudó), and the Netherlands Antilles and islands off Venezuela. Winter migrants from North America, and probably also from the Antilles, occur throughout these same regions and on to Bogotá in Colombia, to Venezuela and Trinidad, although the species was not recorded by Mees who states that the very similar striated heron (*Butorides striatus*) is the most common heron on both Trinidad and Tobago. Phelps and Phelps (1958) have found the green heron nesting on Las Aves, Los Roques, La Orchila, La Tortuga, and La Blanquilla off Venezuela, and say that migrants of this species reach Surinam (*Guayana Holandesa*) in winter. On this point, Haverschmidt mentions that two specimens of the green heron have been taken in Surinam, one in 1852 and another in 1898, and adds: "It is certainly a very rare straggler in Surinam." Bond (1960) considers it "one of the commonest of West Indian water birds."

Fossil remains of the green heron have been found in the Pleistocene of California and Florida.

PLATE 8
LITTLE BLUE HERON (*Florida caerulea*)

Other names: Blue gaulin, white gaulin (immature), garza azul, garza común, garza pinta, garza blanca (immature), crabier noir, crabier blanc (immature), aigrette bleue, aigrette blanche (immature) (*West Indies*); garcita moreno, garcita blanca (immature) (*Yucatán*); garza azul (*Venezuela, Netherlands Antilles*); kleine blauwe reiger (*Netherlands Antilles*); blue crane, calico crane, blue egret (U.S.); levee-walker (*Texas*). "Blew crane" of Mark Catesby (1771).

Description: Rather small and slender. Dainty. Body dark slate blue, head and neck maroon (brownish red). Bill of adult bluish and black-tipped. Legs dark blue-gray. Young are uniformally white (for about first year), pied or "calico" in appearance when molting to adult plumage.

Range: Found in suitable habitats from northern Mexico (Sonora), Oklahoma, Missouri, and Massachusetts south to Central America and throughout the West Indies to Peru and Uruguay. Robertson found it the only common heron on St. John, Virgin Islands. It is "the commonest member of the family" in Jamaica (Lady Taylor). May Jeffrey-Smith says that on this same island it can be seen on the Ferry marshes near Kingston, on open pastures between Jackson Town and Clark's Town, in mangroves by the road to Montego Bay just west of Falmouth, in trees on the riverbank at Bog Walk Bridge, and by the Irrigation Dam near Spanish Town. In Cuba, Rutten found it everywhere, including arid savannas and high up in the Trinidad Mountains.

On Tobago, Belcher (quoted in Alford) suggests looking for this species along the sandy beaches and at the mouths of rivers running down from the Main Ridge. On Trinidad I saw them in the Caroni Swamp near Port of Spain. There is scarcely a place in the Caribbean where little blues will not be observed, but nesting locations are not so common, especially in the extreme south.

This bird is a notable wanderer, the urge to take off in all directions at once sending it to many distant regions beyond its normal breeding range after the close of each breeding season. Young-of-the-year are chiefly concerned in these dispersals, which have carried the little blue heron to Newfoundland, Labrador, and Greenland, and south as far as Argentina. Apparently this wanderlust is an extraordinary extension of the natural urge to expand the range outward, which in some degree is shared by many living organisms, including, under certain conditions, man himself.

PLATE 9
CATTLE EGRET (*Bubulcus ibis*)

Other names: Cattle gaulin, garrapatosa, garza Africana, garza del ganado, crabier garde-boeuf (*West Indies*); reznero (*Venezuela*); koereiger (*Dutch*); héron garde-boeuf (*French*); buff-backed heron, African cattle egret.

Description: A small, white, stocky heron. Rather short-billed and thick-necked. When feeding, extends neck and sways head back and forth like a short-stroked metronome. Unusually tame and highly sociable, feeding among grazing cattle and other livestock. In breeding season has buff on crown, breast, and back; legs and bill become orange or red. Otherwise appears all-white, bill yellow and legs greenish-brown.

Range: A resident of the Western Hemisphere since about 1930. Original range: southern Spain, Africa, and parts of Asia. Appeared first in British Guiana, extending its New World distribution by 1950 to Surinam (1946), Venezuela, and Colombia. Now abundant in Trinidad. First recorded in U.S. in 1952, when there was a widespread invasion (Sudbury Valley, Mass., Cape May, N. J., and Lake Okeechobee, Fla.). Other reports followed, including one bird in the vicinity of Chicago. First breeding record for the U.S. was in 1953 on King's Bar, an Audubon Society sanctuary in Lake Okeechobee, Florida. Since then the cattle egret has spread through the West Indies (Cuba, Great Inagua, Jamaica, Dominican Republic, Puerto Rico, St. Croix), and is an established breeding bird in a number of colonies in Florida, along the Gulf Coast to Texas, and up the eastern seaboard to New Jersey.

In the Old World it breeds on the Iberian Peninsula, in western Asia from the Caspian Sea to Persia, in southwest Arabia, and throughout most of Africa.

PLATE 10
SNOWY EGRET (*Leucophoyx thula*)

Other names: White gaulin, garza blanca, garza de rizos, crabier blanc, aigrette blanche (*West Indies*); garcita blanca (*Yucatán, Venezuela*); garza blancu, Amerikaanse kleine zilverreiger (*Netherlands Antilles*); little egret, snowy heron, golden slippers, bonnet martyr (*obsolete*), little plume bird (*obsolete*); Brewster's egret (*western U.S. and Mexico*).

Description: A medium-sized white heron, with elegant head, breast, and back plumes, a black bill, and black legs with yellow feet. The plumes on the back are recurved at the ends, exquisite in appearance, and number about 50 distinct feathers. Spirited, dashing, and extremely graceful in its movements. Young birds are without plumes. Their legs are dark but have a yellow stripe up back (legs of white-plumaged young little blue herons are uniformly dull greenish-yellow). Bill of young

snowy egret is black, that of immature little blue is blue-gray with a black tip.

Range: Spotty distribution in the U.S., one population (Brewster's egret) breeding in a limited number of sites from northern California, southeast Idaho, and Colorado south to Lower California and Mexico (Sonora and Sinaloa). Another and larger population breeds locally from Oklahoma, on the Gulf Coast east to Alabama, and along the Atlantic Coast from Florida to New Jersey, south through Central America and the West Indies to South America, where it reaches central Chile and central Argentina. Formerly nested in Nebraska, Illinois, and Indiana.

Like the little blue heron, these birds wander after the breeding season, but not on so grand a scale. Recorded in Oregon on the one hand and Newfoundland on the other. There is a record for Bermuda.

In Yucatán, Paynter found them the most common of the smaller herons. They are not abundant in the West Indies generally, breeding only in the Greater Antilles. Rare in the Bahamas and Lesser Antilles (Bond, 1960). Hummelinck found them less common in the Netherlands Antilles than the little blue, but present in small numbers on all three of the Leeward Group (Aruba, Curaçao, Bonaire). In the Windward Group, Voous (1955) states that it is known only from St. Martin. There is a single nesting record for Curaçao (in 1955 at Sint Michiel). In Venezuela, however, Phelps and Phelps (1958) say that the snowy egret nests by the thousands, "*especialmente por los ríos Apure y Arauca.*" On Trinidad and Tobago, Junge and Mees list it as an "uncommon resident." In Surinam it has been found breeding in May–June and August (Haverschmidt).

PLATE 11
COMMON EGRET (*Casmerodius albus*)

Other names: White gaulin, white morgan, garzón, garzón blanco, garza blanca, garza real, crabier blanc (*West Indies*); white gaulding (*Barbados*); garza real (*Venezuela*); garza blancu, grote zilverreiger (*Netherlands Antilles*); yellow-billed egret, long white, big egret, plume bird, white crane (*U.S.*); great white heron (*Europe*). "Le Grande Aigrette" of Buffon (1783).

Description: The largest white heron, except for the great white heron (*Ardea occidentalis*) of extreme south Florida. Yellow bill and black legs (the great white heron of Florida has yellow legs, which are pink or red at breeding time). Long train of 40 to 50 plumes on back, extending beyond tail. No plumes on head. Flight easy and graceful. Young birds similar, but without back plumes.

Range: Found on all continents. In the Western Hemisphere, especially the U.S., the breeding range has gone through many changes since the late nineteenth century. Currently its limits are southern Oregon south through Mexico; the Upper Mississippi drainage south to the Gulf of Mexico; the Gulf Coast to Florida; the Atlantic Seaboard from Massachusetts (irregularly) to the Florida Keys; and on south through the West Indies (breeding in Greater Antilles, Virgin Islands, and possibly Puerto Rico), Central America, and South America (including the Galápagos Islands) to Chile (Gulf of Peñas) and western Santa Cruz, Patagonia (Lago Buenos Aires).

Breeding within many of these regions is more often than not rather spotty and limited to small nesting groups. Large colonies are rare, at least in the U.S. and West Indies. In the U.S. many major breeding and feeding sites have been destroyed by drainage and other "development."

In the Old World, breeds in southeast Europe, has bred in Czechoslovakia. A vagrant to Sweden, Great Britain, and the Balearics (Peterson, 1954). Also the Volga Delta, Turkestan, southern Siberia, northern China, Japan, and south locally to South Africa, Iran, India, Ceylon, Burma, the Malay Peninsula, the East Indies, Australia, and New Zealand (South Island).

This bird is another notable wanderer. Records also from the Baltic States, the Azores, Canary Islands, southern Canada (isolated breeding records), Newfoundland, the Straits of Magellan, and the Falkland Islands.

PLATE 12
BLACK-CROWNED NIGHT-HERON (*Nycticorax nycticorax*)

Other names: Gaulin, night gaulin, crab-catcher, guanabá lominegro, guanabá de la Florida, yaboa real, rey Congo, gallinaza (immature), coq de nuit, coq d'eau, crabier (*West Indies*); yaboa, yaboa real (*Puerto Rico, Virgin Islands*); quock, qua-bird (*Jamaica*); kwak, galina di awa (*Netherlands Antilles*); quock, squawk, night-heron, Indian pullet (*U.S.*).

Description: A stocky heron with short thick bill and short legs. Sits and flies with neck hunched. Plumage black, white, and gray. Adults greenish-black on crown, rest of head and throat white. Wings gray. One or two white plumes on head. Bill black. Legs and feet yellow, changing to pink and ruby red during early stages of courtship. Young are brownish, spotted and streaked with grayish-white. Bill yellow, legs and feet greenish-yellow.

Range: Universal distribution. In the Western Hemisphere, from Washington, southern areas of Idaho, Saskatchewan, Manitoba, Ontario and Quebec, New Brunswick, south through Mexico, Central America, and the West Indies to southern South America and the Falkland Islands. In the Old World, from the Netherlands, Germany, Hungary, Rumania, southern Russia, Turkestan, southern Manchuria, and Japan (Honshu) south to South Africa, Iraq, Iran, Baluchistan, southern India, Ceylon, Burma, the Malay Peninsula, Sumatra, Borneo, Java, the Kangean Islands, the Philippines, Celebes, and the Moluccas. Also the Hawaiian Islands (Niihau to Hawaii).

Wanders to Micronesia (Marianas, Yap), Great Britain, Norway, Finland, northwest Russia, British Columbia, and Newfoundland.

Most black-crowns seen in the West Indies are probably migrants from North America (Bond, 1960). Generally distributed in coastal mangroves, rivers, lagoons, and swamps of the Tropical Zone in Venezuela, including the offshore islands (Phelps and Phelps, 1958). Rather rare in the Netherlands Antilles, although there are apparent records from both Curaçao and Bonaire (the yellow-crowned night-heron—locally the kra-bèchi— is more numerous on these islands than the present species). In Surinam, Haverschmidt says that the black-crown is rather common along the coast and on some of the rivers (Coppename and Saramacca).

PLATE 13
SCARLET IBIS (*Eudocimus ruber*)

Other names: Corocoro, corocoro colorado, sidra (*Venezuela*); flamingo (*Trinidad*). "red curlew" of Mark Catesby (1771).

Description: The only long-legged wading bird with a thin decurved bill and deep scarlet plumage. Color solid throughout except for tips of the four outer flight feathers, which are black. Young birds are similar to young white ibis: grayish-brown and white above, white on lower back, rump, thighs, and underparts. Late juvenal plumage shows a mixed brown, gray, rose, pale orange, and scarlet. Flight and general characteristics like white ibis.

Range: Breeds locally on the northeast coast of South America from Venezuela (Falcón and Apure) and Trinidad (Caroni Swamp) south to Paraná in Brazil. Accidental in Jamaica (none in recent years), Grenada (one record, 1951), Honduras, Texas, Louisiana, and Florida. Bond (1960) doubts the validity of occurrence reports from Cuba and the Bahamas.

For Venezuela, Phelps and Phelps (1958) say: "Distributed locally in suitable locations except in southern Bolívar and the Territory of Amazonas. Falcón (Adicora, Chichiriviche); Aragua (Lago de Valencia, Turiamo); Miranda (Laguna de Tacarigua, Higuerote); Anzoátegui (Barcelona); Sucre (Laguna Campoma); Monagas (Caño San Juan); Guárico (Camaguán, Río Apurito); Barinas (Ciudad Bolivia); Territory of the Amacuro Delta, Apure (San Fernando); Bolívar (Caicara). Margarita Island. Nesting in Falcon and Apure (Zahl, 1954)."

In Surinam Haverschmidt considers the scarlet ibis sadly diminished, owing to continual persecution, but still rather common along the coast. During very dry seasons they move far upstream on the larger rivers (Surinam River, etc.). He has recorded them in Nickerie, Coronie, on the Coppename and Saramacca rivers, on the coast near Paramaribo, in the Commewijne District of Matapica, and at Mot Kreek, Tijerbank, and Pomona Kreek. Kori Kori Bank on the northwest coast of Surinam is doubtless named for these birds.

Although there are specimens of these birds that have been taken in Florida and along the Gulf Coast to Texas, as well as recent reliable sight records from South Florida, there is a strong possibility that some of these individuals may be "escapes" from zoos or bird farms. However, if the plumage is deep scarlet, such a bird may well be a bona-fide "accidental," a stray from its true haunts on the South American coast.

PLATE 14
ROSEATE SPOONBILL (*Ajaia ajaja*)

Other names: Pink curlew, pink, rosy spoonbill, flamingo (*Florida*); pinkie, pink-bird, skatule (*Louisiana*); flamingo (*Texas*); alaloolasetteé (*Seminole*); chocolatera, espátula, garza colorado (*Mexico*); Sevilla (*Cuba, South America*); spatule (*West Indies*); pato cucharo (*Colombia*); garza paleta (*Venezuela*); planeta (*Chile*); colheriro (*Brazil*); espatula rosada (*Argentina*); cuchareta, colherado, garza rosada (*South America*); ayaya (*South American Indian*); tlauhquechul (*Mexico, seventeenth century*). "Rose-coloured curlew" of Audubon (1838). Many additional names have been applied to the spoonbills of Europe, Africa, etc. (see Allen, p. 131).

Description: A sturdy, medium-sized pink wading bird with a flat, spoon-shaped bill. Six well-defined plumages (age groups) have been described, from the nearly all-white juvenal to the full adult, each a little pinker as it progresses toward maturity. The adult in breeding plumage has a bare head, the skin light green to golden buff. Neck and upper back white. Wings and under parts deep pink, with a crimson "drip" along middle of folded wing. Upper and lower tail coverts intense crimson. Patches of saffron yellow on each side of upper breast. Patch of pink to scarlet or crimson feathers, stiff and curly, in middle of breast. Tail deep orange-yellow. Legs lake red.

This plumage requires 33 to 36 months to acquire, and younger birds appear in progressive gradations that may be quite deeply pink but lack some adult features. Individuals from flight age to 12 or 14 months have feathered heads, yellow or yellowish bills. Bill of full adult is horn color, mottled with blackish, greenish, and yellow. Nestlings begin life covered sparsely with short white down, through which the pink skin is visible. This down becomes thick and woolly before first feathers develop.

Range: Breeds from coastal Texas, Louisiana, and Florida south locally through Mexico, Central America, the Bahamas, and Greater Antilles to central Chile, central Argentina, and southern Uruguay. In the U.S., spoonbills are represented by three distinct population groups: (1) a large group that inhabits the eastern Gulf Coast of Mexico, coastal Texas, and southeast coastal Louisiana; (2) a second breeding group originating in Cuba and migrating each fall to eastern Florida Bay where it nests (October–March); (3) another Cuban group, mainly immature birds, dispersing after each nesting season to South Florida (March–September). Formerly there was a spring nesting group in Florida, but spring or early summer nesting records there are now rare and irregular.

In the Bahamas, actual nesting may be confined to one or two colonies on Great Inagua. There are numerous Cuban colonies, on both coasts. Breeding groups may exist in Hispaniola. Griscom (1926) found them nesting at Cayo Culebra and Boca de Paila, Quintana Roo, and more recently Paynter saw a few nests at Cayo Culebra. Phelps and Phelps do not mention nesting sites in Venezuela, where nonetheless it is an uncommon breeding bird in lagoons and mangrove swamps along the north coast. On the offshore islands, including the Netherlands Antilles, it is extremely rare, but has been recorded on Isla Margarita. On Trinidad it is merely a visitor. For Surinam, Haverschmidt says, "not numerous along the coast," and breeding is not recorded. There may be large breeding colonies in the Mato Grosso and in Argentina.

PLATE 15
WEST INDIAN FLAMINGO (*Phoenicopterus ruber*)

Other names: American flamingo, fillymingo (*U.S.*); do-sum-cho-a-bee (*Mikasuki Seminole*); flamant (*Haiti*); chogogo, sjogogo (*Netherlands Antilles*); flamenco, tococo (*Venezuela*); tokoko (*French Guiana*); ganso côr de rosa, ganso do norte, marahão (*Brazil*). Many additional names have been applied to other flamingos around the world (see Allen, p. 261).

Description: The only large wading bird that is pink or red and has excessively long thin neck and legs. Plumage varies from pale pink or salmon to scarlet on head, neck, and wings. Flight feathers black. Bill bent downward in middle. Color fades in captivity. Young birds are grayish-brown with pink on under parts and beneath wings, which have black flight feathers. Nestlings covered with gray down which turns white (*see* color plate). Flamingos fly with neck extended, legs trailing out behind.

Range: A true Caribbean bird, formerly breeding throughout the Bahamas (Abaco, Andros, Rum Cay, Exuma Cays, Long Island, Ragged Cays, Acklins, Mayaguana, Caicos, Great Inagua); Cuba; Hispaniola; Yucatán; Islote Ave; the Netherlands Antilles (Bonaire); islands off Venezuela (Los Roques, La Orchila, Blanquilla, Isla Maria Uespen, Isla Aves); the Guianas (Waini Creek, Surinam River, Hermina Bank, Cayenne); Colombia (Cienga Grande?) and the Galápagos Islands. Large flocks from now extinct colonies on the west coast of Andros wintered in South Florida (to about 1902).

Now much reduced in numbers and breeding restricted to Abaco (?), Great Inagua, Yucatán, Bonaire, and possibly small numbers on Los Roques or La Orchila. A colony may survive in Cuba. A small flock remains in the Galápagos Islands and apparently still breeds there. Flocks observed in Haiti or the Dominican Republic probably represent dispersals from Inagua. Andros flocks may be birds en route to Abaco or wandering non-breeders, possibly from as far away as Inagua. On the coast of Colombia and Venezuela, including offshore islands, flamingos are likely to have an affinity with the large breeding group on Bonaire which disperse in the direction of the mainland. Throughout the Bahamas the origin of birds observed is probably Inagua, the only large Bahamas colony that remains. A few individuals may roam as far as the Guianas and the mouth of the Amazon. Flamingos observed in Florida are almost certainly "escapes" from captive flocks.

PLATE 16
HORNED SCREAMER (*Anhima cornuta*)

Other names: Aruco (*Venezuela*). "anhima" of Marcgrave (1648); "screamer" of Thomas Pennant (1773); "kamichi" of Buffon (1781).

Description: A large, heavily built bird approximately the size of a turkey. Grayish-black on back, white underneath. Crown and lower neck variegated black and white. Small white patches on wings. A frontal horn (length about 3 inches) on forehead and two spurs on the "wrist" or carpal angle of each wing. Large feet, elongated toes, partially palmated.

Range: Through tropical South America from the Cauca Valley in Colombia, Ecuador (one record from Balzar), Venezuela, eastern Peru, and the Guianas south through Amazonia to central-eastern Bolivia (Río Surutu), Mato Grosso and São Paulo (Hellmayr and Conover). In Venezuela these birds are locally distributed and are found in Zulia (Encontrados, Río Catatumbo, Santa Bárbara), in Mérida ("*detrás del Páramo de los Nevados*"), in Anzoátegui (Boca de Tigre), in Sucre (Caño La Brea), in Monagas (Barrancas), and in the Amacuro Delta Territory (Phelps and Phelps, 1958). According to Junge and Mees it is exceedingly rare in Trinidad and probably extirpated there. Not found on Tobago. Rare also in Surinam, where a specimen was collected in 1952 at Galibi on the Marowijne River (Haverschmidt).

PLATE 17
BLACK-BELLIED TREE-DUCK (*Dendrocygna autumnalis*)

Other names: Pichichi, patos maizal (*Mexico*); guirirí (*Venezuela*); yaguaza, chiriría pinta (*Puerto Rico*); black-bellied whistling duck, whistling duck, autumnal tree-duck, cornfield duck, long-legged duck. "Red-billed whistling duck" of Edwards (1751).

Description: A large gooselike duck with long, rather heavy legs. Feet extend beyond tail in flight. Crown rusty brown, cheeks and neck ashy gray, throat white. Lower neck, breast, and back cinnamon brown (in Mexican and Central American birds) to grayish (in South American and West Indian birds). Belly, sides, rump, and tail black. Wings have broad white stripe that appears near fore edge of wing when folded and along entire middle of upper wing surface in flight. Bright coral-pink bill, pink or pinkish-white legs. Sexes alike.

Range: It is found from southern Texas (Rio Grande Delta locally to Rio Grande City, Corpus Christi, San Antonio, Eagle Lake) south through Mexico and Central America to southern Brazil and northern Argentina. In Mexico it breeds as far west as Sinaloa, on both coastal slopes and Cozumel Island. Not found in Baja California. Paynter says that it is not uncommon in northern Yucatán. In Quintana Roo there is one record (Kantunil-Kín). Chapman (1929) saw this species in Panama on Pacora Marsh. Other reported locations include Permé and Port Obaldia, Darien.

In South America the black-bellied tree-duck ranges from northwestern Colombia (Cali) south on the west coast to Ecuador (Arenillas, El Oro) and east of the Andes south through Venezuela, the Guianas, Brazil, Bolivia, and Paraguay to northwestern Argentina (Tucumán, Salta, and Pilcomayo) (Hellmayr and Conover). It occurs on Trinidad (but not Tobago), occasionally breeding, according to Junge and Mees, but greatly diminished by shooting. Haverschmidt makes a similar comment for Surinam.

In the West Indies these birds have been recorded from Barbados, Mustique, St. Vincent, St. Lucia, Martinique, Guadeloupe, St. Croix, and Puerto Rico (Bond, 1960).

PLATE 18
BAHAMA PINTAIL (*Anas bahamensis*)

Other names: White-jaw, white-throat, white-head, white-cheeked pintail, summer duck, brass-wing, pato quijada colorado, pato de la orillo, canard tête-blanche (*West Indies*); Bahama pintail, Bahama duck, pato Criollo, pato de Florida (*Puerto Rico, Virgin Islands*); pato rubio, pato Inglés (*Puerto Rico*); patu, patu morèkè (?), patu di Aña, Bahama pijlstaart (*Netherlands Antilles*); pato Malibú (*Venezuela*). "Ilathera" of Catesby (1771).

Description: In spite of name, does not resemble North American pintail. A smallish duck with white cheeks and throat, contrasting dark-brown crown. Tail pale buff and pointed. Cinnamon-brown above, below grayish-brown with dark-brown splotches. Wings show two broad bands of vinaceous cinnamon (hence "brasswing"). Bill blue-gray, bright red at base. Sexes alike.

Range: The "white-jaw" or Bahama pintail ranges throughout the Bahamas (Abaco, Andros, Watling, Acklins, Long Island, Great and Little Inagua), Caicos Islands, Hispaniola (including Beata Island), Puerto Rico, Virgin Islands, and the northern Lesser Antilles (Anguilla, St. Barts, St. Kitts, Barbuda, Antigua, Guadeloupe), and also from Colombia, Venezuela (rare), Trinidad (uncommon and decreasing), and the Guianas south to Brazil, Argentina, and west through Paraguay to eastern Bolivia and central Chile.

There is one Florida record (Cape Canaveral in 1913). It is pointed out by Pough that South Florida should be an ideal habitat for this duck, and it has been suggested that they may have once been resident but were so vulnerable to hunting that they were wiped out in the very early days of settlement. Casual records also from Wisconsin, Virginia, and Cuba.

PLATE 19
KING VULTURE (*Sarcoramphus papa*)

Other names: Zopilote rey (*Mexico*); rey zamuro (*Venezuela*).

Description: A typical vulture in flight (soars like a turkey vulture), with handsome black-and-white plumage pattern. The shoulders and upper back are pinkish-white, while below it is creamy white. Lower back, tail, and flight feathers black. The bare, orange-red neck emerges from a feathered collar or ruff that is dusky. Head bare and colored red, yellow, orange, and blue. Conspicuous fleshy caruncle at base of bill (like a turkey wattle). Iris white ringed with red (*see* color plate). Young birds resemble turkey vultures but are whitish underneath.

Range: From the humid forests of tropical Mexico south through Central and South America to northern Argentina. Rare on the Yucatán Peninsula, but according to Paynter more common in Campeche than in Quintana Roo. In Mexico generally, Blake says, it inhabits hot lowlands from Sinaloa and Veracruz southward. In Venezuela it is "generally distributed" (Phelps and Phelps, 1958). Haverschmidt finds it not uncommon in forests of the savanna region and in the interior of Surinam. It has been recorded on Trinidad, but evidently is quite rare there. One was shot as recently as 1942 on the Quare Dam Road (Chenery). Not found on Tobago.

PLATE 20
SNAIL KITE (*Rostrhamus sociabilis*)

Other names: Gavilán caracolero, babosero, gavilán babosero (*West Indies*); gavilán caracolero (*Venezuela*); Everglade kite, snail hawk, snail bird, hook-billed hawk (*Florida*).

Description: The adult male is sooty black with a large white patch at base of tail, conspicuous both from above and below in flight. Female sooty brown above, buffy below, heavily streaked with black. Also has white patch at base of tail. Young similar to female. Bill slender and sharply hooked. Legs and feet pink or red. Resembles marsh hawk in size and somewhat in flight, but in this species the flight is more purposeful and direct, less wobbly. Hovers in a style all its own.

Range: The snail kite occurs in Florida (where it is now extremely rare), Cuba and the Isle of Pines, and in Mexico from Veracruz south through Central America and northern and eastern South America to Uruguay and eastern Argentina. Formerly a breeding species throughout much of Florida, from the Wacissa River to the southern Everglades, it has been reduced to a few pairs in

the Lake Okeechobee region. In the West Indies it is found only in Cuba and the Isle of Pines, where it "is becoming scarcer owing to the draining of marsh lands" (Westermann, 1953). In Mexico, Blake says, it occurs in Veracruz and Campeche "principally in fresh-water marshes." Paynter adds records from Quintana Roo (Laguna Bacalar and Xulha) and notes that in Campeche specimens were taken at Palizada, El Vapor, and Pacaytun. It is locally distributed in Venezuela and rather common in suitable habitats in Surinam (and probably the other Guianas), as well as farther south, notably in eastern Argentina.

PLATE 21
ROADSIDE HAWK (*Buteo magnirostris*)

Other names: Ch'uy (*Mexico*); gavilán habado (*Venezuela*); large-billed hawk, tropical broad-winged hawk, insect hawk.

Description: Similar to northern broad-winged hawk in size and proportions. In general, dull grayish-brown above and below, tail brown barred with four or five tawny streaks. Underside of wings pale buff. Some birds show lighter coloration with strongly tawny streaks on tail, others are darker over-all and streaks on tail are very pale. There is considerable variation. Paynter says that this species is highly polymorphic and divisible into approximately 15 subspecies, 5 or 6 in Mexico alone.

Range: This common little hawk is found on both the Pacific and Caribbean slopes of Mexico, from Colima and central Tamaulipas (including Cozumel, Meco, Holbox, and Mujeres Islands) south through Central America to Colombia, Ecuador, Venezuela, the Guianas, and northern Brazil. Phelps and Phelps (1958) find it in the Venezuelan districts of Bolívar and the Territories of the Deltas Amacuro and Amazonas, and generally north of the Orinoco and Rio Apure. Also Isla de Patos. Not noted by Junge and Mees on Trinidad or Tobago. It is the commonest hawk on the cultivated coastal areas in Surinam, as well as in the so-called savanna belt (Haverschmidt).

PLATE 22
ORNATE HAWK-EAGLE (*Spizaetus ornatus*)

Other names: Aguila de penacho (*Venezuela*); ornate eagle-hawk, crested eagle-hawk.

Description: Black and blackish-brown above, hind neck rich chestnut, fore part of face, chin, and throat white, bordered with narrow black streaks. Long black crest. Under parts white with bold horizontal black bars. Tail very long, rounded at tip and barred with black and pale brown. Wings broad, the undersides white barred sparingly with black. Feathered legs. Larger than a northern red-tail but not as large as an eagle.

Range: This extremely handsome hawk-eagle ranges from the humid lowland forests of eastern Mexico (Tamaulipas and Veracruz), Oaxaca, Chiapas, and Yucatán south through Central America, Colombia, Ecuador (and possibly Peru) to Venezuela, Trinidad (very rare), and the Guianas (not common) to southern Brazil and northern Argentina. In Venezuela it occurs in the northern part of the country in Táchira (Burgua), Carabobo (San Esteban), Aragua (Rancho Grande), Guárico (Ortiz, Cojedes El Bául), and Sucre ("Andes de Cumaná"). In the south in Bolívar (Cerro Tigre) and the Territory Amazonas (Nericagua, Cerro Yapacana) (Phelps and Phelps, 1958). There is only a single record from Surinam, a specimen taken on the Johanna Catharina Plantation (Saramacca River) in 1911 (Haverschmidt).

PLATE 23
OSPREY (*Pandion haliaetus*)

Other names: Guincho, guaraguao de mar, aguila de mar, halcón pescador, malfini de la mer, aiglon (*West Indies*); aguila marina (*Puerto Rico, Virgin Islands*); gavilán pescador (*Mexico*); aguila pescadora (*Venezuela*); gabilan piscado, gabilan di laman, visarend (*Netherlands Antilles*); fish hawk, fish eagle.

Description: A very large, eagle-like hawk, seldom observed far from water. Wingspread to 6½ feet. Dark above and white below. In the Bahamas (less so in Cuba) resident birds have almost entirely white head (actually appears all-white in many individuals), but North American ospreys, which are migrant in the West Indies and Caribbean, have dark or dark-tipped feathers on crown and hind neck and broad dark band through eye. Has decided bend in extended wing, and typical way of leaning back and hovering before plunging after fish.

Range: The osprey is cosmopolitan, ranging to all continents, on both temperate and tropical shores, bays, gulfs, and lakes from Alaska, Labrador, northern Europe, and Siberia south to Argentina, southern Africa, India, Malaysia, the Philippines, New Guinea, the Solomons, New Caledonia, Australia, and Tasmania.

In the West Indies and Caribbean it may be observed in every month of the year, but breeds only in the Bahamas, on coastal cays off Cuba (Bond, 1950, lists Cayo Cantiles, Cayo Majás, and Cayo Algodón), the coast of Quintana Roo (*not* Yucatán) and on islands off British Honduras. May breed in the Virgin Islands. Elsewhere, ospreys observed on the Central American coast, in the Lesser Antilles, and in the southern Caribbean are North American migrants and non-breeders in these areas. They also range along the coast of South America and on offshore islands, as far as Peru, Uruguay, and northern Argentina.

Two fossil examples have been found in the Pleistocene deposits of Florida (*see* Wetmore, 1931).

PLATE 24
LIMPKIN (*Aramus guarauna*)

Other names: Carrao, guareao, colas, grand colas, poule-ajoli (*West Indies*); guarauna (*Brazil*); crying-bird, clucking-hen, courlan.

Description: Resembles a very large, long-legged rail (mudhen). Dark brown, streaked and spotted with white. Long, heavy, slightly decurved bill. In flight it demonstrates its close relationship to the cranes (Gruidae) by the flicking upstroke of the wingbeat. Voice unmistakable, a wailing *kur-r-ee-ow, kur-r-ee-ow, kr-ow, kr-ow* (hence local names such as carrao), very loud and mournful. Also a sharp *kwaouk*.

Range: A New World species resident locally from southeastern Georgia through Florida to Cuba, the Isle of Pines, Hispaniola, Jamaica, Mexico (Oaxaca and Veracruz southward, including Campeche, Quintana Roo and Cozumel Island), Central America, and South America east of the Andes to central Argentina.

Apparently there is a more than casual movement of these birds between Cuba and Florida, and migrating limpkins frequently occur on the Florida Keys. In Jamaica they have been seen in the marshes around Black River in St. Elizabeth Parish. In Hispaniola they have occurred near Damien in Haiti and at Barahona in the Dominican Republic (Wetmore and Lincoln). Also on Gonave and Tortue. They have been rare in Puerto Rico for many years. McCandless says: "Considered extirpated, but rumors persist....Last known from Río Arriba south of Arecibo." Paynter found it fairly common along the Río Hondo between Quintana Roo and British Honduras. It is a rare resident on Trinidad and absent on Tobago (Junge and Mees).

Of casual occurrence in South Carolina, on Cay Lobos, Bahamas, and on the Texas coast (Port Arthur–Beaumont area and one old record for Brownsville).

PLATE 25
PURPLE GALLINULE (*Porphyrula martinica*)

Other names: Gallareta platanera, gallareta azul, gallareta Inglesa, poule sultana, poule d'eau à cachet bleu, cascamiol, blue-pated coot, plantain coot (*West Indies*); sultana (*Jamaica*); gallareta Martiniqueña, gallareta, dagareta, cabro (*Puerto Rico, Virgin Islands*); gallineta azul, gallito azul (*Venezuela*). Mudhen, pond-chicken, and blue peter are sometimes used to describe this species, but may apply as well to other gallinules and to the coots.

Description: Resembles the common or Florida gallinule, but in this species the purple plumage is outstanding, the frontal shield is light blue, and the bill red with a yellow tip. Legs yellow. Head, neck, and under parts deep, brilliant purple. Back and wings bluish-green (*see* color plate).

Range: Breeds from coastal Louisiana, Tennessee (Reelfoot Lake and Franklin County), Mississippi, Alabama, and South Carolina south through Georgia and Florida to the Greater Antilles, the Lesser Antilles from Guadeloupe southward, Tobago, and Trinidad. Also, from southern Texas through Mexico and Central America to South America as far as Peru and northern Argentina. Bond (1960) says that it is only a vagrant or wanderer in the Bahamas. It has been reported as uncommon or even rare in Puerto Rico, but McCandless states that it is a fairly common resident and "stays closer to cover than Antillean Gallinule." In Jamaica, May Jeffrey-Smith says, it can be seen at Falmouth and on the Ferry River, as well as on the Río Cobre Irrigation Canal near Spanish Town. It is widely distributed in Venezuela, especially in the northern part, and I have observed it on the shores of Lago de Valencia not far from Maracay. As is to be expected of a bird that requires fresh-water marsh, it is rare or un-known in the Netherlands Antilles and on the Venezuelan islands.

PLATE 26
SUNBITTERN (*Eurypyga helias*)

Other names: Tigana (Venezuela). There are many early "book names" for this curious bird: oiseau de soleil (Ferman, 1769); Surinamische Sonnenreyger (Pallas, 1781); petit paon des roseaux (Rozier, 1772); le caurâle ou petit paon des roses (Buffon, 1781); caurale snipe (Latham, 1785).

Description: Somewhere between a green heron and snowy egret in size, but in general appearance wholly unlike any Caribbean bird. Head black with whitish stripes above and below eye. Throat white. Neck, breast, and upper back brownish, variegated with black. Remainder of back gray and grayish-buff with black barring. The wings have bright chestnut patches, edged with black, and there is a band of similar colors across the tail at the tip. Bill and legs orange. Iris red.

Range: Inhabits the humid lowlands of southern Mexico (Chiapas and Tobasco) south through Central America (except San Salvador) to southeastern Colombia, Venezuela, the Guianas, Brazil, Ecuador, Peru, and Bolivia. It does not occur on the rather dry Yucatán Peninsula, nor is it recorded by Junge and Mees for Trinidad and Tobago.

PLATE 27
AMERICAN JACANA (*Jacana spinosa*)

Other names: Gallito de agua, médecin, poule d'eau dorée chevalier, Brazilian coot, banana coot (*West Indies*); queen bird (*Trelawny Parish, Jamaica*); Spanish coot (*St. Catherine Parish, Jamaica*); pond coot, river chink (*Jamaica*); gallito, gallito de dedos largos (*Puerto Rico*); gallito de agua, gallito de laguna, tigüi-tigüito (*Venezuela*); spur-wing (*Trinidad*); lily-trotter (*Texas*).

Description: About the size of a sora rail, but its long legs, big feet, and lively movements make it seem larger. Bill and frontal shield yellow, wattles reddish. Head, neck, upper back, and breast glossy black. Rest of plumage rusty or deep chestnut. Extensive greenish-yellow wing patches. Yellow spur at bend of wing. Legs and feet greenish, toes excessively long and slender. Immatures are grayish-brown above, whitish below, breast sometimes buffy. Broad whitish stripe over eye. Shield reduced. Immature "slightly suggests Wilson's Phalarope" (Peterson, 1960).

Range: The jacana is a resident species from western and northeastern Mexico (Sinaloa and Tamaulipas) south through Central America to western Panama and the Greater Antilles. Also (if considered as the same species) from Colombia through Venezuela, Trinidad, and the Guianas to eastern Bolivia and Argentina. Very local on the Yucatán Peninsula, where Paynter reported nesting at Laguna Chacanbacab, Quintana Roo. Accidental or casual in Texas (breeding records), Puerto Rico (one record, Río Trujillo about 1880), and Lake Okeechobee, Florida (at least one record, 1899 or 1900).

In the West Indies, breeds in Cuba, the Isle of Pines, Jamaica, and Hispaniola. In Jamaica they are widely distributed in suitable fresh-water habitats (May Jeffrey-Smith found them at Bideford Estate near Jackson, Ferry River, Graham's Pen near Spanish Town, Rio Cobre Dam and Irrigation Canal, Long's Wharf near Old Harbour, and inland ponds in Trelawny and St. Ann). I saw jacanas in small ponds near Hampden, Trelawny Parish. In Venezuela I found them abundant on Lago de Valencia, Aragua. They occur in marshes and rice fields on Trinidad including Laventille Swamp near Port of Spain (Junge and Mees) and Usine Ste. Madeleine, Palmiste, and Oropuche Lagoon (Williams). Not found on Tobago. They are numerous in Surinam.

The birds pictured represent two forms of the wattled jacana, now considered by most authorities as a separate species known as *jacana jacana*. It is found throughout South America and in most of Panama.

PLATE 28
BLACK-NECKED STILT (*Himantopus mexicanus*)

Other names: Zancudo, cachiporra, arcagüete, viuda, echasse, pigeon d'étang, red-shank, soldier, crack-pot soldier, telltale (*West Indies*); yegüita, playante (*Puerto Rico, Virgin Islands*); pink, stilt (*Jamaica*); viuda (*Venezuela*); snepi hudiu, snepi di sabana, caweta di patu, macamba, steltkluut (*Netherlands Antilles*). "Echasse de Mexique" of Brisson (1760).

Description: A noisy, very trim, and handsome

shore bird with incredibly long, thin, pink or red legs. Glossy black above and immaculate white below. Bill long, black, and curved very slightly upward at tip. Voice a sharp *ip-ip-ip*.

Range: Stilts of this species breed from southern Oregon and Utah (Bear River Marshes) south through New Mexico to the Gulf Coast and on south through Central and South America to Ecuador (including the Galápagos Islands) and Peru. Has bred casually in southern Saskatchewan. Also, on the Atlantic slope from South Carolina and Florida south through the Bahamas (Andros, Green Cay, New Providence, Watling, Acklins, Mayaguana, Great Inagua), the Greater Antilles, Virgin Islands, and the northern Lesser Antilles (Anguilla, St. Kitts, Barbuda, Antigua, Monserrat) and in South America (Colombia, Venezuela, the Guianas, and northern Brazil).

In winter the stilt ranges from the San Francisco Bay region of California and the Gulf of Mexico and Mississippi Delta south to Bolivia and Brazil.

This species has been found in the late Pleistocene of Oregon.

PLATE 29
LAUGHING GULL (*Larus atricilla*)

Other names: Gallego común, galleguito, gaviota gallega, gaviota cabecinegra, gaviota boba, mauve à tête noire, goéland, pigeon de la mer, gullie, sea gull, laughing bird (*West Indies*); gaviota (*Mexico*); gaviota forastera, gallego (*Puerto Rico, Virgin Islands*); guanaguanare (*Venezuela*); meuchi (*Netherlands Antilles*).

Description: Bond (1960) points out that this is the only gull apt to be seen in the West Indies. There are three plumages: summer adult, winter adult, and immature. The summer adult is dark gray on the head and throat, the neck, under parts, and tail white, the back and wings dark bluish-gray. Wing-tips black. In flight, the wings have a white border along after edge. Bill and eyelids red, legs reddish-brown. The winter adult has the head white, mottled with grayish-brown. Bill and legs dusky. The immature bird is dark brown with a white rump and black band at tip of tail.

Range: Breeds from the Bird Islands off Nova Scotia south locally along the Atlantic Coast to Florida Bay, the Bahamas, Greater and Lesser Antilles, and around the Gulf Coast to Texas, islands off the Gulf coast of Mexico (Cayo Arcas, Alacrán Reefs, and perhaps others), and the Venezuelan islands (Los Roques, La Orchila, Las Aves, and Isla de Aves). Also in Salton Sea, California, and the Mexican coasts of Sonora and Sinaloa.

In winter from Mexico to the coasts of Ecuador and Peru (Point Pariñas), and from the Gulf of Mexico and North Carolina (Core Sound) south through the West Indies and Caribbean to Colombia, Venezuela, the Guianas, and the Amazon Delta. Accidental in Greenland.

Voous (1955) says that in the Netherlands Antilles they are rare in winter, becoming more abundant by March and April. He suspects breeding on Klein Curaçao and at the Lac on Bonaire. The island of St. Martin is the only place where it is generally observed in the Windward Group. Present in winter around the harbor of Port of Spain, Trinidad. Recorded in every month of the year in Surinam.

PLATE 30
SOOTY TERN (*Sterna fuscata*)

Other names: Gaviota oscura, gaviota monja, oiseau fou, thoiron, egg bird, booby, bubí, hurricane bird (*West Indies*); gaviota (*Mexico*); mauve à manteau noir (*Guadeloupe*); de veras (*Venezuela*); wide-awake. "L'hirondelle-de-mer brune" of Brisson (1760).

Description: The only tern that is black above and white below. Crown black, forehead white. Long wings and tail deeply forked. Bill and legs black. The immature birds are sooty brownish-black, flecked with white on back and wings. The bridled tern (*Sterna anaethetus*) is similar, but is brownish-gray on the back, wings, and tail, rather than black. Also, a white area on the hind neck.

Range: Distribution is pan-tropical, world-wide across all tropical and subtropical seas and oceans. In the Pacific it breeds from the Ryukyu Islands south of Japan across the span of the ocean to the Revilla Gigedo and Tres Marías groups off Mexico, south to New South Wales, Australia, and east to the Galápagos and San Felix off Chile. In the Gulf of Mexico and the Atlantic it breeds locally from the Alacrán Reefs off Yucatán, the Dry Tortugas off Florida (formerly in Texas and Louisiana), through the Bahamas and West Indies and into the South Atlantic on Fernando de Noronha, Ascen-

sion, Martin Vas, and St. Helena. In the Indian Ocean it breeds from the Mascarene, Seychelles, Laccadive, Maldive, and Andaman islands to western Australia.

The sooty tern breeds off Yucatán on Isla Pérez, one of the Alacrán group (Paynter). On Bush Key in the Dry Tortugas there is a notable colony. In the West Indies colonies are known on islands and cayos off Cuba (Cayo Mono Grande, Cayo de las Piedras), Jamaica (Pedro and Morant Cays), Mona Island off Puerto Rico, the Virgin Islands (Tortola?), Guadeloupe (Le Souffloeur), and the Grenadines. Off Venezuela they nest "*en grandes bandadas*" (Phelps and Phelps, 1958) in the Los Hermanos group (Morro Fondeadero, La Horquilla), La Orchila, and Isla de Aves. Also, on Roatán Island, Honduras.

These birds range far and wide in the non-breeding season, and are carried far off their normal routes by hurricanes. They have been reported from Nova Scotia, Bermuda, and at many inland points in the U.S. (including Gatlinburg and Knoxville, Tenn., and Oswego, N.Y.).

PLATE 31
ROYAL TERN (*Thalasseus maximus*)

Other names: Gaviota real, pigeon de la mer, oiseau fou, mauve, sprat bird, gullie, gaby, egg bird (*West Indies*); gaviota (*Mexico*); chirre, gaviota regia (*Puerto Rico, Virgin Islands*); gaviota real (*Venezuela*); bubi chiquitu (*Netherlands Antilles*).

Description: This is the largest commonly observed tern of the West Indies, especially in winter. Black on crown with varied amount of white on forehead, which is often speckled with black. Bushy crest at back of head. Bill orange-red or pale orange. Back and wings very pale bluish-gray. Lower head, neck, breast, and under parts white. Tail deeply forked.

The similar Caspian tern (*Hydroprogne caspia*) is a larger and heavier bird, tail less deeply forked, bill noticeably heavier and deep red. The Cayenne tern (*Sterna eurygnatha*), which occurs in the southern Caribbean, is smaller than the royal, with a rather long, straw-yellow bill. Voous (1955) says that it also has relatively longer wings and a more deeply forked tail.

Range: Breeds from Chincoteague Bay, Md., south to Georgia and irregularly to Florida (Shell Island), and along the Gulf of Mexico in Louisiana and Texas and on Cayo Arcas and the Alacrán Reef off Yucatán. Breeds locally in the West Indies, on the Venezuelan islands, and on the west coast of Africa from Gibraltar to Angola. Also, on the Pacific side from Lower California to the Tres Marías Islands off Nayarit, Mexico.

It nests on Mona Island off Puerto Rico. May nest on small islands off Guadeloupe and in similar locations elsewhere. A few pairs have bred on Bonaire and Curaçao in colonies of Cayenne terns (Hummelinck). On the Venezuelan islands, Phelps and Phelps (1958) have found it breeding on Las Aves and Los Roques. Bond (1950) says that it breeds on many islands and cays in the West Indies, but definite records appear to be scarce.

In winter, south to Peru (Payta), Uruguay, and central Argentina. Individuals banded in South Carolina have been recovered in the Dominican Republic (Wetmore and Lincoln).

PLATE 32
BLACK SKIMMER (*Rynchops nigra*)

Other names: Pico de tijera (*Cuba, Venezuela*); shearwater, scissorbill, seadog, storm gull. "Cutwater" of Catesby (1771). The present name was bestowed by Pennant in 1773, who wrote: "I call it *Skimmer* from the manner of its collecting its food with the lower mandible as it flies along the surface of the water."

Description: No other bird has a bill like this—long, bladelike, flat vertically, red at base and black at tip, the lower mandible longer than the upper. Plumage black above and white below. Wings very long, legs very short. Voice a "sharp *yap*, *yap*, like a pack of hounds on the trail" (Chapman, 1926).

Range: Breeds locally from Massachusetts southward along the Atlantic and Gulf coasts, possibly to Yucatán, and in South America to central Argentina. On the Pacific side it breeds from northwestern Mexico (Sonora, Sinaloa, and Nayarit) south to the Straits of Magellan. Does not breed in the West Indies, but has been recorded in winter in the Bahamas (Bimini, New Providence, Great Inagua), Cuba, the Virgin Islands (between St. Thomas and St. Croix), off the northern coast of Hispaniola, Guadeloupe, and Grenada.

In Mexico it occurs on both coasts. On the Yucatán Peninsula it has been observed on Isla Holbox, at Celestún, and on Isla Cozumel. It is locally distributed in Venezuela, both along the coast and inland on lakes and rivers. In Trinidad it has been seen on one of the open lakes in Caroni Swamp (Junge and Mees). It is quite numerous in Surinam, chiefly along the coast and in the mouths of the big rivers. It is less numerous upstream (Haverschmidt). It breeds on sandbars and mudflats along the larger rivers in northern and eastern South America.

PLATE 33
WHITE-TIPPED DOVE (*Leptotila verreauxi*)

Other names: White-fronted dove (*Texas*); tsutsuy (*Yucatán*); paloma turca (*Venezuela*); ala duru, buladeifi di hoffi, rukuku (*Aruba, Curaçao*); patrushi (*Bonaire*).

Description: A large, terrestrial dove, dark above, white below, with a rounded, white-tipped tail. White forehead. No black-and-white pattern on wings, which show reddish (cinnamon) underneath in flight. Voice owl-like, a very low, soft *cowhoooooooo*.

Range: From northwest Mexico (Sonora) and the lower Rio Grande Valley of Texas south through Central and South America as far as southern Brazil, Uruguay, and northern Argentina. Also resident on the Leeward Group of the Netherlands Antilles (Aruba, Curaçao, and Bonaire), on Islas de Patos, Los Testigos, and Margarita off Venezuela and on both Trinidad and Tobago. Common in suitable habitats in Surinam.

Not recorded from Baja California (Blake).

PLATE 34
BLUE-HEADED QUAIL-DOVE (*Starnoenas cyanocephala*)

Other names: Perdiz, paloma perdiz (*Cuba*).

Description: A large, brown quail-dove, found only in Cuba. Bright blue crown, black line through eye, white line under eye. Throat glossy black with a narrow white "bib" along bottom edge. Purplish-brown above, rufous brown underneath, the breast tinged with purple. Wings and tail brown. No rufous on wings. Bill and feet deep red. "Unlike any other Cuban dove" (Bond, 1960).

Range: Cuba. Charles Dornay Cory in 1889 reported it common in parts of the interior. Rutten saw one bird of this species, in the Sierra de Cubitas,

Camagüey. Now extremely rare. Of doubtful occurrence on the Isle of Pines. Albrecht (1862) reported it from Jamaica, but this has never been confirmed, nor has the species been seen there since.

PLATE 35
SCARLET MACAW (*Ara macao*)

Other name: Guacamayo bandera (*Venezuela*).

Description: A very large red, blue, and yellow macaw. Head and neck scarlet or vermilion. Wing coverts rich chrome yellow. Flight feathers deep blue. Lower back, rump, and tail coverts azure blue. Tail scarlet and extremely long. The cheeks are bare and pale pinkish-white.

Range: Found in tropical Middle America (except British Honduras) and South America, to Bolivia and Brazil. In Mexico, the humid forests of southern Tamaulipas, Veracruz, Tobasco, Campeche, Oaxaca, and Chiapas (Blake). Traylor saw this species a number of times at Pacaytun (Río Candelaria), southern Campeche. Paynter failed to find it along the Río Hondo, which flows between Quintana Roo and British Honduras. Phelps and Phelps (1958) mention a number of localities in Venezuela where it has been recorded and state that it inhabits forest clearings and savannas. In Surinam it is a bird of the hill forests of the interior, less numerous near the coast (Haverschmidt).

PLATE 36
BLUE-AND-YELLOW MACAW (*Ara ararauna*)

Other name: Guacamayo azul y amarillo (*Venezuela*).

Description: Large. Massive bill. Extremely long, wedge-shaped tail. Horizontal black lines beneath eye. White lower cheek patch of naked skin, rimmed with black feathers. Black on throat. Blue on back of head, back, and wings. Crown yellow. Under parts yellow and orange-yellow. Undersides of wings yellowish.

Range: From eastern Panama to Ecuador, eastern Peru, Bolivia, northern Paraguay, and locally through Venezuela and the Guianas to Brazil. In Venezuela, Phelps and Phelps (1958) report this species is very local in its distribution, having been recorded north of the Orinoco in Monagas (Caicara, Guanipa, La Ceiba on the Río Guara-

piche), and south of the Orinoco in the Territory of Delta Amacuro (Isla Corosima, Río Toro, Piacoa). Also, farther south in Amazonas Territory (Cerro Yapacana and east of the Siapa and Padauiri rivers on the Brazilian frontier). In Surinam, Haverschmidt reports sight records at an unnamed location in Nickerie and along the Wayombo, Coppename, Saramacca, and Cottica rivers. Also a specimen from Coronie. The blue-and-yellow macaw occurs on the island of Trinidad, but is absent from Tobago. According to Ray Johnson, both this species and the scarlet macaw (*Ara macao*) can be observed around Nariva Swamp, inland from the middle east coast of Trinidad and south of Upper Manzanilla. I have seen *Ara ararauna* at Brigand Hill, at the north end of Nariva.

PLATE 37
ST. VINCENT PARROT (*Amazona guildingii*)

Other name: Parrot (*St. Vincent*).

Description: One of the larger Amazonas. Beautifully plumaged. Head white, yellow, and violet. Neck predominantly green. Back, rump, upper tail coverts, and wing coverts golden brown. Under parts brown washed with green. Wings variegated with green, violet-blue, brown, and yellow. Tail green and violet-blue, with broad yellow tip. Young entirely green. "The only parrot on St. Vincent" (Bond, 1960).

Range: St. Vincent in the Lesser Antilles. "Rather rare but found throughout the mountainous districts" (Bond, 1950).

PLATE 38
CARIBBEAN PARAKEET (*Aratinga pertinax*)

Other names: Parakeet (*St. Thomas*); prikichi, parkiet, West-Indische parkiet (*Aruba*, *Curaçao*, *Bonaire*); brown-throated parakeet, veragua parakeet (*Panama*); perico cara sucia (*Venezuela*).

Description: Smaller than the Amazona parrots, tail long and pointed as in typical parakeets, flight very rapid and voice a loud screech. Bright green upper parts, under parts greenish-yellow. Some of flight feathers blue. Head and throat generally yellow or orange-buff (except in Panama), dull brownish-orange on upper breast, but there is considerable variation, both individual and geographical, chiefly in the color and pattern of the head. There are two geographic forms in Colombia and Venezuela and one each on Isla La Tortuga, Margarita, and Los Frailes, in the Guianas and on Aruba, Curaçao, and Bonaire. For details and discussion see Hummelinck, (1957), and Phelps and Phelps (1958).

Range: This parakeet is resident on islands in the southern Caribbean (*see above*), and on the mainland in Panama (Pacific slope), Colombia, Venezuela, and the Guianas. It has been introduced on St. Thomas (apparently from Curaçao) where Bond (1960) says it is most numerous in the eastern part.

PLATE 39
SMOOTH-BILLED ANI (*Crotophaga ani*)

Other names: Tick-bird, black daw, long-tailed crow, old Arnold, Chapman bird, corbeau, Juif bilbitin (*West Indies*); Judío, garrapatero, black witch (*Puerto Rico*); bouts-tabac (*Haiti*); black parrot, savanna blackbird, merle corbeau (*Jamaica*); old witch (*Trinidad*); garrapatero, judío (*Venezuela*); tickbird, Cuban parrot (*Florida*). "Great black-bird" of Sloane (1705–25). In Mexico the groove-billed ani (*Crotophaga sulcirostris*) is known as garrapatero or chick-bul, and in the Leeward Group of the Netherlands Antilles as chuchubi pretu or chuchubi hudiu. In Venezuela this same species is called curtidor, and the greater ani (*Crotophaga major*) is called garrapatero grande.

Description: Looks like a blackbird or grackle except for parrot-like, high-ridged bill. Plumage black with iridescent gloss. Tail loose-jointed and often held at strange angle. Flaps and glides in an uncertain manner of flight. Voice shrill and querulous.

Range: (*Smooth-billed ani*). This species ranges from South Florida (rare and local) and the Bahamas through the Greater Antilles to South America (Colombia, Venezuela, the Guianas to southern Brazil and northern Argentina). In the Lesser Antilles it occurs only from Guadeloupe south to Grenada, but is absent on Barbados and only recently on Martinique. Present on many of the western Caribbean islands and locally on the Pacific side of Central America from southwest Costa Rica to Panama (including the Pearl Islands) and Ecuador. One record (1891) from Isla Holbox, several from Cozumel (where it presumably meets *C. sulcirostris*). Off Venezuela, recorded on Islas de Patos and Margarita.

(*Groove-billed ani*). This smaller species ranges from Baja California, southern Sonora (Mexico), and the lower Rio Grande Valley of Texas south through Central America to Peru and British Guiana. Resident on Aruba, Curaçao, Bonaire, Trinidad, and Tobago, but not recorded on the Venezuelan islands.

(*Greater ani*). This species, larger and glossier than the other two, ranges from central Panama east of the Andes to northern Argentina. Not found on islands in the southern Caribbean or on Tobago, but present on Trinidad (Caroni Swamp, Tacarigua River).

PLATE 40
BARN OWL (*Tyto alba*)

Other names: Night owl, death owl, death bird, jumbie bird, lechuza (*West Indies*); frezaie (*Haiti*); chat-huant (*Lesser Antilles*); screech owl, white owl (*Jamaica*); lechuza de campanario, rajatrapo, quiebrahueso (*Venezuela*); palabrúa, kerkuil (*Curaçao, Bonaire*); monkey-faced owl, white owl (*U.S.*).

Description: A fairly big owl with large head and long legs, heart-shaped face, and no ear tufts. Plumage very pale to nearly white. Upper parts variegated with buff, rusty or grayish, under parts nearly pure white with sprinkling of dark spots to buffy with pronounced dark spots. Appears all-white at night ("ghostly," says Peterson). When perched the long legs are "knock-kneed." There is considerable variation in the plumage among the different geographic races (*see* Bond, 1960).

Range: The barn owl is virtually cosmopolitan, ranging from Great Britain, the Baltic, and southern Russia south through Africa and east through Palestine, Iraq, Arabia, India, Burma, Indochina, Java, and New Guinea to Australia. Found on the Society Islands and elsewhere in the Pacific (Mayr notes that there are 4 or 5 races in the Southwest Pacific). In the Western Hemisphere it is a breeding bird from British Columbia across the continent to southern Ontario and New England, south through the West Indies, Central America, and South America to Tierra del Fuego.

The barn owl has been discovered in the Pleistocene of California, Nuevo León (Mexico), and Florida.

In the West Indies, according to Bond (1960), the barn owl is represented by five races resident in

(1) Cuba, Isle of Pines, Jamaica, Grand Cayman, Cayman Brac; (2) Grand Bahama, Abaco, Andros, New Providence, Inagua; (3) Hispaniola, Tortue (?), Navassa (?); (4) St. Vincent, Bequia, Union, Carriacou, Grenada; (5) Dominica.

PLATE 41
FERRUGINOUS PYGMY-OWL (Glaucidium brasilianum)

Other names: Ferruginous owl, streaked pygmy-owl (*U.S.*); vieja, toj-caj-xnuk (*Yucatán*); little owl, jumbie or jumby bird, jumby (*Trinidad*); pavita, monjita, morocoto (*Venezuela*). The only owl of this genus in the West Indies is the Cuban pygmy-owl (*Glaucidium siju*), known locally as sijú, sijucito, and sijú platanero. It occurs in Cuba and on the Isle of Pines.

Description: Very small (*see* color plate). Not much larger than a sparrow. Small head with fine pale streaks on top and no ear tufts. Rusty brown above, white or buffy white below with bold reddish-brown streaks on breast, sides, and flanks. An irregular black-and-white band on hind neck ("suggests eyes on back of head," Peterson, 1960). Rather long tail with three or four white or reddish bars. Flipping motion of tail is characteristic. Junge and Mees mention a rufous or chestnut phase and a dark sepia-brown phase on Trinidad.

Range: This miniature owl is resident from south-central Arizona (Phoenix and Tucson west to Agua Caliente), Sonora, and the lower Rio Grande Valley (where it is rare) south in the lowlands and locally on the central plateau (below 4000 feet) to central America and South America to the Straits of Magellan. Not found on Baja California. Phelps and Phelps (1958) list five races of this species that range from northeastern Colombia through Venezuela (including Isla de Margarita), Ecuador, Peru, and Bolivia. Not present on Aruba, Curaçao, or Bonaire, and not recorded by Haverschmidt in Surinam. Resident in Trinidad, but not in Tobago.

Other species of pygmy-owls occur in Canada south to California, Arizona, New Mexico, Mexico, Guatemala, Costa Rica, and Panama.

PLATE 42
SPECTACLED OWL (Pulsatrix perspicillata)

Other names: El buho (*Panama*); titiriji (*Venezuela*); black-breasted owl, collared owl (*Trinidad*).

Description: A large black, white, and buffy owl without ear tufts. Upper parts uniform dark sooty brown, nearly black. Wide chest band of same color. White band above and between eyes. Throat buffy white, under parts pale tawny buff. Black "spectacles" around eyes, contrasting markedly with the white brows and forehead.

Range: Ranges from the lowland forests of Veracruz, Oaxaca, and Chiapas in Mexico south through Central America to Peru and from eastern Colombia, Venezuela, and the Guianas to Brazil. Resident in Trinidad but not in Tobago. Phelps and Phelps (1958) say that it is locally distributed in Venezuela, most abundant in the vicinity of the Orinoco. In Surinam it has been recorded at Java Weg, Paramaribo, Republiek, and along the Surinam River (Haverschmidt).

PLATE 43
BURROWING OWL (Speotyto cunicularia)

Other names: Ground owl, howdy owl (*Florida*); cuckoo bird (*Bahamas*); cucú, coucou, coucouterre (*West Indies*); chogó (*Aruba*); mochuelo de hoyo (*Venezuela*).

Description: A small, brown, terrestrial owl with long legs and no ear tufts. Bobs up and down and bows (hence "howdy owl") when excited. Upper parts brown, heavily spotted with white. Under parts barred horizontally with gray-brown and white. Tail quite short. Usually active in the daytime (diurnal).

Range: Widely distributed, ranging from southwest Canada (southern British Columbia) south to Tierra del Fuego. It breeds locally throughout its range, in Florida on prairies of central and southern parts of state from Osceola County south to Miami International Airport (*see text*). In the West Indies it occurs in the Bahamas (Grand Bahama, Abaco, Andros, New Providence, Eleuthera, Cat Island, Samana Cay, Cay Sal, Great Inagua, subfossil bone from Exuma), Cuba (accidental), and Hispaniola, including Gonave and Beata islands. Formerly also on Antigua, Nevis, St. Kitts, and Marie Galante (exterminated by mongoose in the late nineteenth century). In Mexico this owl occurs wherever there are plains and barren open country (Blake). Rare and probably only an irregular visitor in Yucatán (Paynter). In Central America it is of local distribution and not reported from British Honduras or Nicaragua (Eisenmann, 1955). It is found in the savanna regions of Venezuela and at Río Branco, Bôa Vista, Brazil. On the southern Caribbean islands it has been recorded from Aruba and Islas de Margarita and La Borracha (Anzoátegui).

PLATE 44
GUÁCHARO (*Steatornis caripensis*)

Other names: Diablotin (*Trinidad*); oil bird. Guácharo, the name used in Venezuela and elsewhere in South America, is said to be an obsolete Spanish word signifying one that cries or laments loudly.

Description: Resembles a very large nightjar (whip-poor-will), but belongs in a family of its own (*Steatornithidae*). Upper parts chestnut and gray, barred and streaked with dark brown or black, and with white spots on the wings. Under parts pale chestnut with small white spots. Bill strong and sharply hooked. Wingspread over three feet.

Range: The guácharo or oil bird is very local in its distribution and restricted to Colombia, Venezuela, British Guiana, Ecuador, Peru, and the island of Trinidad. Phelps and Phelps (1958) say that in Venezuela it is locally distributed in caves of the mountainous regions. There are records from Zulia, in Perijá (Ayapa); Falcón (Cocoy Cave); Mérida (Capaz, Carbonera, Páramo de la Culata, Pregonero); Cojedes (Las Murracas, La Sierra); Aragua (Rancho Grande); Miranda (El Encantado, Petare); Monagas (Cerro Negro, Caripe, El Guácharo), and Bolívar (the Hills of Roraima and Tabarerupá, Río Paragua, and near Salto Guaiquinima).

PLATE 45
RUFOUS NIGHTJAR (*Caprimulgus rufus*)

Other names: Cent-coups-de-couteau, Jacques-pas-papa-vous (*St. Lucia*); aguaitacamino rufo (*Venezuela*).

Description: Larger than the whip-poor-will or nighthawk. Resembles the chuck-will's-widow (*Caprimulgus carolinensis*), but is darker and more rufescent (Bond, 1960). Plumage mouse gray to ochraceous buff, finely vermiculated with cinnamon buff and mottled with black. Wings spotted with cinnamon buff. Tail tawny, barred and streaked with black except that the male has im-

maculate patches on outer tailfeathers, white above and tawny below. Throat mainly cinnamon, bordered by transverse white band. Female lacks clear white or tawny patches on tail. The color plate shows a dark-phase bird.

Range: This southern representative of the chuck-will's-widow is found in Costa Rica, Panama, Colombia, and Venezuela. Also in the Lesser Antilles (St. Lucia). Phelps and Phelps (1958) state that it is locally distributed in the forested mountain regions of northern Venezuela and very locally in Amazonas Territory and Bolívar.

PLATE 46
PAURAQUE (*Nyctidromus albicollis*)

Other names: Parauque (*Mexico, Panama*); tapa-camino, pujuy (*Yucatán*); aguaitacamino, aguait-camino común (*Venezuela*); road nighthawk (*Trinidad*).

Description: Grayish-brown and buff above, buff below, narrowly barred with sooty. Cheeks pale chestnut, throat dusky brown, bordered by a conspicuous white crescent. Scapulars mainly black. Broad white band across the flight feathers (buff in female). Tail long, slightly notched at tip, and with white on some of the outer feathers. Some individuals tend to be predominantly gray, others brown, often quite dark.

Range: From south Texas (lower Rio Grande Valley north to Beeville and Rockport) and western Mexico (Sinaloa) south through Central America to eastern Peru, Bolivia, Paraguay, northeastern Argentina (Entre Ríos), and southern Brazil (Rio Grande do Sul). Also, on Tres Marías Islands on the Pacific side and the islands of Mujeres, Holbox, and Cozumel off the Yucatán Peninsula. Absent from Baja California and Sonora. Generally distributed throughout Venezuela and in Trinidad (but not Tobago). Perhaps the commonest "nighthawk" in the coastal region of Surinam (Haverschmidt).

PLATE 47
BLACK-THROATED MANGO (*Anthracothorax nigricollis*)

Other name: Chupa flor pechinegro (*Venezuela*).

Description: The male has iridescent green upper parts and is extensively black underneath, except bright turquoise blue under eye and along neck and border of throat and upper breast. Under tail coverts turquoise blue. Tail coppery with purplish reflections and pale blue tips. Female has iridescent green upper parts, white underneath with vertical black streak down center of throat and breast, wider on breast.

Range: From eastern Panama to Colombia, Venezuela, Trinidad, Tobago, and the Guianas south to Peru, eastern Bolivia, Paraguay, eastern Argentina, and southern Brazil. In Venezuela it is widely distributed throughout the country except southern portion of Amazonas Territory. It occurs in the Tropical Zone and in the lower Subtropical Zone up to about 5000 feet (Phelps and Phelps, 1958). In Surinam it is known from all districts, being quite common in the coastal areas and the savanna belt. One of the most numerous hummingbirds (Haverschmidt).

PLATE 48
RUBY-TOPAZ HUMMINGBIRD (*Chrysolampis mosquitus*)

Other names: Colibrí rubí (*Venezuela*); blenchi tornasol, tornasol (male), blenchi, blenchi hudiu (female) (*Aruba, Curaçao, Bonaire*).

Description: The male has upper parts dark metallic greenish-brown, crown orange-red or glistening dark purplish-red. In favorable lights a fiery red gorget on throat and upper breast, but can appear wholly black as light changes. Tail coppery with dark tips. Female is pale greenish-brown on upper parts, whitish underneath, but may have some orange-red patches on head and throat. "Usually do not have such a conspicuous white eye-line as female Emerald Hummers" (Voous, 1955).

Range: This striking hummer ranges widely through northern and eastern South America from Colombia through Venezuela and the Guianas to Brazil. Occurs on both Trinidad and Tobago. In Venezuela it is generally distributed except in Delta Amacuro Territory and in Amazonas Territory found only in the north in Sanariapo, Cerro Yaví, and San Juan de Manapiare. Occurs also on the Caribbean islands of Los Testigos, Los Frailes, Margarita, Coche, Los Hermanos, Blanquilla, La Tortuga, Tortuguilla de Sotavento, La Orchila, and Cayo Sal. Resident also on Aruba, Curaçao, and Bonaire (Phelps and Phelps, 1958). In Surinam it is common in both the coastal areas and the savanna belt (Haverschmidt).

PLATE 49
TUFTED COQUETTE (*Lophornis ornata*)

Other names: Coqueta de abanico (*Venezuela*); coquette, whiskerando, huppe-col, king or queen (*Trinidad*).

Description: One of the smallest hummingbirds. The male has a conspicuous erectile crest, chestnut brown in color. Elongated feathers stand out from sides of neck, pale cinnamon with glittering dark-green spots. Upper parts mainly light iridescent green. Pale buffy band across rump. Forehead and throat glittering green. Under parts grayish-green. Tail cinnamon edged with green. Female lacks crest and elongated feathers on neck. Throat cinnamon. Bill brownish-red with black tip. Legs and feet black. Iris dark brown.

Range: Restricted to northeast Venezuela, the Guianas, and Trinidad. Not recorded on Tobago. In Venezuela it is very local in distribution, being confined to the extreme northeast part of the country in Sucre (San Rafael, Mirasol, Cerro Azul) and south of the Orinoco in Bolívar (Cerros Roraima, Tonoro and Auyan-tepui, Caño Pácara, Suapure, Santa Rosalía, and Caicara). Vertically it moves out of the Tropical Zone and is occasionally found in the lower Subtropical Zone (Phelps and Phelps, 1958). In Surinam it is not uncommon in the coastal areas and savanna belt (Paramaribo, Surinam River, Albina) (Haverschmidt). On Trinidad it has been recorded at Tacarigua, Providence Estate, El Cerro del Aripo (Junge and Mees).

PLATE 50
CUBAN EMERALD (*Chlorostilbon ricordii*)

Other names: Zunzún, zumbador, picaflor, colibrí (*Cuba*); hummingbird, god bird (*Bahamas*); Ricord's hummer, Ricord's emerald hummingbird.

Description: Male mainly brilliant green with white under tail coverts. From a distance appears black. Tail black and conspicuously forked. Lower mandible pinkish. Female has upper parts bronze green, under parts grayish with green along sides. Throat pale gray or whitish. Tail dusky violet. "Can be told from female Ruby-throat by pink on bill and deeply forked tail. (Female Ruby-throat has *rounded* tail showing *white spots*)" (Peterson, 1947).

Range: Throughout Cuba and the Isle of Pines, including coastal islands and cays, and in the northern Bahamas (Grand Bahama, Abaco, Andros). "Apparently accidental on New Providence; may also occur on the Caicos Islands (sight record on East Caicos—Bartsch)" (Bond, 1950). There have been sight records of this species at Coconut Grove, Florida (1943) and south of Coco, Florida (1953) (Sprunt).

PLATE 51
STREAMER-TAIL (*Trochilus polytmus*)

Other names: Streamer-tailed hummingbird; doctor-bird; long-tail; long-tail doctor-bird; scissors-tail.

Description: The adult male is a vivid, iridescent green, with top of head and crest black. The flight feathers and two greatly elongated tailfeathers are black. Bill red, except that streamer-tails in eastern Jamaica have a black bill. The female is a less vivid green above, brownish on the head and white underneath, from the throat to the under tail coverts. The tail of the female is of normal length, without elongated tailfeathers, and black with the outer tips white. In various lights the male appears to be a metallic bronze green or emerald, and the wings and under tail coverts show a dusky violet or blue-black. Young males are less brilliant and lack the long tailfeathers.

Range: Occurs only in Jamaica, where it is extremely common. The red-billed form is found abundantly throughout the island, but does not occur in the extreme northeastern and eastern parts, where it is replaced by the black-billed streamer-tail (*Trochilus polytmus scitulus*). According to Bond (1950), the red-billed is found as far east as Blue Mountain Peak (7402 feet), and along the south coast to extreme western St. Thomas Parish. Bond also mentions Port Antonio, Preistman's River, Cuna Cuna Pass, and Bath as within the range of the black-billed variety. Although the red-billed may be observed from semi-arid lowlands to the highest mountains, the black-billed seems to be more confined to humid areas of heavy rainfall, mainly on the northern slopes, according to Bond.

PLATE 52
COPPER-RUMPED HUMMINGBIRD (*Amazilia tobaci*)

Other names: Amazilia (*Venezuela*); common emerald (*Trinidad*).

Description: Upper parts dark coppery or bronze green. Head and breast emerald. Under parts glittering green. Tail bluish to dark bluish-purple. Under tail coverts reddish-brown. Rump coppery bronze. Bill black, pink on lower mandible except tip. Legs and feet black. Breast feathers appear emerald or brown, depending on light.

Range: Venezuela, Trinidad, and Tobago. In Venezuela it is widely distributed in the mountainous regions and the Llanos of the northern part of the country, as well as south of the Orinoco in Bolívar and northern Amazonas Territory. Also Margarita Island.

PLATE 53
GLITTERING-THROATED EMERALD (*Amazilia fimbriata*)

Other name: Tucusito (*Venezuela*).

Description: Upper parts purplish-brown, throat glittering green. Under parts white, including under tail coverts, but purplish-brown on sides and flanks. Tail bluish-purple. Bill reddish at base, black-tipped.

Range: Eastern Colombia, Venezuela, the Guianas, and northern Brazil. In Venezuela it is found in the western Llanos of Apure, Táchira, Barinas, Portuguesa, Cojedes, and Guárico, and south of the Orinoco in southeast Bolívar (Phelps and Phelps, 1958). In Surinam it is known from all districts and is the most numerous hummingbird of the coastal area (Haverschmidt).

PLATE 54
BELTED KINGFISHER (*Ceryle alcyon*)

Other names: Martin pescador, martin zambullidor, pitirre de agua, pitirre de río, pitirre de mangle (i.e. mangrove), pájaro del rey, martin-pêcheur, pie (*West Indies*); matraca, fraile miguelete (*Puerto Rico, Virgin Islands*); martín pescador (*Yucatán*); pescador (*Mexico*); martín pescador migratorio (*Venezuela*); bandijivogel, kingfisher (*Netherlands Antilles*). Many of these local names are also applied to the ringed kingfisher (*Ceryle torquata*).

Description: Big-headed and large-billed, with a bushy crest. Blue-gray above, white below, the male with a gray band across the breast, the female with an additional, narrower rufous band across the belly. Adept at hovering, helicopter style. Voice a loud, high-pitched rattle.

Range: Widely distributed, breeding from north-western Alaska across the continent to central Labrador, south to the Gulf Coast and Florida. In winter, south to Mexico, Central America, the West Indies, and Caribbean to Curaçao, Bonaire, and Trinidad. Also Bermuda. Recorded at Store Bay, Tobago (Junge and Mees). In Venezuela this species is seen occasionally on the offshore islands and coast, including the islands of Los Testigos, Margarita, La Tortuga, La Blanquilla, and Los Roques. Also, the coasts of Colombia (Santa Marta) and British Guiana (Phelps and Phelps, 1958).

Stragglers have been recorded in Greenland, Iceland, England, the Netherlands, and the Azores.

PLATE 55
BLUE-CROWNED MOTMOT (*Momotus momota*)

Other names: Guardabarranca (*Mexico*); jut jut (*Yucatán*); arriero, pájaro león (*Venezuela*); king of the woods, gray king of the woods (*Trinidad*); houton (*South American Indian*); blue-diademed motmot (Skutch, 1954).

Description: Chiefly olive green above and chestnut or rufous below, but there is variation in birds of this species from different geographic regions. In Trinidad the above description holds good, but this same species in Mexico is "essentially greenish olive" above and below, the upper back and under-parts sometimes strongly tinged with rufous (Blake). The colors on the crown likewise vary. Trinidad birds have a black crown with the forehead cobalt blue, an ultramarine band behind the crown, and black around the eyes (Junge and Mees). In Mexico, according to Blake, the crown is wholly blue in birds from Nuevo León and central Tamaulipas south to Puebla and northern Veracruz or black bordered with blue in other parts of the country. Lores and cheeks black and a black chest patch. The middle tailfeathers are "racket-tipped" in this species, the blobs at the tips blue with black edges.

See Edwards for concise plumage comparisons and plate showing the distinctive features of the six motmots found in Mexico.

Range: This large motmot ranges from north-eastern Mexico south through Oaxaca, Chiapas, the Yucatán Peninsula, and Central America to Colombia, Ecuador, Venezuela, the Guianas, and northern Brazil. Haverschmidt defines the southern limits of its range as the Tropical Zone of South America

from the Orinoco to Cayenne, south to southern Venezuela and the north bank of the Amazon.

PLATE 56
CUBAN TODY (*Todus multicolor*)

Other names: Pedorrera, cartacuba, barranco-río (*Cuba*). There are five species of todies and, depending on their location, each has had common names applied to it. These are listed by Bond (1960) as follows: barrancolí, pichuí, colibrí, tête-sèche, chicorette (the narrow-billed tody of *Hispaniola*); San Pedrito, medio peso, papagayo, barrancolino (the Puerto Rican tody of *Puerto Rico*); robin, robin redbreast (the Jamaican tody of *Jamaica*); barrancolí, barranquero, colibrí (the broad-billed tody of *Hispaniola* and *Gonave Island*). Wetmore (1927) adds the name verdadon for the Puerto Rican species and Lady Taylor (1955) the name Jamaican robin for the Jamaican bird. "Green sparrow" and "green hummingbird" of Sloane (1705–1725).

Description: Very small, brightly colored birds that look superficially like miniature kingfishers or plump hummingbirds. This species has vivid grass-green upper parts with a yellow tinge in front of the eye. There is a bright red patch on the throat (as in other todies), but in this bird there is also a blue area on the side of the neck. Under parts mainly white, but pink on the flanks and with the under tail coverts yellow or yellowish-green. Bill orange-red on lower mandible, feet pink.

For a description of the four other species of todies see Bond (1960), and especially plate 7 in Eckelberry.

Range: Todies are confined to the Greater Antilles, this species being found only in Cuba and the Isle of Pines. Other todies inhabit Hispaniola, Gonave Island, Puerto Rico, and Jamaica.

PLATE 57
RUFOUS-TAILED JACAMAR (*Galbula ruficauda*)

Other names: Black-faced jacamar; woodpecker (*Tobago*); tucuso de montaña, barranquero (*Venezuela*).

Description: Resembles an out-size hummingbird or long-tailed kingfisher. The adult male is a bright metallic green on the head, breast, back, and tail, except that the three outer tailfeathers are tawny rufous. The green shows copper reflections. Throat a white triangular patch, but the chin is sometimes flecked with dusky. Tawny rufous beneath. Tail-feathers decidedly graduated. Bill very long, pointed, and black. Adult female similar, except that the throat is pale buff.

Range: Tropical Middle America (except San Salvador) to western Panama and South America. In Mexico this species occupies humid lowland forests in Veracruz and Chiapas (Blake). Phelps and Phelps (1958) give the South American distribution of this species as northern Colombia, northern Brazil (Río Branco), the Guianas, and Trinidad and Tobago. Geographic races have been described from Santa Marta in northern Colombia and Rio Zulia in northwest Colombia. In Venezuela, Phelps states, the "tucuso de montaña" is very generally distributed in the region north of the Orinoco and Arauca rivers, including northwest Táchira (Ureña). South of the Orinoco they occur around Araguaimujo the Territory of Delta Amacuro, and at Caicara, Altagarcia, Río Cuchivero, Caño Guaniamo, and Raudal Alto in northwestern Bolívar. In Surinam Haverschmidt lists the following localities: Apoura (Corantijn River); Coronie; Coppename River; Paramaribo; Java Weg, Lelydorp; Surinam River; Republiek; Zanderij.

PLATE 58
CHANNEL-BILLED TOUCAN (*Ramphastos vitellinus*)

Other names: Piapoco, diostedé, diostedé pico acanalado (*Venezuela*); yellow-and-white-breasted toucan.

Description: A typical toucan with over-sized bill, in this species black with greenish-yellow on ridge of upper mandible and at base. Upper parts black, except upper tail coverts, which are scarlet. Sides of neck, throat, and breast white, tinged with pale to orange-yellow. Scarlet on lower breast, abdomen and tail black. Under tail coverts scarlet. Space around eyes blue.

Range: From northern Colombia through Venezuela to Trinidad, the Guianas, and Brazil north of the Amazon. In Venezuela, according to Phelps and Phelps (1958), north of the Orinoco it is locally distributed in northwest Lara (El Cerrón and El Cogollal), the southern slopes of the Andes in Táchira (Santo Domingo, Burgua), and Barinas (La Veguita), and generally distributed on the Upper Orinoco in Amazonas Territory (Cataniapo and Cuao, Munduapo, Nericagua, San Fernando de Atabapo, Esmeralda, Las Carmelitas, Boca de Sina, El Carmen). Also distributed locally northeast of the basin of Lago de Maracaibo in the Perijá, in Zulia (La Sierra, Ayapa, Panapicho, Los Motilones, Río Yasa), the northern slopes of the Andes in Táchira (La Fría), and in Mérida (Santa Elena). In addition, it is known from eastern Sucre (Cerro Papelón) and is generally distributed in the south of the Delta Amacuro Territory (San Francisco de Guayo, Jobure, Caño Vagre) and Bolívar (Nuria, El Dorado, Carabobo, Auyan-tepui, Chimantá-tepui and Paurai-tepui, La Paragua, Guaiquinima, Arebuchi and María Espuma, Caño Antabari, Salto Pará, La Prisión, Suapure, El Cambur, Santa Rosalía). Generally, in forests of the Tropical Zone and the lower Subtropical Zone to 1700 meters.

Resident in Trinidad but not in Tobago. In Surinam this species is common in forests of the savanna region and in the interior (Haverschmidt).

PLATE 59
CUBAN GREEN WOODPECKER (*Xiphidiopicus percussus*)

Other names: Carpintero verde, carpintero tajá, carpintero roán (*Cuba*).

Description: About the size of a hairy woodpecker. Back and upper surface of wings yellowish-green. Two central tailfeathers black with grayish tinge, under surface barred pale brown and gray. Crown and hind neck of male bright red (black with white streaks in female). Forehead and sides of head white, black line from eye along neck. Narrow black stripe center of throat ending in bright red patch on extreme upper breast. Remainder of breast yellow with vertical black stripes. Flanks and under parts barred horizontally with pale brown and gray. "No other Cuban woodpecker has green upper parts....Voice: A mewing or squealing reminiscent of Yellow-bellied Sapsucker" (Bond, 1960).

Range: Cuba and the Isle of Pines. Endemic.

PLATE 60
RED-BILLED SCYTHEBILL (*Campylorhamphus trochilirostris*)

Other names: Tanguero, pico de garfio (*Venezuela*); sickle-bill, woodcreeper, woodhewer, trepadore.

Description: Very long, decurved bill. Tailfeathers stiff and sharply pointed. Plumage mainly reddish-brown, with creamy white streaks on head, neck, breast, sides, and back. Legs and feet dull pea green. Iris brown.

Range: From central Panama to Colombia, northern Venezuela, the upper Río Negro region of Brazil (?), western Ecuador, and northwestern Peru. In Colombia it is of spotty distribution in the tropical zone of the northern part, the Magdalena Valley, the eastern Llanos, and the Pacific slope to the Baudó region (Río Baudó) and Nariño (de Schauensee). In Venezuela it is found in the north from Zulia and Táchira to Sucre, through the Llanos from Anzoátequi to Apure and north-western Bolívar in the region of Caicara, and in southern Bolívar in the Alto Caura, Alto Paragua, Santa Teresa de Uairén (Phelps and Phelps, 1950).

PLATE 61
PALE-BREASTED SPINETAIL (*Synallaxis albescens*)

Other names: Guitío gargantiblanco (*Venezuela*); white-throated spinetail (de Schauensee).

Description: Upper parts earth brown, the crown patch and upper wing coverts chestnut brown. Throat whitish, remainder of under parts ash gray. Tail long and spiny and brown in color. The iris of the male is orange-brown, that of the female grayish-brown. The upper mandible is black, the lower bluish-gray with a black tip. Legs and feet grayish-green. Some geographic races are darker than others. Wetmore (1926) describes the outstanding plumage differences between certain races, and compares this spinetail with others of the same genus.

Range: From Costa Rica to Panama and from Colombia, Venezuela, Trinidad, British Guiana, and Surinam south to Bolivia and Argentina. Occurs on Margarita Island off Venezuela, but not on Tobago. In Colombia it is found within the Tropical and lower Subtropical Zones of all three Andean ranges, in the upper Magdalena and Cauca valleys, the Santa Marta Mountains between 600 and 1900 meters, the Caribbean coast region from the lower Atrato east to the western base of the Santa Marta, and on the Guajira Peninsula (de Schauensee). It likewise occurs throughout Venezuela, from the Caribbean coast south through Apure and Bolívar to Amazonas Territory (Phelps and Phelps, 1950).

PLATE 62
RUFOUS-FRONTED THORNBIRD (*Phacellodomus rufifrons*)

Other names: Guaití (*Venezuela*).

Description: A rather nondescript brown bird, approximately sparrow-size. Upper parts brownish, under parts whitish to pale gray. Eckelberry describes their general appearance, when clambering about their remarkable nests, as similar to that of a large, plainly colored wren.

Range: This species inhabits open country in the Tropical Zone of Venezuela, in the northern part of the country from Sucre (San Félix) and Monagas (Guanguana) to Lara (Bucarito) and the Llanos from Guárico (Santa María de Ipire) to the west as far as Barinas (Ciudad Bolivia) and Apure (San Fernando and Guasdualito) (Phelps and Phelps, 1950). Also south to Tucuman, Argentina (Wetmore, 1926).

PLATE 63
BARRED ANTSHRIKE (*Thamnophilus doliatus*)

Other names: Balan-ch'ich' (*Yucatán*); pavita hormiguero (*Venezuela*); bush Guinea bird, Guinea bird, white-barred bush-shrike, pin'ade (*Trinidad*); cata-bird, qua-qua (*Tobago*).

Description: Male and female entirely unlike. Male strongly barred with black and white above and below, heavier black bars on back and wings, white areas wider on under parts. White crown patch, feathers of crown elongated forming an erectile crest. Female rufous, darker on crown. Sides of head, neck, and nape whitish, streaked with black. Throat finely streaked with pale buff and white.

Range: From the Caribbean slopes of Mexico, locally on the Yucatán Peninsula (including adjacent islands), and the Pacific slope of Chiapas, south through Central America to Venezuela, the Guianas, and adjacent parts of northern Brazil. Resident on Trinidad and Tobago.

PLATE 64
WHITE-BEARDED MANAKIN (*Manacus manacus*)

Other names: Casse-noisette (*Trinidad*).

Description: A small, chubby bird with typically

large head and short tail. Sexes totally different. The male is black on crown, lower back, wings, and tail. Tail coverts grayish. Otherwise white on throat, cheeks, neck, upper back, and under parts. Female grass green above, yellowish-green below.

Range: Trinidad, the Guianas, and northern Brazil. Not found in Tobago. In Surinam, Haverschmidt says, it is common in forests of the coastal area, the savanna region, and the interior.

PLATE 65
GOLDEN-HEADED MANAKIN (*Pipra erythrocephala*)

Other name: Saltarin cabecidorado (*Venezuela*).

Description: Small and chubby with large head and short tail as in other manakins. Plumage of male glossy, purplish-black throughout, except that head and face are golden yellow. Chin and throat black. Thighs carmine. Female olive green (leaf green) above, yellowish below.

Range: From eastern Panama through Colombia, Venezuela, and the Guianas to extreme northern Brazil. Resident in Trinidad but not in Tobago. A forest bird in Surinam, it is found in the savanna region and in the interior (Haverschmidt).

PLATE 66
PURPLE-THROATED FRUITCROW (*Querula purpurata*)

Other name: Toro montañero (*Venezuela*).

Description: A noisy, gregarious species. Upper parts glossy black. Throat, breast, and abdomen orange-red, but in the male the throat is purplish, crimson, or maroon, "visible only from certain angles" (Chapman, 1929).

Range: From Costa Rica and Panama into South America. It occurs in forests of the Tropical Zone in Colombia, except that it is absent in the arid sections of the Caribbean coast, the Cauca and Magdalena valleys, and from the Santa Marta region. Also, Ecuador, Peru, eastern Venezuela, the entire Amazon Valley, the Guianas, and north-western Brazil (Phelps and Phelps, 1950; de Schauensee). In Surinam it is a common bird of the forests of the savanna region and the interior (Haverschmidt).

PLATE 67
WHITE BELLBIRD (*Procnias alba*)

Other name: Campañero (*Venezuela, Trinidad*).

Description: A plain white, pigeon-size cotinga, remarkable only for its amazingly loud, ringing call.

Range: This species inhabits forests in Venezuela, the Guianas, and northern Brazil (Rio Negro). In Venezuela, according to Phelps and Phelps (1950), it is to be found in eastern Bolívar in the Sierra de Imataca (Altiplanicie de Nuria, Cerro Tomasote) and in the region of the Gran Sabana (the hill regions of Roraima, Auyan-tepui and Paurai-tepui). Haverschmidt records it in Surinam from Zanderij and Nassau Mountain (Marowijne).

PLATE 68
GUIANA COCK-OF-THE-ROCK (*Rupicola rupicola*)

Other names: Gallito de las rocas (*Venezuela*); golden cock-of-the-rock. "Rupicola" of Brisson (1760).

Description: About the size of a large Amazona parrot. The male is a brilliant golden orange throughout, blackish-brown on wings and tail. Upper wing coverts curled and greatly elongated. Crest disk like, laterally compressed and extending from the tip of the bill, which it nearly obscures, to the back of the head. Female generally olive brown. Wings short and rounded. Tail short. Legs short, feet large and strong.

Range: This handsome species inhabits forested hills, always on the lower slopes where there are rocky cliffs or outcrops, in eastern Colombia (Orinoco and Río Vaupés), southern Venezuela, and the Guianas to the Río Negro region of Brazil (de Schauensee). In Venezuela it occurs in Amazona Territory and to the east in Bolívar, from the Río Cuchivero across the Ríos Caura and Paragua to the region of the Gran Sabana and the Alto Cuyuni (Phelps and Phelps, 1950). In Surinam it is found in forests of the interior "wherever there are rocky outcrops" (Haverschmidt). "Its preference for hilly country is more a preference for rocky cliffs and slopes than for altitude" (Friedmann, 1948).

Another species (*Rupicola peruviana*) occurs in western Venezuela, Ecuador, and northern Peru; blood red where the present species is orange.

PLATE 69
BLACK PHOEBE (*Sayornis nigricans*)

Other names: None known.

Description: Identical in size with eastern phoebe and wags tail in same manner. Almost entirely black, darkest on head ("The only *black-breasted* flycatcher," Peterson, 1960). Most races are white on abdomen *and* under tail coverts. South American representatives of this species have two narrow white bars on each wing.

Range: Breeds in both the Nearctic and Neotropical regions, from northern California through Nevada, Utah, Arizona, New Mexico, and Texas south through Mexico (except the Caribbean lowlands and Yucatán Peninsula), the highlands of Central America (except British Honduras) to South America as far south as Argentina. The Central American range is well described by Skutch (1960): "Essentially a bird of mountainous regions, in South America it is confined to the Andean countries and the hilly parts of Venezuela east of the Andes. In Central America, as in South America, it occurs on both sides of the Cordillera. In Guatemala it has been recorded in the Pacific lowlands, and I have met it at points ranging from 1100 feet above sea level along the Río Copom in northern El Quiché, where one was present in midwinter, to 7000 feet in the neighborhood of Tecpán in the Department of Chimaltenango. In Costa Rica I saw a single individual at about 1200 feet on the Río General in August, but in this region it is rarely encountered below 3000 feet. On the opposite side of the country, it is abundant on the Caribbean slope at the elevation of 2000 feet, whence it extends upward into the intensively cultivated central highlands to possibly 6000 feet above sea level. In Ecuador I met it only on the middle reaches of the Andean streams, up to 6000 feet. Thus in the intertropical portion of its range the Black Phoebe inhabits chiefly the Tropical and Subtropical altitudinal zones, although in Guatemala it reaches into the lower edge of the Temperate Zone."

PLATE 70
PIED WATER-TYRANT (*Fluvicola pica*)

Other names: The washer-woman (*Trinidad*); Viudita acuática (*Venezuela*); white-shouldered water-tyrant.

Description: Smaller than a phoebe. White with black wings and tail, the tail edged with white, the shoulders and scapulars conspicuously white. A black streak extends from rear of crown along hind neck and down middle of back. Rump and upper tail coverts white. Iris sepia brown. Legs and feet black.

Range: This species ranges from eastern Panama to eastern Colombia (marshes of the Tropical Zone throughout the entire country with the exception of the Pacific slope). Also, Venezuela, Trinidad, and the Guianas south to Bolivia and northern Brazil. Not on Tobago. In Venezuela it inhabits the northern part of the country south to the Orinoco, the Delta Amacuro Territory and northern Bolívar (including the Bajo Caura), the Alto Apure (Guasdualito), Apure, through Amazonas Territory (Isla Ratón) to the Río Ventuari (Las Carmelitas) (de Schauensee; Phelps and Phelps, 1950).

PLATE 71
GREAT KISKADEE (*Pitangus sulphuratus*)

Other names: Xtakay (*Yucatán*); cristofué, cristofué Venezolano (*Venezuela*); qu'est-ce-qu'il-dit, common keskadee (*Trinidad*); kiskadee flycatcher, derby flycatcher.

Description: A big-headed, loud, conspicuous flycatcher with striking head pattern. Crown black with partly concealed yellow crest. Broad white eyebrow line from forehead around hind neck. Wide black line through eye. Throat white. Upper parts olive brown or brown, wings and tail cinnamon rufous. Breast and under parts bright lemon yellow. Bill large and black. May be confused with the convergent species *Megarhynchus pitangua*, the boat-billed flycatcher, but latter has much broader, thicker bill and very little cinnamon on wings and tail (Blake, 1953).

Range: The kiskadee ranges from Sonora and southern Texas (lower Rio Grande Valley) south through Mexico and Central America to northwest Panama (Bocas del Toro) and South America to Argentina. In South America several races have been described and these are distributed rather generally from northeastern Peru, eastern Ecuador, Colombia, Venezuela, Trinidad, and the Guianas southward to the Amazon and northern Brazil and Argentina. Casual in central Texas

(Devils Lake, Santa Anna) and Louisiana (Chenier au Tigre).

PLATE 72
COMMON TODY-FLYCATCHER (*Todirostrum cinereum*)

Other names: Titirijí lomicenizo guayanés, titirijí lomicenizo marabino (*Venezuela*); white-tipped tody-flycatcher (Blake); northern tody-flycatcher, black-crowned tody-flycatcher, black-fronted tody-flycatcher (Skutch, 1930, 1960); grey-backed tody-tyrant, white-chinned tody-tyrant (de Schauensee).

Description: One of the very small tropical American flycatchers. Large head, long, flattened bill, and short rounded tail, which it characteristically holds erect. Crown and sides of head black, back slaty gray, rump and wings tinged with olive. Wing coverts and tail edged with yellow. Tail black tipped with white. Lower face and entire under parts sulphur yellow. Iris white or pale yellow; Skutch (1960) adds: "... except just above the pupil, where it is suffused with deep red in curious fashion."

Range: This species ranges from the lowlands of southeastern Mexico, including the Yucatán Peninsula, south through Central America to Peru, Brazil, and the Guianas. In Central America it inhabits the lowlands of both coasts, up to 4500 feet above sea level in Costa Rica and Guatemala. De Schauensee describes its distribution in Colombia as within the Tropical and lower Subtropical Zones. It is rather generally distributed in suitable environments in Venezuela, chiefly in the Tropical Zone, more casually in the Subtropical (Phelps and Phelps, 1950). Known throughout Surinam in both the coastal areas and the savanna region (Haverschmidt).

PLATE 73
LESSER ANTILLEAN ELAENIA (*Elaenia martinica*)

Other names: Siffleur, siffleur blanc, judad bird (*West Indies*); ruiseñor pequeño, Juí blanco (*Virgin Islands* and islands east of Puerto Rico); piole or peole (*Dominica, St. Lucia*); pee-whistler or pee-whittler (*Barbados*); para bobo (*Curaçao*); chon-chorogai (*Bonaire*); cheery-cheer, whistler (*St. Martin, Saba, St. Eustatius*); Caribbean elaenia.

Description: A plain, olive-gray flycatcher with two grayish-white wing-bars and a stubby tail. Upper parts dark olive gray. Under parts grayish-white

tinged with pale yellow. Concealed white crown patch.

Range: A bird of the smaller Caribbean islands. It inhabits islands east of Puerto Rico (Vieques, Culebra, Culebrita), the U.S. and British Virgin Islands, the Leeward Group of the Netherlands Antilles (St. Martin, Saba, St. Eustatius), and islands of the Lesser Antilles to Barbados and Grenada (doubtful on the Grenadines). Also the Windward Group of the Netherlands Antilles (except possibly Aruba), Old Providence Island (including Santa Catalina), St. Andrew, islands off the Yucatán Peninsula (Holbox, Meco, Isla Mujeres, Cozumel, Banco Chinchorro), the Cayman Islands, and possibly Half Moon Cay off British Honduras.

PLATE 74
ROUGH-WINGED SWALLOW (*Stelgidopteryx ruficollis*)

Other name: Golondrina ala de sierra (*Venezuela*). In Spanish-speaking regions, all swallows are called golondrina.

Description: A brown-backed swallow, without a breast-band as in the bank swallow. Upper parts pale brown, throat and breast dusky gray, darker on the throat. "No other brown-backed swallow has a *uniform grayish throat* and *breast*" (Blake). "Flight unlike Bank Swallow's, more like Barn Swallow's; direct, with wings folded back at end of stroke" (Peterson, 1960).

Range: This unassuming, brown-backed swallow, with the rough-edged or serrated outer primary, has an extensive range, from British Columbia across the continent to southwestern Quebec, south to Peru, Bolivia, Paraguay, and Argentina. In the West Indies it has been recorded only in Cuba (in spring migration). In Mexico it is resident on the Pacific slope and in the southeast from central Veracruz southward, chiefly at lower elevations, an abundant migrant elsewhere (Blake). The northern race winters south to western Panama.

In Central America they are resident from the highlands of western Guatemala south through western British Honduras to Costa Rica (Griscom, 1932). In El Salvador, Dickey and Van Rossem found it common in both the arid Upper and Lower Tropical Zones, breeding above 2000 feet, wintering below 1000 feet. Wetmore (1939) says that it is common in the coastal range above Maracay, Venezuela, and elsewhere in the foothill country back of the north coastal plain. It also is resident across northern Venezuela south to the Orinoco drainage basin and west into Colombia (Friedmann and Smith, 1950). Fairly common and resident on the coast and in open country in Trinidad and Surinam. Not recorded on Tobago.

PLATE 75
GREEN JAY (*Cyanocorax yncas*)

Other names: Ses-ib (*Yucatán*); querrequerre (*Colombia*); querrequerre, piarra, kinkin, quin-quin (*Venezuela*); galeated jay, ynca jay, blue-backed jay (de Schauensee).

Description: No other jay in this region is green. Crown and cheeks bright blue. Forehead white. Stripe through eye, sides of neck and throat patch black. Back and wings bright green. Under parts vary from pale green to yellow or greenish-yellow depending on the location (geographic race). Tail has inner feathers bright green, bluish toward tips. Lateral tailfeathers bright yellow.

Range: From the south tip of Texas south through Mexico (except Baja California and the northwest), the highlands of Guatemala, and northern Honduras, and from the Subtropical Zones of Colombia and northern Venezuela south to Ecuador, Peru, and northern Bolivia.

PLATE 76
SOUTHERN HOUSE-WREN (*Troglodytes musculus*)

Other names: Rock bird, wall bird, god bird, oiseau bon dieu, rossignol (*Lesser Antilles*); Saltapared, xan-coti (*Yucatán*); churrita (*Guatemala*); cucarachero (*Venezuela*); god bird (*Trinidad*).

Description: Very similar to the well-known northern House-Wren, even the song and scolding notes being nearly identical. A small, energetic brown bird. Wings and tail barred with black. In different regions the under parts may be whitish or tinged with dull cinnamon buff. "It is distinguished from the Northern House-Wren by its more richly colored underparts, *buffy* (not grayish) *crissum* (i.e., under tail coverts) and fairly *distinct superciliaries* (i.e., stripe over eye)" (Blake).

Range: This tropical representative of the house-wren ranges from eastern and southern Mexico (the Caribbean slope from southern Tamaulipas to Yucatán, Cozumel Island, Oaxaca, and Chiapas) south through Central America to eastern Colombia, Peru, Venezuela, Trinidad, Tobago, and the Guianas south through Brazil to Argentina. Also in the Lesser Antilles (Grenada, St. Vincent, St. Lucia, Dominica). Formerly resident on Martinique (not since 1886) and Guadeloupe (not since 1914).

PLATE 77
BARE-EYED THRUSH (*Turdus nudigenis*)

Other names: Yellow-eyed grive, yam bird, grive à paupières jaunes, grive à Lunette (*West Indies*); bare-cheeked thrush, yellow-eyed thrush (*Trinidad*); ojo de candil (*Venezuela*).

Description: About the size and general appearance of the American robin. Song similar. Upper parts olive brown to dark olive gray. Under parts pale brownish-gray to buffy brown. Abdomen and under tail coverts whitish. Chin and throat whitish streaked with dusky or dark brown. Bare skin around eye greenish-yellow. Eyelid orange-yellow. Iris orange-brown.

Range: This abundant thrush ranges through the southern Lesser Antilles from Martinique southward, including St. Vincent, the Grenadines, and Grenada (but excluding Barbados). Rare north of St. Vincent, where it is apparently a recent arrival (St. Lucia and Martinique). Also Tobago, Trinidad, Islas de Margarita and Patos (off Venezuela), and the South American mainland from eastern Colombia to Peru and western Ecuador and east through Venezuela to the Guianas and south to the Amazon Valley and northwestern Brazil (Bond, 1950, 1960; de Schauensee).

PLATE 78
ORANGE-BILLED NIGHTINGALE-THRUSH (*Catharus aurantiirostris*)

Other name: Mirla avileña (*Venezuela*).

Description: A small, long-legged thrush. Upper parts uniform tawny olive, cinnamon rufous, or bright ochraceous brown. Breast light gray. Throat, abdomen, and under tail coverts white. Bare skin around eye orange. Eyelid orange. Iris brown. Bill orange. Legs and feet yellowish-orange.

Range: This little thrush lives in high mountain forests from central and southern Mexico south through Central America (except British Honduras) to western Panama and, in northern South America, from Colombia east through western and northern Venezuela to Trinidad. In Central America it is found in the higher parts of the Humid Tropical Zone from about 1400 to 7000 feet. In Colombia it occupies the Upper Tropical Zone of the Santa Marta Mountains, from about 2000 to 5000 feet. Also, northwest Norte de Santander in the region about Ocaña and Pamplona, the upper Magdalena Valley, and the Cauca and upper Patía valleys south to the upper Guáitara Valley in the Andes of Nariño. In Venezuela it is found in the states of Zulia, Táchira, Mérida, Trujillo, and Lara to the Caracas region (de Schauensee). In Trinidad it inhabits the undergrowth of forests in the higher parts of the Northern Range (Junge and Mees).

PLATE 79
RED-LEGGED THRUSH (*Mimocichla plumbea*)

Other names: Blue thrasher, red-legged blue thrasher, thrush, blue Jane, robin, sigüa calandria, Pierrot vantard (*West Indies*); zorzal real (*Cuba*); zorzal, zorzal azul, zorzal de patas coloradas (*Puerto Rico*); caleçon rouge, merle, rossignol de montagne, ouète-ouète, couète-couète (*Haiti*); Pierrot vanta (*Dominica*). "Caleçon rouge" ("red pants") of Moreau de Saint-Méry (1798).

Description: A large, blue-gray, robin-like thrush with red legs and feet. Tail black with conspicuous white tips on the outer feathers. Under tail coverts white. Red ring around eye. Iris brown. Bill reddish. The throat is white streaked heavily with black, but this varies, according to locale ("The chin and throat are variously black and white..." Bond, 1960). Color of under parts also varies—birds from central and western Cuba, the Isle of Pines, and Cayman Brac have abdomen ochraceous, but on Puerto Rico the abdomen is white, the breast streaked with gray, etc. "The mannerisms are wholly those of a robin" (Wetmore and Swales, 1931).

Range: This endemic West Indian thrush ranges through the northern Bahamas (including Grand Bahama, Abaco, Andros, New Providence, Eleuthera, Cat Island, the Exumas), Cuba, Isle of Pines, Puerto Rico, Hispaniola, Gonave and Tortue islands, and Dominica. Rare or absent on Cayman Brac. Extirpated from Swan Island (since 1887).

PLATE 80
RUFOUS-BROWED PEPPERSHRIKE (*Cyclarhis gujanensis*)

Other names: Pájaro perico (*Panama*); sirirí (*Venezuela*); si trih (*Toba Indian, Formosa, Argentina*); yellow-breasted pepper-shrike (Wetmore, 1957); pale-billed pepper-shrike.

Description: Upper parts olive green to bright green. Under parts pale greenish-yellow to buffy white. Abdomen whitish-gray. Forehead and sides of crown rufous, center of crown gray or brown. Cheeks and hind neck pale gray. The bill is heavy and hooked at tip. "No similar bird has a *powerful, hooked bill*" (Blake).

Range: This species ranges from southeast and southern Mexico (Veracruz, Puebla, Campeche, Yucatán, and Quintana Roo, including Meco and Cozumel islands) south through Central America and in South America from eastern Colombia, Venezuela, Trinidad, and Guianas south to Argentina.

PLATE 81
BANANAQUIT (*Coereba flaveola*)

Other names: Porto Rican honeycreeper, reina, gusanero (*Puerto Rico*); beany bird (*St. Mary Parish, Jamaica*); Bessie Coban (*St. Thomas Parish, Jamaica*); Psyche, John Croppie (*Trelawny Parish, Jamaica*); Hispaniolan honeycreeper (*Haiti, Dominican Republic*); sucrier, sugar-eater, sugar bird (*Trinidad, Tobago*); barica geel, barica heel (*Aruba, Curaçao*); chibichibi, bachi pretu, suikerdiefje, sugar-thief (*Bonaire*); reinita (*Puerto Rico, Venezuela*); banana bird, yellow-breast, paw-paw bird, yellow bird, marley quit, sugar bird, honey-sucker, molasses bird, yellow see-see, sigüita (*West Indies*); black see-see (*St. Vincent, Grenada*).

Description: A tiny bird, less than sparrow-size (length four to five inches). Considerable geographical variation in color of plumage. Upper parts sooty gray in most races, sooty black in others. Superciliary stripe over eye white in adults, yellow in immatures. Rump generally yellow, greenish-yellow in some races. The white wing patch, often obscure, also varies in size and may be nearly or totally absent. Under parts yellow, but great variation in color of throat, which may be grayish-white or sooty black, with additional local variations (Bonaire birds have a white throat with a small patch of black on the chin). Variation also in size of different races. On some islands in the Lesser Antilles (St. Vincent, Grenada) most individuals are black (melanic phase), with a greenish-yellow wash on breast and upper tail coverts, but this last is not apparent in the field according to Bond. Black individuals also on Los Testigos and El Gran Roque (Islas Los Roques) off Venezuela. Bill decurved and black.

Range: Widespread in Middle America (Mexico to Panama, except not reported in El Salvador and Honduras), South America, the West Indies (except Cuba), and on extralimital islands of the Caribbean. Accidental in Florida.

There are more than 30 geographical races or subspecies, 17 in the West Indies alone. In Mexico they occur in the lowlands of the southeastern part, and also on Holbox and Cozumel islands (Blake). Danforth (1939) says that on Monserrat Island (Leeward Islands) these birds are common at lower elevations, but scarce in the mountain forests, whereas Hummelinck observes that they are met with throughout all parts of Curaçao and Bonaire (Netherlands Antilles), "from the driest and most thorny xerophytic bush to fruit gardens and farm yards and the summit of Christoffel Mountain" (1220 feet). Occurs throughout the Bahamas, but more abundantly on the southern islands of this group. As elsewhere in its range, this species is the most abundant and most widely distributed bird on Puerto Rico and, according to Wetmore (1927), is not only present wherever there is cover—from mangrove shores to cane fields, pastures, coffee plantations, and neighborhood cafés—but is the only common bird in the dense, humid rain forests on the higher slopes of El Yunque (3484 feet). In the Virgin Islands, Danforth (1935) lists the bananaquit as present on Vieques, Culebra, Louis Peña, Culebrita, Cayo Norte, St. Thomas, St. John, Jost van Dyke, Tortola, Beef Island, Virgin Gorda, and Anegada. It doubtless occurs also on many smaller islands not mentioned, if there is cover. Bond (1950) found them on Green Island, a tiny islet adjacent to Grenada "that could scarcely accommodate more than two pairs." On Guadeloupe, Noble found them in greatest numbers around the banana plantations, but said that they occur "everywhere in the lowlands and as far up the mountains as the Grand Bois extends." This would be about 4000 feet, or the beginning of the so-called mountain barrens. Similarly, its distribution is widespread elsewhere—in Haiti and the Dominican Republic,

Wetmore and Lincoln (1933) found bananaquits in all habitats, the desert area north of Habanero and the wet forests of the Pic de Macaya at close to 7000 feet. They occur in Jamaica, all three of the Caymans, on Holbox and Cozumel (as mentioned earlier), and on the little islands of St. Andrews, Old Providence, and Santa Catalina. In a word, this ubiquitous and highly successful little bird completely encircles the Caribbean, but with one glaring and unexplainable exception— Cuba. Bond says that this "may be due chiefly to climatic and ecological conditions," but adds, "I cannot suggest a logical reason for its absence from Oriente Province," which, of course, has mountainous terrain much like that in Jamaica and Hispaniola, where the bananaquit is abundant. Although this species is probably of South American origin, few birds are more typical of the Caribbean and the West Indian islands.

PLATE 82
YELLOW-LEGGED HONEYCREEPER (*Cyanerpes caeruleus*)

Other names: Copeicillo violáceo (*Venezuela*); grampo, Yellow-legged grampo (*Trinidad*); purple honey-creeper.

Description: Male a brilliant purplish-blue, except patch through eye; throat, wings, and tail black. Bill long, decurved, and black. Legs and feet yellow. Female has green upper parts, throat and patch through eye rusty. "Mustache" streak pale blue. Breast and abdomen yellow, streaked with blue and green.

Range: From northern Colombia through northern Venezuela, Trinidad, and the Guianas to Brazil (Maranhão and Mato Grosso), as well as eastern Ecuador, eastern Peru, and Bolivia.

PLATE 83
CHESTNUT-BELLIED CHLOROPHONIA (*Chlorophonia pyrrhophrys*)

Other name: Verdin de vientre castaño (*Venezuela*).

Description: A sparrow-size, chunky little tanager, with stubby tail and short bill. Larger than the closely related euphonias. Plumage mainly green, the males beautifully patterned about the head, neck, and throat with blues, yellows, and greens. Females similar but duller.

Range: This chlorophonia ranges from Colombia to eastern Ecuador and western Venezuela. In Venezuela it is found in the Andes of Trujillo (Páramo de Misisí, Cerro Niquitaz), Mérida (Páramo Aricagua), and Táchira (Boca del Monte). It inhabits forests of the Subtropical Zone (Phelps and Phelps, 1950). In Colombia it occurs in both the Subtropical and Temperate Zones and has been recorded from both slopes of the Eastern and Central Andes, the eastern slope of the Western Andes, in the Department Cauca, and the Pacific slope of the Andes of Nariño (de Schauensee).

PLATE 84
LESSER ANTILLEAN GRACKLE (*Quiscalus lugubris*)

Other names: Tordo negro (*Venezuela*); boat-tail (*Trinidad*); blackbird, bequia-sweet, merle (*West Indies*); Carib grackle, Swainson's grackle.

Description: Typical grackle appearance, a large black bird with a V-shaped tail. Male black throughout with violaceous and greenish gloss. Iris may appear white, but is pale yellowish-brown. Female smaller. Black throughout but duller than male and brownish underneath. Females in some areas are paler than others, and those from Martinique to Montserrat incline to white on the under parts, particularly on the throat (Bond, 1960). Bill, legs, and feet black.

Range: The Lesser Antillean grackle (perhaps "Carib grackle" is a more appropriate name) ranges from eastern Colombia across northern Venezuela to Trinidad, Tobago, and the Guianas, and in the Lesser Antilles from Grenada and Barbados to Guadeloupe and Montserrat. Introduced on Barbuda, Antigua, and St. Kitts. Also occurs on Islas Margarita, Los Frailes (Puerto Real), Los Hermanos (La Horquilla, El Fondeadero), and Los Testigos (Testigo Grande) (Phelps and Phelps, 1950).

PLATE 85
GLOSSY COWBIRD (*Molothrus bonariensis*)

Other names: Mirlo (*Venezuela*); merle de barbade (*St. Lucia*); merle de Sainte Lucie (*Martinique*); blackbird's cousin, corn bird, tordo (*West Indies*); tordo (*Argentina*); shiny cowbird.

Description: Male glossy purplish-black. Female drab gray-brown above, dusky brown on wings and tail, brownish-gray underneath. Bill, legs, and feet black. Iris dark brown. Usually seen in flocks.

Range: The glossy cowbird has an extensive range, being distributed from eastern Panama through South America to Bolivia, Uruguay, and Argentina, and from Trinidad and Tobago northward through the Lesser Antilles to Grenada, the Grenadines, St. Vincent, and St. Lucia as far as Martinique. Spreading. Accidental on St. Croix, St. John, Vieques, and northeastern Puerto Rico. Common in the coastal region of Surinam.

PLATE 86
MONTEZUMA OROPENDOLA (*Gymnostinops montezuma*)

Other name: Oropéndola (*Mexico*).

Description: Large as a crow. Head, neck, and upper breast black, remainder of plumage deep chestnut. Central tailfeathers brownish-black, outer feathers bright yellow. Tail appears all-yellow below. Long, sharp bill, black at base, tip orange. Frontal shield of male edged with orange on posterior margin. Cheek bare and white or pink, faintly tinged with blue. Males also have a long, fleshy protuberance along side of chin, orange in color. Females decidedly smaller, otherwise more or less similar.

Range: This largest of the family Icteridae is restricted to tropical Middle America, ranging from southern Mexico through Central America (except San Salvador) to the Panama Canal Zone. In Mexico it occurs in the lowlands of southern Tamaulipas, Veracruz, Oaxaca, Tobasco, and Quintana Roo. Skutch (1954) writes: "Where the continental divide is high and broad, as in Guatemala, it is restricted to the Caribbean slope, but where the barrier is low, as in parts of Costa Rica and Panamá, it spills over to the Pacific side. In northern Costa Rica where the divide is low, this oropéndola is not uncommon on the moister parts of the Pacific slope; but in the southern part of the country, where the Cordillera de Talamanca forms a great barrier between 8000 and 12,000 feet in height, I have not met the bird on the Pacific side, although the forests of the Térraba Valley much resemble those on the Caribbean slope at the same altitude and conditions would seem to be favorable to it. Most abundant at lower altitudes, the oropéndola is occasionally seen in suitable localities as high as 4500 feet above sea level. . . ."

PLATE 87
COMMON TROUPIAL (*Icterus icterus*)

Other names: Trupial (*Aruba, Curaçao*); turpial (*Venezuela*). "Le troupiale" of Brisson (1760).

Description: Larger than the yellow oriole, with black head, neck, throat, and upper breast and conspicuous orange-and-black plumage pattern. Nape, lower breast and abdomen, rump and both upper and lower tail coverts deep orange. In addition to head, throat, etc., the back, wings, and tail are also black. Scapulars white, appearing as conspicuous white "mirrors" in the black wings. Bill black, the base of the lower mandible bluish-gray. Iris yellow or yellowish-white. Legs and feet bluish-gray. Sexes alike. Hummelinck says that the orange colors are subject to considerable fading and sun-bleaching.

Range: Inhabits northeastern Colombia, including the arid coastal region from the Guajira Peninsula west to the middle Cesare Valley, Venezuela north to the Orinoco and the Caribbean islands of Aruba, Curaçao, and Margarita. Not recorded on Bonaire.
  Bond (1960) says: "Introduced (apparently from Curaçao) and established in Puerto Rico and St. Thomas, including Water Island; also reported from Jamaica, St. John, Antigua, Dominica and Grenada (escaped cage birds?)." Of its status in Puerto Rico, McCandless writes: "Uncommon local resident. Possibly introduced many years ago, although may be native. Found only along the south coast west of Ponce. Commonest in Guanica State Forest."

PLATE 88
COMMON MEADOWLARK (*Sturnella magna*)

Other names: Frijolera, tortilla con chile (*Mexico*); perdigón, mochila vacia (*Venezuela*); sabanero (*Cuba*); eastern meadowlark. "Stourne ou merle à fer-à-cheval" of Buffon (1781).

Description: A stocky, short-tailed bird, brownish above, with conspicuous white outer tailfeathers. Yellow underneath with a black V-shaped patch in center of upper breast. In characteristic flight the wing beats are rapid with intervals of sailing. The upper parts are sooty brown streaked with buff or tawny. Sharply contrasted black-and-white striping on head.

Range: Across the U.S. east of the Rockies from Arizona and New Mexico to northern Minnesota, Ontario, Quebec, and central Nova Scotia south through Mexico (except Baja California) and Central America to Colombia, Venezuela, British Guiana, Surinam, and northeastern Brazil. Also, Cuba and the Isle of Pines.
  Another species, the western meadowlark (*Sturnella neglecta*) ranges widely over western North America, breeding from British Columbia to western Ontario and south to Baja California, central Mexico, Texas, and Louisiana.

PLATE 89
SWALLOW-TANAGER (*Tersina viridis*)

Other name: Azulejo golondrina (*Venezuela*).

Description: The male bright turquoise blue, with velvet black on face and throat, belly and under tail coverts pure white. Narrow black barrings on flanks. In direct light the turquoise blue changes to emerald green. The female bright green, barred with dark green and black on the flanks. Throat grayish, belly and under tail coverts pale yellow streaked faintly with gray. For detailed description of immature and subadult plumages, see Schaefer.

Range: The swallow-tanager ranges from eastern Panama (Darien) throughout virtually all of tropical South America, including Trinidad, south to Bolivia and northeastern Argentina. In Colombia it is found in the Tropical and Subtropical Zones, including the Santa Marta Mountains up to 1600 meters and Miraflores (2040 meters). Not recorded from the lower Magdalena Valley (de Schauensee). "Its local and seasonal distribution in Venezuela in general, and the Parque Nacional in particular, is extremely interesting. Like many other passerine birds, *Tersina viridis* is not sedentary but semi-migratory. During the breeding season (February to August), in the broadest sense of the word, *Tersina viridis* seems to be confined to hilly or mountainous areas. This seems to apply not only to the northern mountains, the main Andes (states of Táchira, Mérida, Trujillo), but also to the coast range (Cordillera de la Costa), the Perijá Mountains on the Colombian border, and the vast mountainous regions south of the Llanos and the Orinoco River....During their migration, the tersinas apparently do not follow the Cordillera de la Costa, but use the transverse valley to reach their breeding grounds" (Schaefer).

PLATE 90
COPPER-CROWNED TANAGER (*Tangara cayana*)

Other names: Monjita (*Venezuela*). "Le tangara verd de Cayenne" of Brisson (1760).

Description: This tanager has a coppery rufous crown and a broad black patch through the eye. The upper parts are pale greenish, light ochraceous on rump, the upper tail coverts blue. Wings and tail blue edged with black. Under parts opalescent light ochraceous. Throat and foreneck more or less tinged bluish. Sexes generally similar.

Range: The copper-crowned tanager ranges from eastern Colombia, Venezuela, and the Guianas south to northern Bolivia, eastern Peru, southern Brazil, and Mato Grosso. In Venezuela it is generally distributed in suitable habitats throughout the northern part of the country, and south of the Orinoco it is found in Bolívar and Amazonas Territory from Puerto Ayacucho to the Cerro Yapacana and San Antonio (Phelps and Phelps, 1950). According to Haverschmidt it is at present very rare in the coastal areas of Surinam, but "still common on the sandy savannas dotted over with low trees and bushes."

PLATE 91
BLUE-GRAY TANAGER (*Thraupis virens*)

Other names: Azulejo (*Panama*); viuda (*Costa Rica*); azulejo de jardines (*Venezuela*); bluejeans (*Tobago*); blue bird (*Trinidad*); gray tanager, bishop tanager.

Description: Very pale blue-gray, darker on back and rump, with greenish tinge on back, wings, and rump in certain lights. Wings and tail sky blue, the lesser coverts bright lilac blue. Bill black, bluish-gray on lower mandible. Legs and feet black, gray, or lead color. Iris brown. Sexes alike.

Range: This abundant tanager ranges from the lowlands of southern Veracruz, Tabasco, and Quintana Roo south through Central America to northern Bolivia and Maranhão, Brazil. Exceedingly rare on the Yucatán Peninsula (Paynter), but "wearisomely abundant in the tropical lowlands of nearly the whole of Central America" (Griscom, 1932). Skutch (1954) says that it has a wide altitudinal range in Central America, "extending from the seacoasts up to about 5000 feet in Guatemala, 4500 feet in El Salvador and 7500 feet in Costa Rica." In South America it is found in Colombia, Venezuela, Trinidad, and Tobago, to Ecuador, Peru, and in Brazil "Southward to the Río Tapajoz and Río Madeira, possibly to northern Bolivia" (de Schauensee).

PLATE 92
SCARLET-RUMPED TANAGER (*Ramphocelus passerinii*)

Other names: Song tanager, black tanager, velvet tanager, passerini tanager.

Description: Male velvety black, except rump, lower back, and upper tail coverts which are bright scarlet. Female has head and neck brownish to brownish-gray, back olive with greenish tinge. Rest of plumage orange-olive, brightest on breast and rump, but these brighter colors vary from orange to dull yellowish. Tail dull brown. Bill in both sexes thick, light blue in color with black tip. Iris red. Legs and feet blackish in male, plumbeous in female.

Range: This beautiful tanager inhabits humid forests from southern Mexico (Tabasco) to western Panama, where its extreme southern limit of distribution is Almirante. There are two geographic races, one on the Caribbean slopes from Mexico to Nicaragua, the other in the region of high rainfall in southern Costa Rica and adjacent Panama. Breeding has been recorded from sea level to 4000-feet elevation.

PLATE 93
SILVER-BEAKED TANAGER (*Ramphocelus carbo*)

Other names: Sangre de toro, sangre de toro apagado, pico de plata (*Venezuela*); silver beak, bec d'argent (*Trinidad*).

Description: Over-all plumage dark velvety crimson, more blackish above, brighter on breast, the throat and upper breast a rich crimson. Female duller above, the under parts reddish with some variation geographically. Very conspicuous bluish-gray or silvery patch on lower mandible of male. Otherwise, mandibles black. Legs and feet black. Iris red.

Range: The silver-beaked tanager ranges from eastern Colombia to eastern Ecuador, northeastern Peru, and through Venezuela and the Amazon Valley of northern Brazil to Trinidad and the

Guianas. Not in Tobago. Common and widespread throughout its range. In Surinam it occurs in "light forests, plantations and gardens in the coastal area and the savanna region" (Haverschmidt).

PLATE 94
RUDDY-BREASTED SEEDEATER (*Sporophila minuta*)

Other names: Espiguero pigmeo (*Venezuela*); small red-bellied finch (*Trinidad*). Lesser seedeater, minute seedeater.

Description: Very small and undistinguished (Blake). The male has the upper parts, including entire head and hind neck, ashy gray to dusky grayish-brown. Under parts and rump dull cinnamon rufous or chestnut. Inner secondaries and wing coverts edged with grayish-brown. A small white patch at base of primaries. Tail blackish-brown. Female has the upper parts buffy brown, earthy brown, or pale olive brown. Under parts pale buff or pale ochraceous brown, paler on abdomen. Inner secondaries and wing coverts edged with ochraceous gray. Two pale wing-bars.

Range: This tiny finch ranges from the arid lowlands of Nayarit, Oaxaca, and Chiapas, in Mexico, south through Central America to Colombia and northwest Ecuador, Venezuela, Trinidad, Tobago, the Guianas, and the lower Amazon Valley to southern Brazil, eastern Bolivia, and Argentina (de Schauensee). In Venezuela it occurs in suitable situations throughout the northern parts of the country to the Orinoco and Apure rivers, and south of the Orinoco in eastern Bolívar to the Gran Sabana and northwest Bolívar and Amazonas Territory as far as San Fernando de Atabapo, Islas Los Frailes (Puerto Real) (Phelps and Phelps, 1950).

PLATE 95
SAFFRON FINCH (*Sicalis flaveola*)

Other names: Canary, wild canary, Jamaican canary, wild canary of Jamaica (*Jamaica*); canario de tejado (*Venezuela*).

Description: The male has the upper parts bright olive yellow, forehead and crown bright orange. Under parts bright yellow. Female similar but less bright, especially on forehead and forepart of crown. Immature birds have upper parts brownish to yellowish-green with dark streaks, the under parts whitish to yellowish and streaked. Bill dull yellow with dark tip on lower mandible. Legs and feet greenish or yellowish-gray. Iris dark brown.

Range: The saffron finch ranges over most of South America, south to northern Argentina, Uruguay, and southern Bolivia. It may be locally distributed in many areas. In Venezuela it inhabits open fields and gardens in the Tropical Zone (up to 1500 meters) and casually to a higher elevation (Phelps and Phelps, 1950). In Trinidad it is local, "probably being confined to the large artificial savannahs between Port-of-Spain and Tacarigua" (Junge and Mees). Haverschmidt says that it is apparently rare in Surinam, where Hellmayr recorded it at Paramaribo. Introduced in Jamaica in the vicinity of Black River early in the nineteenth century and now common and widespread (Kingston, Mandeville, Montego Bay, etc.).

PLATE 96
BLACK-FACED GRASSQUIT (*Tiaris bicolor*)

Other names: Barbito (*Cuba*); chamorro, gorrión, chamorro bicolor, chamorro negro, gorrión negro (*Puerto Rico*); chee-chee bird, tobacco bird (*Saba*); petit z'herbes (*Haiti*); moffi (*Aruba, Curaçao, Bonaire*); tordito común (*Venezuela*); Carib grassquit. Bond (1960) also gives these West Indian names: parson bird, parson sparrow, sin bird, chitty bird, black sparrow, white see-see (female), grass sparrow, ground sparrow, grass bird, straw bird, cane sparrow, tobacco seed, parakeet, grass quit, juana maruca, petit des herbes ("Ti-zeb"), ci-ci des herbes ("Si-si-zeb").

Description: A very small sparrow-like bird with a heavy finch's bill. The male has upper parts dark olive green to grayish-green, sides of head and under parts black except flanks grayish or grayish-green, more or less tinged with olive. Abdomen dull white. Female plain brownish-olive-green or grayish-olive throughout, except white or with tinge of buffish-white underneath. Young males similar to females.

Range: The black-faced grassquit ranges throughout the West Indies with the notable exception of the Cuban mainland, where it is replaced by the Cuban grassquit (*Tiaris canora*). However, it occurs on many small islands and cayos off northern Las Villas Province and locally on the adjacent mainland near Isabela de Sagua, and perhaps elsewhere off the coast. Also, Isle of Pines, the Cayman Islands,

Swan Islands, and St. Andrew, Old Providence, and Santa Catalina in the southwest Caribbean. In addition, coastal regions of Colombia and Venezuela, as well as Aruba, Curaçao, Bonaire, Blanquilla, Los Hermanos, Tortuga, Trinidad, and Tobago. One record for Florida (Miami, 1871).

PLATE 97
GRAYISH SALTATOR (*Saltator coerulescens*)

Other names: Primavera (*Veracruz*); paraulata ajicera, lechosero (*Venezuela*).

Description: "Big, slender, long-tailed, and thick-billed, with olive-green or grayish plumage quite lacking in brilliant colors, the saltators form a distinct group in the great finch family" (Skutch, 1954). The present species is large and grayish, with a white stripe or superciliary line over the eye and a white throat patch, the latter bordered on each side with a conspicuous black streak. "No similar bird has a grayish, *unpatterned chest*, and buffy abdomen" (Blake).

Range: From Sinaloa, Durango, southern Tamaulipas, and the Yucatán Peninsula southward through Mexico, Central and South America to Bolivia and Argentina. In Colombia it occurs in the Tropical Zone of the Caribbean coast, the lower Magdalena Valley, the eastern slope of the Andes in Norte de Santander and the eastern base of the Andes from Meta southward. Also northern Venezuela north of the Orinoco, Trinidad, the Guianas, and northeastern Brazil (de Schauensee).

PLATE 98
RUFOUS-COLLARED SPARROW (*Zonotrichia capensis*)

Other names: Coronadas, coronalitas (*Guatemala*); correporsuelo (*Venezuela*); chonchorogai (*Aruba, Curaçao*); sigua, siguita (*Dominican Republic*).

Description: Resembles the white-throated sparrow (*Zonotrichia albicollis*) but has gray instead of white head stripes, a black chest patch, and considerable rufous or chestnut on sides of neck and hind neck. Head gray streaked heavily with black. Throat white. Upper parts grayish-brown or olive brown broadly streaked with black on back and scapulars. Two vague wing-bars. Under parts pale grayish to dull white, sides and flanks olive brown.

Range: A widely distributed mountain species that ranges from the highlands of Middle America (except British Honduras) south through most of South America to Tierra del Fuego, as well as the Cordillera Central of Hispaniola in the Greater Antilles and the islands of Aruba and Curaçao. In Mexico it occurs in the mountains of Chiapas (San Cristobal and Pinabete near Comitán) (Blake). In the Guatemalan highlands, Griscom (1932) found them ranging from about 3000 to 11000 feet, and Wetmore (1941) saw them on Volcán de Agua at 8000 feet. In El Salvador, Van Rossem found them resident in the higher parts of the arid upper Tropical Zone on Los Esesmiles and also on the summit of Volcán de Santa Ana. "The vertical range is from 4500 to 8000 feet" (Dickey and Van Rossem, 1938).

In Colombia these sparrows occur in the Subtropical and Temperate Zones of the Andes and the Santa Marta Mountains, but are not rare in the upper Tropical Zone, occasionally as low as 1200 feet, but reaching 12,000 feet elsewhere (de Schauensee). The Venezuelan range is in the Andes from Táchira to southern Lara, the Cadena del Litoral de la Cordillera de la Costa, the eastern Cordillera de la Costa in Anzoátegui, Sucre, Monagas, and northwest Bolívar. Also in the Gran Sabana, including the summit of Cerro Roraima, Cerro Guaiquinima in Bolívar, and Cerro Yaví in Amazonas Territory (Phelps and Phelps, 1950).

On Aruba and Curaçao it is generally distributed, even at sea level, but is most abundant in such habitats as the Arikok Hills on Aruba.

In Hispaniola it is known only from the Cordillera Central in the Dominican Republic to elevations above 3500 feet.

The Photographers

Like any of the arts, photography is a highly democratic field that is open to all comers and may be excelled in by persons of both sexes and from varied walks of life. Most of the pictures in this book were taken by professional photographers, many of whom make a specialty of birds and other animal subjects, but a surprising number are the work of semi-pros, part-time camera bugs who do something else for a living and consider photography a pleasant and exciting hobby. Among those contributing to this collection are two college students, a postman, the president of a great industrial empire, and a certified public accountant. One of the pros is best known, perhaps, for his outstanding portraits of children.

So many of us take pictures these days that what was once the exclusive parlance of the expert is now understood by all, amateur and professional alike, and the extra lenses and other camera equipment we see slung around the neck of many a tourist is no longer cause for expressions of astonishment, but a badge of identity, like the tartan of a clan.

Because of this general and, at the same time, very personal interest in cameras, lenses, and techniques, it seemed to me that it would be useful to include here a brief note on each of the contributors to this book, along with whatever information I was able to glean as to how they obtained their photographs. Twenty-three names are concerned, and these account for all of the pictures herein except one, the sunbittern (*Plate 26*), which was supplied by *Paris-Match* and is of a captive bird.

Dr. Arthur Augustus Allen, who photographed the laughing gulls in flight (*Plate 29a*) and the black-throated mango on its nest (*Plate 47*), is unquestionably the dean of American bird photographers. After a long and illustrious career (1906-1953) as professor of ornithology at Cornell University, Dr. Allen is now honorary director of the Laboratory of Ornithology and professor emeritus of that institution. He has photographed in color over 500 species of North American birds. Many of his pictures have appeared in the *National Geographic Magazine*, and in his books.

Dr. Allen writes us that the laughing gull photograph was taken from a car window on the pier at Aransas Pass, Texas. "By throwing out bread we soon had a flock hovering about us, and it was a simple matter to snap them on Superanscochrome, 1/500 at $f/8$." The black-throated mango was photographed on the shore of Barro Colorado Island in Gatun Lake, Panama Canal Zone. A blind was left near the nest and after several days the picture was taken without difficulty. "At that time (1945) Kodachrome had a speed of 6 and I believe I regularly used 1/50 second at $f/5.6$ when taking close-ups in bright sunshine."

Arthur W. Ambler has contributed eight of the photographs. Although he has taken pictures of many birds in their natural surroundings, the eight pictures used here happen to have been taken at the Bronx Zoo. These are the blue-headed quail-dove (*Plate 34*); St. Vincent parrot (*Plate 37*); tufted coquette (*Plate 49*); blue-crowned motmot

(*Plate 55*); Cuban tody (*Plate 56*); white-bearded manakin (*Plate 64*); golden-headed manakin (*Plate 65*); and chestnut-bellied chlorophonia (*Plate 83*).

Mr. Ambler uses an Exacta 35-mm camera equipped with either a 135-mm or 200-mm Schneider lens, plus a No. 1 supplementary lens to shorten the focal length. Also, a Nikon F reflex and Nikon 135-mm lens. Anscochrome daylight regular (EI32) film was used for all pictures. For lighting he prefers a small 100 Ws Ultrablitz portable electronic flash, without a filter, as this light has a color temperature of about 5600 K.

G. RONALD AUSTING, who lives in Ohio, took the photograph of the belted kingfisher (*Plate 54*). Mr. Austing worked with this species in captivity in order to obtain close-up shots of these lively birds catching fish—something that is next to impossible to accomplish in the wild. This picture is of one of his captive birds. A Crown Graphic was used, with Ektachrome film, a 300-mm Schneider lens and a lens opening of $f/16$. Lighting was provided by Speedlight at 1/10,000 second.

ALLAN DUDLEY CRUICKSHANK, well-known wildlife photographer and lecturer on the National Audubon Society circuit, was born in the Virgin Islands while his family was en route to the Bronx, where he was raised. An early member of the Bronx Bird Club, Cruickshank is one of the most accomplished "bird listers" in the country, has written a book on the subject of field identification —*Cruickshank's Pocket Guide to the Birds* (New York; Dodd, Mead, 1953)—and is editor of the Audubon Christmas Bird Count. His beautiful, portrait-like photographs of birds have been published in many books and magazines, including scientific monographs. The Cruickshanks live in Rockledge, Florida.

Allan Cruickshank has contributed six photographs to this collection. He has sent us the following data on each of them.

Brown pelican (*Plate 2*) taken at Gulfport, Florida, with 4×5 Graflex, 17-inch lens at 1/110 sec., $f/6.5$.

Frigatebirds (*Plate 5*) at Dry Tortugas off Florida, 4×5 Speed Graphic, 4-inch lens at 1/40 sec., $f/11$.

Snowy egret (*Plate 10*) on Carroll Island, San Antonio Bay, Texas, 4×5 Graflex, 17-inch lens at 1/40 sec., $f/12$.

Roseate spoonbill (*Plate 14a*) at the Vingt'un Islands, Galveston Bay, Texas, 4×5 Graflex, 17-inch lens, at 1/40 sec., $f/10$.

Black-necked stilt (*Plate 28*) at Port Canaveral, Florida, 4×5 Graflex, 17-inch lens, at 1/40, $f/9$.

Black phoebe (*Plate 69*) at Morro Bay, California, 4×5 Speed Graphic, 17-inch lens, at 1/40, $f/16$ and synchroflash.

Kodachrome film was used for all photographs except that of the stilt, which was shot on Ektachrome.

CRAWFORD H. GREENEWALT, seven of whose photographs appear in these pages, is a chemical engineer by profession and, since 1948, president of E. I. DuPont de Nemours and Company. When the speed of a ruby-throated hummingbird proved too much for Mr. Greenewalt's camera equipment, he went to work with characteristic ability to develop something that would do the job. His recently published *Hummingbirds* (New York: Doubleday, 1960) is the highly creditable result.

In this book, Mr. Greenewalt's contributions include the white-tailed tropicbird (*Plate 1*), which he photographed at a nesting colony on his place in Bermuda. He comments: "I am sure I used high-speed Ektachrome in a Leica with a 135-mm lens and, if I remember it rightly, the exposure time was one-thousandth of a second at an aperture of $f/11$." The Cuban emerald (*Plate 50*) was photographed on her nest in a small patio at a resort hotel in Varadero, Cuba. The glittering-throated emerald (*Plate 53*), yellow-legged honeycreeper (*Plate 82*) and copper-crowned tanager (*Plate 90*) were photographed at the Phelps residence on the outskirts of Caracas, Venezuela. The honeycreeper and tanager were aviary birds. The Cuban green woodpecker (*Plate 59*) and red-legged thrush (*Plate 79*) were wild birds, both nesting on the Irenee DuPont estate near Varadero. The last six birds in the above list were photographed with special high-speed equipment designed and developed by Mr. Greenewalt and his associates. He writes me that with such equipment, "apertures and times have very little significance. The best I can suggest is that you put in a reference to my hummingbird book, which has in it a chapter describing my technique in general." (This would be Chapter 4).

SAMUEL ANDREW GRIMES, a printer and photoengraver by trade, lives in Jacksonville, Florida, and has been interested in birds since the age of five. Photography began as a hobby for Mr. Grimes and has become his chief outside interest; his bird pictures have appeared in many books and magazines. Three of his photographs are included here, all taken on the Okeechobee Prairie in Central Florida. The cattle egret (*Plate 9*) and common meadowlark (*Plate 88*) are both hand-held shots taken from a car window with a Leica mounted on a gunstock. The egret picture was made with a 16-inch Kilar lens and the meadowlark with a 20-inch Bausch and Lomb. The photograph of the male snail kite (*Plate 20*) was taken with a 12-inch Kilar lens from a boat concealed some 200 feet from the nest, which was built over water that was five feet in depth. The tripod had to be strapped to long bamboo poles. Several exposures were made by the use of a Leicamotor. Mr. Grimes tells me that as all of the pictures were taken when Kodachrome had a Weston rating of 8, and all subjects were in direct sunlight, the exposures must have been 1/60 at $f/6.3$.

SHELLY GROSSMAN, who lives in New York City, is a professional photographer of wide experience. His pictures have received important awards and have been exhibited at leading galleries. He has contributed two of the photographs in this book, the roadside hawk (*Plate 21*) and the spectacled owl (*Plate 42*), both of which were captive birds belonging to a friend. A Hasselblad camera was used, loaded with Ektachrome EP 120 film. The hawk shot was made with Speedlight, 1/2500 sec., at $f/11$. The owl was a daylight shot, 1/250 sec., at $f/11$.

ROBERT C. HERMES, now a resident of Homestead, Florida, was a commercial artist in his early years, but later turned to wildlife photography and lecturing. He has had wide experience in both fields and has twice captured first prize in the International Graflex competition. Six of his pictures appear in this book: the sooty terns (*Plate 30*), scarlet macaw (*Plate 35*), Caribbean parakeets (*Plate 38*), white bellbird (*Plate 67*), Montezuma oropéndola (*Plate 86*) and common troupial (*Plate 87*). All were captive birds except the terns, which were photographed in the famous colony on the Dry Tortugas off Florida.

ERIC HOSKING lives in London, the city of his birth. He took his first photograph at the age of 6, of a song thrush's nest, and since then has amassed a collection of over 30,000 negatives covering most of the birds and mammals of Europe. Mr. Hosking writes me that for most serious work he prefers a $3^1/_4 \times 4^1/_4$ inch camera fitted with a 21-cm lens, but he also uses a 35-mm camera with a

600-mm lens, "for stalking or when using a 'wait and see' blind," as he puts it. Mr. Hosking pioneered the use of flash bulbs for bird photography and was the first to apply high-speed flash with photoelectric shutter release for taking pictures of birds in flight. He is active in photographic and bird-protection affairs, serves as photographic editor of the *New Naturalist* and *British Birds*, and, besides being co-author of ten bird books, has contributed photographs to more than 500 others. We feel that perhaps we should apologize for including only one of Mr. Hosking's photographs in this book, but he has never been to the Caribbean, or it might have been different! The black-crowned night-heron on its nest (*Plate 12*) was taken in the Coto Doñana of southern Spain, using a Brand 17 camera fitted with an $8^1/_2$-inch Zeiss Tessar lens stopped down to $f/11$ and with an exposure of 1/25 second on Ektachrome film.

TORREY JACKSON, whose home is in Marblehead, Massachusetts, writes me that he has had a keen interest in wildlife since the age of 5, began taking pictures of birds at age 12, started lecturing at age 14, and has now reached "the ripe old age of 23." Torrey's photographs appearing in this book—the green heron (*Plate 7*), laughing gull on its nest (*Plate 29b*) and black skimmer (*Plate 32*)— were made when he was 18 and on vacation at Stone Harbor, New Jersey. The heron was photographed from a blind with a 4 × 5 Speed Graphic with $2^1/_4$ roll film adapter, and Ektachrome film. A blue flash bulb was used. Exposure was 1/100 sec. at $f/16$. Torrey noted that when an airplane approached overhead the heron "would crane its neck vigorously and then stand as though in reverence until the plane had passed out of sight before settling back to incubation chores."

The laughing gull on its nest was taken in a colony of some 10,000 birds, from a "walkaway" blind set-up. A strobe was used, but "blew up" after this one shot. The camera was a 4 × 5 Speed Graphic, Ektachrome film and strobe light (Dormitzer 200) at $f/16$. The same equipment was used for the skimmer shot, which was made in late afternoon, under an overcast sky and with a strong wind blowing, which caused the skimmer to raise its wings as it struggled to remain on the nest. This time the strobe behaved perfectly.

MARVIN PHILIP KAHL, JR., a native of Indianapolis, is at this writing a graduate student at the University of Georgia, where he holds a fellowship under the National Education Defense Act. Phil is a promising young ornithologist who has already done outstanding research work for the National Audubon Society on the ecology and behavior of the wood stork. His one contribution to this book, the royal terns (*Plate 31*), was taken at Cocoa Beach, Florida, with a Contaflex I camera and Phil's own special combination of a 40-mm lens and a 15 × Bausch and Lomb spottingscope, which he estimates as giving a magnification equal to that of a 600-mm telephoto lens. Phil writes: "Such a combination of a single-lens reflex camera and spottingscope or binoculars is a convenient and economical method for obtaining close-ups of wildlife subjects." The terns were approximately 50 feet from the camera, facing into a fairly stiff breeze. The lens settings were 1/60 second at $f/2.8$ with Ektachrome film.

Russ KINNE, a native Rhode Islander who now makes his home in New York City (although he is more likely to be found in Trinidad or Wyoming), is an all-round professional photographer, equally at ease taking pictures of birds or racing sloops or underwater coral formations on a Bahama reef. He is one of the most active wildlife photographers in the business. In addition to exposing a lot of film, Russ is the author of a bi-monthly column called "Nature Camera" for *Popular Photography* magazine, and two books, *Life on a Coral Reef* and *Fur, Film and Feathers*. His contributions to this book number 20 pictures covering 17 species. These are as follows:

Double-crested cormorant (*Plate 3*). Taken with Hexacon camera, 300-mm Kilfitt lens, 1/200 sec. at $f/5.6$. Location: Florida Bay.

Anhinga (*Plate 4*). A lightly overcast sky and diffused light permitted an exposure of 1/100 at $f/5.6$. Hasselblad camera, 300-mm Kilfitt lens, no filter. Ektachrome film. Location: Anhinga Trail, Everglades National Park, Florida.

Great blue heron (*Plate 6*). Hasselblad camera, 300-mm Kilfitt lens, 1/100 at $f/8$. Late afternoon sunlight and nearly horizontal lighting. Location: Anhinga Trail.

Little blue heron (*Plate 8*). Praktina camera, 300-mm Kilfitt lens, 1/100 at $f/5.6$. Late afternoon sun. Low light separated bird from background. Location: Anhinga Trail.

Scarlet ibis (*Plates 13 a* and *b*). Both pictures were taken in the Caroni Swamp in Trinidad, on daylight Ektachrome with a Praktina camera and 300-mm Kilfitt lens, 1/200 at $f/5.6$.

Roseate spoonbill (*Plates 14 a, b, c*). All three pictures were taken at the Cowpens colony in Florida Bay, using a Hexacon camera, 300-mm Kilfitt lens, 1/200 at $f/6.3$. Ektachrome film and no filter.

West Indian flamingo (*Plate 15a*). Captive birds at Sarasota Jungle Gardens in Florida. Photographed with a Hexacon camera, 135-mm Kilfitt lens, 1/100 at $f/4.5$. Ektachrome film, no filter. Late afternoon and no direct sunlight.

Black-bellied tree-duck (*Plate 17*). Hasselblad camera, 300-mm Kilfitt lens, 1/100 at $f/7$. Ektachrome film, no filter. Late afternoon and low sunlight. Location: Sarasota Jungle Gardens.

Ornate hawk-eagle (*Plate 22*). Hasselblad camera, 150-mm Kilfitt lens, 1/250 at $f/5.6$. Ektachrome film, no filter. Location: Hamlet's "Birds of Prey," Ocala, Florida.

Purple gallinule (*Plate 25*). Hasselblad camera, 150-mm Kilfitt lens, 1/100 at $f/4.5$. Ektachrome film, skylight filter. Location: Anhinga Trail.

American jacana (*Plate 27*). Praktina camera, $f/2$ Biotar lens, High-Speed Ektachrome film, daylight type, 1/50 at $f/2.2$. Skylight filter. Photographed at Bronx Zoo, New York. Light from overhead skylight. Cloudy day and lighting very diffused.

Blue-and-yellow macaw (*Plate 36*). Hasselblad camera, 150-mm Kilfitt lens with extension tube to allow close-up pictures. 1/100 at $f/8$ in bright sunlight, with sun directly overhead, the sandy ground acting as a reflector. Ektachrome film. Captive bird at "Africa, U.S.A." in Florida.

Ferruginous pygmy-owl (*Plate 41*). Hasselblad camera, normal lens (80 mm Tessar), 1/100 at $f/9$. Ektachrome film. Photograph is of a captive bird at Hamlet's "Birds of Prey."

Burrowing owl (*Plate 43*). Photograph is of a wild bird on its nest mound near Immokalee, Florida, and was taken after sunset from 13 feet with a Hexacon camera, 300-mm Kilfitt lens, 1/200 at $f/5.6$ on Ektachrome film with no filter.

Guácharo (*Plate 44*). Hasselblad camera, 150-mm Kilfitt lens, Ektachrome film, operated with a small strobe unit mounted as close to the lens as possible and lens setting of $f/4$. Skylight filter. Photographed in the Spring Hill colony in Trinidad, in almost total darkness.

Streamer-tail (*Plate 51*). Photographed through glass partition at Bronx Zoo, using two small strobe units placed on either side of camera to avoid heavy shadows. Duration of flash about 1/800 second. Hasselblad camera, normal 80-mm lens, skylight filter. Daylight Ektachrome film and lens setting of $f/16$.

Guiana cock-of-the-rock (*Plate 68*). Also photographed through glass at the Bronx Zoo. Same equipment as with streamer-tail, except only one strobe unit was used, placed on one side. Glass directly in front of camera lens was shielded.

GEORGE LAMB photographed the smooth-billed ani (*Plate 39*) near Manzanillo, Oriente Province, Cuba, using a Leica III F Reflex housing, 300-mm Kilfitt lens set at $f/5.6$ and Ektachrome film. This picture was taken in January 1956 when George was in Cuba studying the ivory-billed woodpecker on a fellowship from the International Council for Bird Protection.

J. F. AMEDEE LA TOUR, better known as Cy La Tour, is a veteran free-lance "photo-journalist" who has been a civil engineer, newspaper reporter, feature writer, picture-page editor, wire-service editor, sports radio commentator and newsreel cameraman. In recent years he has been doing what he loves best, photographing wildlife. His contribution to this book is the channel-billed toucan (*Plate 58*), a captive bird in his own collection. As befits a photographer with his background, Cy La Tour uses Graflex and Speed Graphic equipment almost exclusively.

JOHN MARKHAM is a Londoner and photography is both his work and his hobby. His delightful portrait of a barn owl (*Plate 40*) was made with an M. P. P. Technical 5×4 inch on Ektachrome sheet film with an $8^1/_2$-inch Ross Xpres lens set at $f/16$, shutter speed 1/50 second. A G. E. C. 22 blue flash bulb provided the light.

KARL HERBERT MASLOWSKI, who lives in Cincinnati, Ohio, has been taking pictures since he was 16. He has specialized in motion pictures of wildlife and conservation subjects for many years and is a well-known lecturer. The common egrets (*Plate 11*) were photographed in the famous colony on Reelfoot Lake, Tennessee, using an Auto-Graflex with 10-inch Eastman Extar lens, 1/50 at $f/8$, on $3^1/_2 \times 4^1/_2$ inch Kodachrome film. The two birds were about a hundred feet above the ground in a huge cypress.

KARL MAYER, a native of Austria who lives in Kralendijk on Bonaire Island in the Netherlands Antilles, is a photographer with a highly sensitive gift for the artistic. His color pictures of flowers are beautiful examples of this, but his skill has also been equal to the task of recording on film the color and high drama of a flock of wild flamingos (*Plate 15c*). An appealing portrait is his photograph of a newly hatched flamingo chick (*Plate 15b*). Mr. Mayer uses a Leica camera.

DR. T. W. ROTH, who took the photographs of the purple-throated fruitcrow (*Plate 66*), and the scarlet-rumped tanager (*Plate 92*), uses a Hasselblad camera and four electronic flash units. The fruitcrow is a captive.

PAUL A. SCHWARTZ is a native of York, Pennsylvania, who has lived for some years in Venezuela, where he is an air-conditioning engineer. He has made a major contribution to this book, which contains 32 of his outstanding photographs representing a total of 31 Venezuelan birds. These are listed here in their proper order:

White-tipped dove (*Plate 33*)
Rufous nightjar (*Plate 45*)
Pauraque (*Plate 46*)
Ruby-topaz hummingbird (*Plate 48*)
Copper-rumped hummingbird (*Plate 52*)
Rufous-tailed jacamar (*Plate 57*)
Red-billed scythebill (*Plate 60*)
Pale-breasted spinetail (*Plate 61*)
Rufous-fronted thornbird (*Plate 62*)
Barred antshrike (*male and female*) (*Plate 63*)
Pied water-tyrant (*Plate 70*)
Great kiskadee (*Plate 71*)
Common tody-flycatcher (*Plate 72*)
Lesser Antillean elaenia (*Plate 73*)
Rough-winged swallow (*Plate 74*)
Green jay (*Plate 75*)
Southern house-wren (*Plate 76*)
Bare-eyed thrush (*Plate 77*)
Orange-billed nightingale-thrush (*Plate 78*)
Rufous-browed peppershrike (*Plate 80*)
Bananaquit (*Plate 81*)
Lesser Antillean grackle (*Plate 84*)
Glossy cowbird (*Plate 85*)
Swallow-tanager (*Plate 89*)
Blue-gray tanager (*Plate 91*)
Silver-beaked tanager (*Plate 93*)
Ruddy-breasted seedeater (*Plate 94*)
Saffron finch (*Plate 95*)
Black-faced grassquit (*Plate 96*)
Grayish saltator (*Plate 97*)
Rufous-collared sparrow (*Plate 98*)

PHILIPPA SCOTT was born in South Africa and educated at St. Georges School, Ascot. She began taking pictures of pet animals at the age of nine—with a box Brownie, of course—and photography did not become her "serious hobby" until after World War II. In 1951 she married Peter Scott, founder of the Wildlife Trust at Slimbridge, England, and with him she has traveled as a still-camera photographer on expeditions to Patagonia, Bolivia, Australia, New Zealand, New Guinea, Fiji, Uganda, Trinidad, Panama, Ecuador and the Galapagos Islands. Her picture of the Bahama pintail (*Plate 18*) was taken of one of the pen-reared birds at Slimbridge; she used an Exacta Varex camera with High Speed Ektachrome film.

FREDERICK KENT TRUSLOW, a native of New Jersey who, since retirement from the wire and cable business, has been spending his winters in Florida, is responsible for the interesting photographs of the osprey (*Plate 23*) and the limpkin (*Plate 24*). The word "retirement" is merely a term of convenience, for Fred Truslow is one of the most energetic wildlife photographers on the present-day scene, his hobby taking him to Tobago, Mexico, Canada and many parts of the U.S. He has written and provided the photographs for any number of recent articles in the *National Geographic*

Magazine, including one on the bald eagle that has stirred nation-wide comment and interest.

The osprey was photographed on Palm Key in Everglades National Park, with a Pentex camera, Leitz 400 Telyt lens, 1/125 second at $f/6.5$. The limpkin picture was taken at Wakulla Springs, Florida, with an Exacta camera, Astro lens, 300 mm, 1/125 second at $f/6.3$.

R. VAN NOSTRAND, whose credit line reads "Van Nostrand, San Diego Zoo," is a postman by profession, but for the last ten years has been the official zoo photographer at San Diego. His pictures of the king vulture (*Plate 19*) and horned screamer (*Plate 16*) were both taken at the zoo, with a 4 × 5 Speed Graphic and Ektachrome film.

KARL WEIDMAN writes from South America, where he has lived for the past 14 years, that he is "basically a nature lover who took up free-lance photography to make a living." We can believe every word of this when he also tells us that to obtain his scarlet ibis picture (*Plate 13c*) he stood in water for 9 and 10 hours at a time, with the air temperature reaching 118 degrees inside the blind! He uses an Exacta VX equipped with a 300-mm Kilar lens. The exposure for this shot was 1/50 second at $f/8$.

Bibliography

Titles are limited for the most part to those that are referred to directly in the body of the text. However, some additional items containing useful reference material are also included and may be helpful to the reader who wishes to pursue some of these matters on his own. The reader's attention is called in particular to the regional bibliography in Eugene Eisenmann's *The Species of Middle American Birds.*

Alford, Commander C. E. R.
  1953. *The Island of Tobago (British West Indies).* Dorchester, Longmans.

Allen, Robert Porter
  1942. *The Roseate Spoonbill.* New York: National Audubon Society.
  1956. *The Flamingos: Their Life History and Survival.* New York: National Audubon Society.

Barbour, Thomas
  1943. "Cuban Ornithology." *Memoirs of the Nuttall Ornithological Club, No. 9.*

Baynard, Oscar E.
  1912. "Food of Herons and Ibises." *Wilson Bulletin,* 24 : 167–169.

Belcher, Charles, and G. D. Smooker
  1934–1937. *Birds of the Colony of Trinidad and Tobago.*
      Part I, Tinamidae—Accipitrides. *Ibis* (13), 4 : 572–595.
      Part II, Cracidae—Rynchopidae. *Ibis* (13), 5 : 279–297.
      Part III, Columbidae—Trochilidae. *Ibis* (13), 6 : 1–35.
      Part IV, Trogonidae—Cotingidae. *Ibis* (13), 6 : 792–813.
      Part V, Pipridae—Tyrannidae. *Ibis* (14), 1 : 225–249.
      Part VI, Hirundinidae—Fringillidae. *Ibis* (14), 1 : 504–550.

Biaggi, Virgilio, Jr.
  1955. "The Puerto Rican Honeycreeper (*Reinita*)." *Special Publication,* Agricultural Experiment Station, University of Puerto Rico.

Blake, Emmet Reid
  1953. *Birds of Mexico. A Guide for Field Identification.* Chicago: University of Chicago Press.

Bond, James
  1928. "On the Birds of Dominica, St. Lucia, St. Vincent, and Barbados, B. W. I." *Academy of Natural Sciences of Philadelphia, Proceedings,* LXXX : 523–545.
  1934. "The Distribution and Origin of the West Indian Avifauna." *Journal of the American Philosophical Society,* 73 : 341–349.
  1942. "Additional Notes on West Indian Birds." *Academy of Natural Sciences of Philadelphia, Proceedings* XCIV : 89–106.
  1946. "The Birds of Mona Island." *Notulae Naturae,* 176 : 1–10. Academy of Natural Sciences of Philadelphia.
  1947. "A Plea for Conservation in the West Indies." *Audubon Magazine,* 49 : 6 : 348–354.
  1948. "Origin of the Bird Fauna of the West Indies." *Wilson Bulletin* 60 : 4 : 207–229.
  1950. *Check-List of Birds of the West Indies.* Academy of Natural Sciences of Philadelphia.
  1960. *Birds of the West Indies.* London: Collins.

Carr, Archie
  1956. *The Windward Road.* New York: Knopf.

Carriker, M. A., Jr.
  1910. "An Annotated List of the Birds of Costa Rica Including Cocos Island." *Annals of the Carnegie Museum* 6 : 7 : 314–970.
  1931. "The Cave Birds of the Island of Trinidad." *Auk,* 48 : 2 : 186–194.

Chapman, Frank Michler

1894. "On the Birds of the Island of Trinidad." *Bulletin of the American Museum of Natural History*, VI : 1–86.

1895. "Further Notes on Trinidad Birds, with a Description of a New Species of Synallaxis." *Bulletin of the American Museum of Natural History*, VII : 321–326.

1926. *Handbook of Birds of Eastern North America.* New York: Appleton.

1929. *My Tropical Air Castle. Nature Studies in Panama.* New York: Appleton.

1938. *My Life in an Air Castle.* New York: Appleton.

Chenery, E. M.

1956. "The King Vulture in Trinidad." *Journal of the Trinidad Field Naturalists' Club*, p. 24.

Coffey, Ben Barry, Jr.

1948. "Southward Migration of Herons." *Bird-Banding*, 19 : 1–5.

Collins, Henry Hill

1956. *Birds and Fish of the Netherlands Antilles.* Bronxville, N.Y.: Caribou Press.

Conway, William Gaylord

1959. "The Mossy-throated Bellbird, an Ornithological Mystery." *Animal Kingdom* 62 : 3 : 66–76.

Dalquest, Walter W. *See* Lowery, George H., Jr., and Walter W. Dalquest.

Danforth, Stuart Taylor

1935. "Supplementary Account of the Birds of the Virgin Islands, including Culebra and Adjacent Islands Pertaining to Puerto Rico, with Notes on their Food Habits." *Journal of Agriculture of the University of Puerto Rico*, 19 : 4 : 439–472.

1939. "Birds of Guadeloupe and Adjacent Islands." *Journal of Agriculture of the University of Puerto Rico*, 23 : 1 : 9–46.

de Phelps, Kathleen Deery

1954. "Aves Venezolanas. Cien de las màs conocidas." *Enero* 15: 1–103. Caracas: Creole Petroleum Corporation.

de Schauensee, Rodolphe Meyer

1950–1951. "The Birds of the Republic of Colombia. Their Distribution and Keys for their Identification." *Caldasia (Boletín del Instituto de Ciencias Naturales de la Universidad Nacional de Colombia)*, Pt. III, 5 : 24 : 645–871; Pt. IV, 5 : 25 : 873–1112.

Devas, Fr. Raymund

1950. *Visitors' Book of Birds. Trinidad and Tobago.* Port-of-Spain: Muir, Marshall.

Dickey, Donald R., and A. J. Van Rossem

1938. "The Birds of El Salvador." *Field Museum of Natural History, Zoological Series*, 23: 1–609 (Publication 406).

Eastman, Whitney and Karen

1956. "Birding in Jamaica." *Bulletin of the Massachusetts Audubon Society*, 40: 9: 497–498.

1958. "Birding in the West Indies." *The Flicker*, 30: 2: 47–49 (June).

Edwards, Ernest Preston

1955. *Finding Birds in Mexico.* Amherst, Va.: Amherst Publishing Co.

Eisenmann, Eugene

1952. "Annotated List of Birds of Barro Colorado Island, Panama Canal Zone." *Smithsonian Institution, Miscellaneous Collections*, 72 : 5 : 1–62.

1955. *The Species of Middle American Birds. A List of All Species Recorded from Mexico to Panama, with Suggested English Names, Outlines of Range, and a Distributional Bibliography. Transactions of the Linnaean Society of New York*, VII.

1957. "Notes on the Birds of the Province of Bocas del Toro." *Condor*, 49: 247–262.

Friedmann, Herbert

1948. "Birds Collected by the National Geographic Society's Expeditions to Northern Brazil and Southern Venezuela." *Proceedings of the U.S. National Museum* (No. 3219), 97: 373–569.

Friedmann, Herbert, and Foster D. Smith, Jr.

1950. "A Contribution to the Ornithology of Northeastern Venezuela." *Proceedings of the U.S. National Museum* (No. 3268), 100: 411–538.

1955. "A Further Contribution to the Ornithology of Northeastern Venezuela." *Proceedings of the U.S. National Museum* (No. 3345), 104: 463–524.

Frost, W.

1910. "The Cock of the Rock." *Aviculture Magazine* (3) 1: 319–324.

Greenewalt, Crawford H.

1960. *Hummingbirds.* New York: Doubleday.

Greenway, James Cowan, Jr.

1958. "Extinct and Vanishing Birds of the World." *American Committee for International Wild Life Protection, Special Publication*, No. 13.

Griffin, Donald R.

1954. "Bird Sonar." *Scientific American*, 190: 3: 78–83.

Griscom, Ludlow
1926. *The Ornithological Results of the Mason-Spinden Expedition to Yucatan: Part 2, Chinchorro Bank and Cozumel Island. American Museum of Natural History*, Novitates, No. 236.
1932. "The Distribution of Bird-life in Guatemala. A Contribution to a Study of the Origin of Central American Bird-life." *American Museum of Natural History*, Bulletin, 64: 1–439.

Griscom, Ludlow, Alexander Sprunt, Jr., et al.
1957. *The Warblers of North America*. New York: Devin-Adair.

Griswold, Oliver
1959. "Blithe, Beautiful, Tiny and the First Tody to be Exhibited Alive." *Animal Kingdom*, 62: 4: 98–105.

Haverschmidt, François
1955. *List of the Birds of Surinam. Publications of the Foundation for Scientific Research in Surinam and the Netherlands Antilles*, No. 13 (Utrecht).

Hellmayr, Charles E., and Boardman Conover
1948. *Catalogue of Birds of the Americas*, Part I, No. 2. *Zoological Series, Field Museum of Natural History*, XIII (Publication 615).

Hernandez, R.
1953. "Scarlet Ibis Come Home Again." *Trinidad Guardian* (August 7).

Holt, Ernest Golsan
1933. "Journey by Jungle Rivers to the Home of the Cock of the Rock." *National Geographic Magazine*, 64: 585–630.

Hummelinck, P. Wagenaar
1957. *Studies of the Fauna of Curaçao and other Caribbean Islands*, No. 29 (Vol. VII). *Publications of the Foundation for Scientific Research in Surinam and the Netherlands Antilles* (Utrecht).

Jeffrey-Smith, May
1956. *Bird-Watching in Jamaica*. Kingston: Pioneer Press.

Junge, G. C. A., and G. F. Mees
1958. *The Avifauna of Trinidad and Tobago. Zoölogische Verhandelingen, Uitgegeven door het Rijksmuseum van Natuurlijke Historie te Leiden*, No. 37. Leiden: Brill.

Lamb, George R.
1957. *On the Endangered Species of Birds in the U.S. Virgin Islands. Research Report No. 2*, Pan-American Section, International Committee for Bird Preservation.

Léotaud, Antoine
1866. *Oiseaux de l'île de la Trinidad*. Port d'Espagne: Chronicle Publishing Office.

Lowery, George H., Jr., and Walter W. Dalquest
1951. "Birds from the State of Veracruz, Mexico." *University of Kansas Publications, Museum of Natural History*, 3: 4: 531–649.

Mason, Charles Russell
1960. "Jamaica–Puerto Rico Tour Enjoyed." *Florida Naturalist*, 33: 2A.

McCandless, James B.
1958. *A Field Guide to the Birds of Puerto Rico. Being a Supplement to Roger Tory Peterson's Field Guide to the Birds*. San Germán: I. A. U. Press.

Mayr, Ernst
1942. *Systematics and the Origin of Species*. New York: Columbia University Press.
1946. "The Number of Species of Birds." *Auk*, 63: 1: 64–69.

Mees, G. F. *See* Junge, G. C. A., and G. F. Mees.

Meyerriecks, Andrew Joseph
1960. *Comparative Breeding Behavior of Four Species of North American Herons. Publications of the Nuttall Ornithological Club*, No. 2.

Newton, Alfred
1893–1896. *A Dictionary of Birds*. London: Adam and Charles Black.

Noble, G. Kingsley
1916. "The Resident Birds of Guadeloupe." *Bulletin of the Museum of Comparative Zoölogy*, 60: 10: 359–396.

Paynter, Raymond Andrew, Jr.
1955. *The Ornithogeography of the Yucatán Peninsula. Peabody Museum of Natural History*, Bulletin 9.

Peterson, Roger Tory
1947. *A Field Guide to the Birds*. Boston: Houghton Mifflin.
1960. *A Field Guide to the Birds of Texas*. Boston: Houghton Mifflin.

Peterson, Roger Tory, Guy Mountfort, and P. A. D. Hollom
1954. A Field Guide to the Birds of Britain and Europe. Boston, Houghton Mifflin.

Phelps, Kathleen Deery de. *See* de Phelps.

Phelps, William H., and William H. Phelps, Jr.
1950. *Lista de las Aves de Venezuela con su Distribución*. Parte 2, Passeriformes. Extracto del *Boletín de la Sociedad Venezolana de Ciencias Naturales*, Tomo XII, No. 75. Caracas.
1958. *Lista de las Aves Venezuela con su Distribución*. Tomo II, Parte I, No Passeriformes. Separata del *Boletín de la Sociedad Venezolana de Ciencias Naturales*, XIX, 90. Caracas.

Pough, Richard Hooper
  1951. *Audubon Water Bird Guide.* New York: Doubleday.
Quesnel, V. C.
  1956. "The Density of the Population of Breeding Kiskadees in Port-of-Spain." *Journal of the Trinidad Field Naturalists' Club.*
Rand, Austin L., and Melvin L. Traylor
  1954. *Manual de las Aves de El Salvador.* San Salvador, El Salvador: Universidad de El Salvador.
Robertson, William B., Jr.
  1960. *Observations on the Birds of St. John, Virgin Islands. National Park Service, Project Completion Report,* 1–72.
Rodriguez-Vidal, José A.
  1959. "Puerto Rican Parrot (*Amazona vittata vittata*) Study." *Monographs of the Department of Agriculture and Commerce,* 1: 1–15.
Rothschild, W.
  1905. "On Extinct and Living Parrots of the West Indies." *Bulletin of the British Ornithological Club,* 16: 13–14.
Rutten, M.
  1934. "Observations on Cuban Birds." *Ardea,* 33: 3–4: 108–126.
Schaefer, Ernst
  1953, "Contribution to the Life History of the Swallow-Tanager." *Auk,* 70: 4: 403–460 (Pls. 11–18).
Skutch, Alexander F.
  1930. "The Habits and Nesting Activities of the Northern Tody Flycatcher in Panama." *Auk,* 47: 313–322.
  1950. "Outline for an Ecological Life History of a Bird." *Ecology,* 31: 464–469.
  1954. "Life Histories of Central American Birds, Families Fringillidae, Thraupidae, Icteridae, Parulidae and Coerebidae." *Cooper Ornithological Society. Pacific Coast Avifauna,* No. 31, 1–448.
  1960. "Life Histories of Central American Birds, II. Families Vireonidae, Sylviidae, Turdidae, Troglodytidae, Paridae, Corvidae, Hirundinidae and Tyrannidae." *Cooper Ornithological Society, Pacific Coast Avifauna,* No. 34, 1–593.
Slud, Paul
  1960. "The Birds of Finca 'La Selva,' Costa Rica: A Tropical Wet Forest Locality." *Bulletin, American Museum of Natural History,* vol. 12, art. 2.
Smith, Foster D., Jr. *See* Friedmann and Smith.

Sprunt, Alexander, Jr.
  1954. *Florida Bird Life.* New York: Coward-McCann.
Street, Phillips B.
  1946. "Some Notes on Trinidad Birds." *Auk,* 63: 3: 369–378.
Sturgis, Bertha B.
  1928. *Field Book of Birds of the Panama Canal Zone.* New York: Putnam.
Taylor (Lady) R. G.
  1955. *Introduction to the Birds of Jamaica.* London: Macmillan.
Traylor, Melvin Alvah, Jr.
  1941. "Birds from the Yucatan Peninsula." Field Museum of Natural History, *Publication* 493, *Zoological Series* 24: 19: 195–225.
Urich, F. W.
  1895. "Visit to the Oropuche Guacharo Cave." *Journal of the Trinidad Field Naturalists' Club,* II, pp. 231–234.
van Tyne, Josselyn, and Andrew J. Berger
  1959. *Fundamentals of Ornithology.* New York: John Wiley.
Voous, Karel H.
  1953. "Vogeltrek op de Nederlandse Benedenwindse Eilanden." *De West-Indische Gids,* 33, 183–190. (English Summary).
  1955. De Vogels van de Nederlandse Antillen (Birds of the Netherlands Antilles). Uitgaven van de "Natuurwetenschappelijke Werkgroep Nederlandse Antillen," Curaçao.
  1957. "The Birds of Aruba, Curaçao and Bonaire." *Studies on the Fauna of Curaçao and other Caribbean Islands,* vol. 7, no. 29. The Hague: Martinus Nijhoff.
Voous, K. H., and H. J. Koelers
  1959. "Animal Life in the Netherlands Antilles." *Schakels,* 28. The Hague: Netherlands Ministry of Overseas Affairs.
Walkinshaw, Lawrence H., and Bernard W. Baker
  1946. "Notes on the Birds of the Isle of Pines, Cuba." *Wilson Bulletin* 58: 3: 133-142.
Westermann, J. H.
  1946. "Bird Preservation in the Territory of Curaçao." Reprinted from *Uitgaven Studiekring Suriname Curaçao,* Jaarboek 1945–1946. Utrecht.
  1952. "Conservation in the Caribbean. A Review of Literature on the Destruction and Conservation of Renewable Natural Resources in the Caribbean Area, with reference to the Population Problem." *Foundation for*

Scientific Research in Surinam and the Netherlands Antilles, No. 7.

1953. "Nature Preservation in the Caribbean. A Review of Literature on the Destruction and Preservation of Flora and Fauna in the Caribbean Area." *Foundation for Scientific Research in Surinam and the Netherlands Antilles*, No. 9.

Westermann, J. H., and J. I. S. Zonneveld
1956. "Photo-Geological Observations and Land Capability and Land Use Survey of the Island of Bonaire (Netherlands Antilles)." *Royal Tropical Institute*, CXXIII, No. 47.

Wetmore, Alexander
1916. "Birds of Puerto Rico." *U.S. Department of Agriculture*, Bulletin No. 326, 1–140. (also published as *Bulletin 15, Insular Experiment Station*, Río Piedras, P.R., March 24, 1916.)
1926. "Observations on the Birds of Argentina, Paraguay, Uruguay, and Chile." *U.S. National Museum, Bulletin*, 133: 1–448.
1927. "The Birds of Porto Rico and the Virgin Islands." *Scientific Survey of Porto Rico and the Virgin Islands*, Vol. IX, pts 3–4. New York Academy of Sciences.
1931. "The Avifauna of the Pleistocene of Florida." *Smithsonian Institution, Miscellaneous Collections*, 85: 2: 41.
1932. "Birds Collected in Cuba and Haiti by the Parish-Smithsonian Expedition of 1930." *Proceedings of the U.S. National Museum* (No. 2925), 81: 1–40.

1939. "Observations on the Birds of Northern Venezuela." *Proceedings of the U.S. National Museum* (No. 3037), 87: 173–260.
1941. "Notes on Birds of the Guatemalan Highlands." *Proceedings of the U.S. National Museum* (No. 3105), 89: 523–581.
1943. "The Birds of Southern Veracruz, Mexico." *Proceedings of the U.S. National Museum* (No. 3164), 93: 215–340.
1944. "A Collection of Birds from Northern Guanacasta, Costa Rica." *Proceedings of the U.S. National Museum* (No. 3179), 95: 25–80.
1957. "The Birds of Isla Coiba, Panamá." *Smithsonian Institution, Miscellaneous Collections*, 134: 9: 1–105.

Wetmore, Alexander, and Frederick C. Lincoln
1933. "Additional Notes on the Birds of Haiti and the Dominican Republic." *Proceedings of the U.S. National Museum* (No. 2966), 82: 1–68.

Wetmore, Alexander, and Bradshaw H. Swales
1931. "The Birds of Haiti and the Dominican Republic." *U.S. National Museum, Bulletin*, 155: 1–483.

Williams, C. B.
1922. *Trinidad Birds. Notes on the Food and Habits of Some Trinidad Birds. Bulletin of the Department of Agriculture, Trinidad and Tobago.*

Zahl, Paul A.
1954. *Coro-coro. The World of the Scarlet Ibis.* New York: Bobbs-Merrill.

Index to the plates

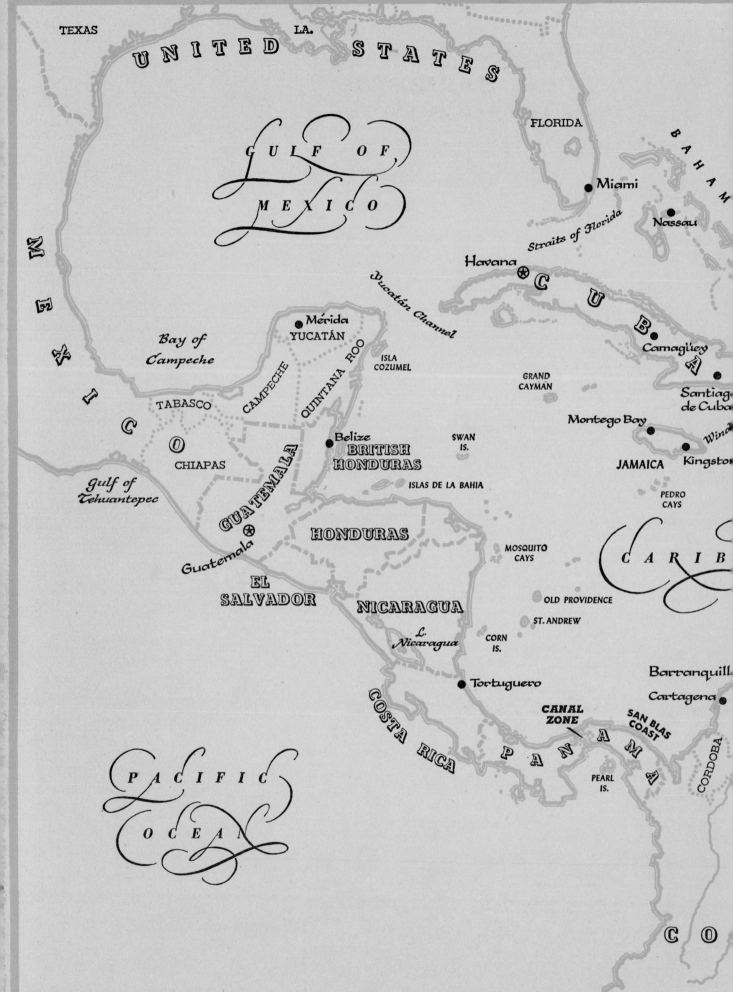

TEXAS
LA.
UNITED STATES
FLORIDA
● Miami
BAHAM
Nassau ●
Straits of Florida
GULF OF
MEXICO
Havana
Yucatán Channel
⊛ CUBA
Camagüey ●
Mérida ●
YUCATÁN
Bay of
Campeche
ISLA
COZUMEL
GRAND
CAYMAN
Santiago
de Cuba
CAMPECHE
QUINTANA ROO
Montego Bay ●
TABASCO
MEXICO
Belize ●
BRITISH
HONDURAS
SWAN
IS.
JAMAICA
Kingston
Wind
CHIAPAS
GUATEMALA
ISLAS DE LA BAHIA
PEDRO
CAYS
Gulf of
Tehuantepec
HONDURAS
MOSQUITO
CAYS
CARIB
⊛
Guatemala
OLD PROVIDENCE
EL
SALVADOR
NICARAGUA
ST. ANDREW
L.
Nicaragua
CORN
IS.
Barranquill
Cartagena
● Tortuguero
COSTA RICA
CANAL
ZONE
SAN BLAS
COAST
PANAMA
CORDOBA
PACIFIC
PEARL
IS.
OCEAN

CO